Introduction to
physical education
health education
and recreation

MARGARET M. DUNCAN, ED.D. • MACMURRAY COLLEGE

RALPH H. JOHNSON, ED.D. • UNIVERSITY OF ILLINOIS

Introduction to

physical education

health education

and recreation

PRENTICE-HALL, INC.

ENGLEWOOD CLIFFS, N. J.

PRENTICE-HALL PHYSICAL EDUCATION SERIES

Elmer D. Mitchell, *Editor*

First printing....September, 1954
Second printing....October, 1955
Third printing........June, 1959
Fourth printing..November, 1964

PRINTED IN THE UNITED STATES OF AMERICA

49274

Preface

This book was planned and written for young men and women beginning preparation for careers in physical education, health education, and recreation. It has three purposes:

1. To indicate the interests, abilities, and personal characteristics that are important to professional workers in physical education, health education, and recreation.

2. To explain the professional qualifications needed for successful work.

3. To assist students in planning for future careers as qualified teachers and leaders.

The first three chapters discuss physical education, health education, and recreation as professional careers, provide information on opportunities in these areas and in related fields, and examine the problems of estimating and appraising personal qualifications. Chapters 4 through 7 present the problems of college life and adjustment, the importance of leadership abilities, and provisions for developing professional competencies during undergraduate years. Chapters 8 and 9 deal with the aims and purposes of physical education, health education, and recreation and discuss the professional status of these fields. Chapter 10 presents information concerning opportunities for employment and methods of securing placement both during undergraduate years and after completing professional preparation. Finally, Chapter 11 provides practical suggestions for continued professional growth in a career. The appendixes include related materials that supplement chapter discussions.

The problems at the end of each chapter, the selected chapter references, and the final bibliography offer an opportunity for further study.

Several hundred professional students have contributed questions about their undergraduate work, their future careers, and the possibilities for advancement in their professions. Many of these questions have been answered; other questions must be answered by each person for himself. The information in the text, the problems, and the sources of reference, combined with the reader's practical experiences as a major in physical education, health education, or recreation, should provide answers to such questions as:

1. Do I really want to work with boys and girls?

2. Do I have the personal qualities and the abilities that are needed by teachers?

3. Do I enjoy playing for my own personal benefit and fun more than I would like teaching young people?

4. Am I sincerely interested in the health and welfare of other people?

5. Would I be a good teacher and leader of boys and girls?

6. What are my personal goals for the future?

M. M. D.

R. H. J.

Acknowledgments

The authors wish to express appreciation to the many leaders of physical education, health education, and recreation who have contributed their suggestions and assistance to the preparation of this book. Special acknowledgment is tendered to Seward C. Staley, Howard S. Hoyman, and Charles K. Brightbill, all of the University of Illinois, for their suggestions and resource materials. Thanks for their constructive guidance and critical reading of the manuscript are gratefully extended to Clifford L. Brownell, E. Patricia Hagman, Florence K. Stratemeyer, and John L. Hutchinson, all of the Teachers College, Columbia University, and to Elmer D. Mitchell of the University of Michigan. The authors' sincere appreciation goes to Norma M. Leavitt, University of Florida, for her valuable assistance, and to Graham Johnson, Mary Jo Ivens, Howard Ivens, and Amanda Langemo for their encouragement, their pertinent suggestions, and their critical review of the manuscript. The authors are grateful also to the students, teachers, and recreation leaders who have willingly contributed personal statements for use in the text, and to Barbara Hartman for her assistance in the preparation of the manuscript.

The following publishers and holders of copyrights have kindly given permission to quote from their publications: American Association for Health, Physical Education, and Recreation; American Camping Association; American Recreation Society; Appleton-Century-Crofts, Inc.; A. S. Barnes and Company; Boys Clubs of America; Boy Scouts of America; Harcourt, Brace and Co., Inc.; D. C. Heath and Co.; H. S. Hoyman;

Camilla M. Low; McConnell School Map Co.; McGraw-Hill Book Co., Inc.; National Education Association; Ohio State University; Rinehart and Co., Inc.; E. E. Samuelson; W. B. Saunders Co.; John Wiley and Sons, Inc.; and Yale University Press.

M. M. D.
R. H. J.

Table of contents

PREFACE V

1. YOUR CAREER IN PHYSICAL EDUCATION, HEALTH
EDUCATION, OR RECREATION 3

You and your career 4
The nature of physical education, health education,
and recreation 8
Qualifications 11
Self-appraisal 19
Summary 20

2. PHYSICAL EDUCATION, HEALTH EDUCATION, AND
RECREATION AS CAREERS 25

Physical education as a profession 26
Health education as a profession................ 39
Recreation as a profession 44
Educational preparation 49
Opportunities in physical education, health educa-
tion, and recreation 60
Summary 72

3. CAREERS IN RELATED FIELDS 77

Public and private health agencies 78
Therapeutics 81
Corrective Physical Education 90
Safety education 92
Camping and outdoor education 94
Youth-serving agencies 98
Industrial recreation 113
Commercial recreation 114
Professional athletics 116
Summary 118

4. THE PROFESSIONAL STUDENT AND COLLEGE LIFE ...   125

   Planning a successful college life   125
   Orientation to college   126
   Personal and social development   137
   Summary   148

5. LEADERSHIP DEVELOPMENT   151

   Leadership   153
   Leadership opportunities   154
   Cooperation in leadership   165
   Summary   165

6. UNDERGRADUATE TEACHING AND FIELD WORK
   EXPERIENCES   171

   Purpose of professional laboratory experiences......   171
   Importance of professional laboratory experiences...   173
   The program of professional laboratory experiences.   179
   Opportunities for practical experience............   191
   Summary   196

7. PROFESSIONAL RESPONSIBILITIES AND
   RELATIONSHIPS   203

   Personal responsibilities   204
   Professional relationships   211
   Relationships with young people   218
   Summary   221

8. PROFESSIONAL LEADERSHIP IN PHYSICAL EDUCATION,
   HEALTH EDUCATION, AND RECREATION   225

   Historical background   225
   Professional preparation   232
   Philosophy and aim   235
   Contributions of physical education, health educa-
     tion, and recreation   247
   The role of professional leadership   250
   Summary   262

9. THE NATURE OF A PROFESSION   269

   Characteristics of a profession   269
   The significance of teaching and leadership........   271
   The status of teaching and professional leadership..   273

Status of physical education, health education, and
    recreation 279
The teacher and leader 281
Summary 282

10. LOOKING AHEAD 287

Placement opportunities 288
Placement information and services 294
References and recommendations 298
Letters of application 298
The personal interview 300
Contracts 303
Planning ahead 305
Starting professional work 308
Personal adjustment 310
Summary 310

11. PROFESSIONAL GROWTH 315

Professional literature 316
Affiliation with professional organizations 318
Contributions to your profession 320
Advanced study and specialization 321
Travel 323
Avocational interests 325
Summary 326

APPENDIXES 329

BIBLIOGRAPHY 366

INDEX 379

Introduction to
physical education
health education
and recreation

Courtesy of University of Illinois

CHAPTER ONE

Your career
in physical education
health education
or recreation

The major field you have chosen represents the steppingstone to your future career. You have undoubtedly given careful thought to the selection of a vocation, and to the possibilities in that vocation for an interesting and worth-while career. Now that you are beginning preparation for your profession, there are a number of questions that may occur to you. You may even have a few reasonable doubts as to the wisdom of your choice, and wish to re-examine your reasons for choosing a particular field of work.

The purpose of this book is to answer as many of your questions as possible, to present a survey of the requirements you are expected to meet, and to discuss career opportunities for professional work in physical education, health education, and recreation. The information in the following chapters is designed to explain the steps in professional preparation which qualify you for your profession. The specific purpose of this chapter is to answer such questions as:

1. Have I chosen wisely?

2. What is the nature of professional work in physical education, health education, and recreation?

3. Are programs of physical education, health education, and recreation important to people?

4. What qualifications do I need for the profession I have chosen?

5. What preparation is required to qualify for positions in these fields?

YOU AND YOUR CAREER

The wisdom of your choice is determined to a great extent by your attitude toward your future career, and by what a career means to you personally. Although your original choice is very important, continued planning for your future in that career is equally important. Your life work requires constant, careful, intelligent, and enthusiastic planning. Intelligent planning means investigating, re-evaluating, and improving your personal qualifications for a vocation as well as determining the requirements and opportunities of that vocation. Planning insures against a career based primarily upon interests that are temporary or recreational in nature.

> A career suggests (1) working with a *purpose;* (2) *growth* in a vocational field, planning and using imagination; (3) making a *game* out of work; (4) having a creative aspect. It is not merely work, but work directed toward fulfillment, and it involves interesting experimentation and exploration.[1]

Interest and enjoyment are essential to your success in a career. They must be combined with a realistic understanding of the purpose and nature of the vocation you have chosen; the personal qualities, abilities, and aptitudes demanded for successful accomplishment; and the willingness to work conscientiously in the field you select. A well-chosen career has many of the characteristics of an avocation. If you enjoy what you are doing and are well suited to your work, you will find satisfaction in developing and carrying out creative ideas and growing through your career.

A re-evaluation of yourself and of your choice of a career is of value in verifying or modifying your plans for the future. It is

[1] Reprinted with permission from Fred McKinney, *Psychology of Personal Adjustment,* 2d ed. (New York, John Wiley and Sons, Inc., 1949), p. 301.

important that you be content with the selection you have made. Uncertainty of the wisdom of continuing in a major field may develop into dissatisfaction with your vocation and in loss of interest in professional work. When such dissatisfaction is a matter of record, you may find it difficult to re-establish a good reputation in the same department later if you decide to continue in the same major field. Everyone should develop the habit of re-evaluating his interests and judging his progress from time to time even if he is certain that he has chosen the right career. The suggestions in the Guide for Re-Evaluating Your Choice of Career (Appendix A) may help you to review your selection of a career, and aid you in learning more about that field of work.

The following statements made by freshman students who have selected careers in physical education, health education, and recreation illustrate a variety of reasons for their choice of a career, and a variety of attitudes toward their future professions.

Student A: I chose physical education as my lifetime profession because I am sure that I will be happy in that field. True, I may not make as much money as some other people. However, this will be offset by my knowing that each day I will be doing something different, and life will not be one dull day after another. Then, too, I like to work with boys, and since I've always loved sports, I believe that teaching physical education or coaching is the vocation for me.

Student B: I chose physical education because I feel that it is one of the most important things in the lives of girls and boys. Through physical education, children learn to play and work hard to succeed, to be fair and honest, and to win and lose graciously. They learn to accept others for what they are as people, and not just on the basis of what they have or don't have. I believe that a career in physical education will be the most satisfying way I could possibly find to work with boys and girls. I plan to teach children of grade-school age, and I hope to be able to teach them sports and games they will be able to enjoy all their lives, and many other things that will help them become happy, well-adjusted people.

Student C: There are several things to consider when deciding on a lifetime job. One of these, self-satisfaction, is the main reason.

If you are qualified for the job you are doing, you are going to try just a little harder and just a little longer to be a success. The personal joy that can be derived from your association with people is one of the major fundamentals of happiness and success. Since I like people, I feel that I could help my community by teaching other people the philosophy I will have derived from my college education.

Student D: I believe that I gained more from my classes in physical education during high school than from anything else. My physical education teacher was one of the finest teachers in the school. She was always ready to help any girl who had a problem, or who had any trouble learning any of the games or dances we did. She also started a club for leaders, and spent many hours with us helping us learn how to be good leaders. We often assisted with classes, and learned to officiate. Our teacher was very patient with us—even though many times it would have been easier for her to do things herself, she helped us until we had learned how to do whatever we were working on at that time. As a result of our leader's club, a number of us were able to get jobs during the summer as junior counselors in camps or helping on playgrounds. I decided that I would rather teach physical education or be a recreation leader than anything else that I could think of. I am planning on a major in physical education and a minor in recreation. I hope to be able to finish a minor in health education also, since I believe that good health, and knowing about health, is one of the most important parts of a girl's life. I will be ready for my future work with this preparation.

Student E: I enjoy being around boys and working with them. I enjoy teaching boys all about sports and how to take defeat as well as they have taken victory. I know that the coaching field isn't a field in which to make a big salary, but I feel that being able to work at something that one likes is the biggest factor in selecting your future means of supporting a family.

The statement of a young man who had returned to college after World War II is worthy of consideration since it represents a change in the choice of a vocation. This student had started preparation for a professional career in one of the engineering fields, had an excellent scholastic record, and was apparently well suited to his chosen field. His statement explains his reasons for changing major fields and the basis for his choice of physical education.

My pal and I were together all through high school and we played together on all of the teams. We planned to enter the University and enroll in the College of Engineering. The war came, and at the end of our sophomore year we enlisted in the Navy. We were sent to the same training school and eventually assigned to the same ship. During the South Pacific campaign we were shore-based on many different islands and found that the recreational facilities were pitiful. Between us we managed to bring ship recreation equipment ashore at each of the bases and organized team games and tournaments. It was wonderful to see the effect it had on the men. Soon we were regularly assigned to recreation duty at each new base. We talked over our plans for the future and decided that when we were civilians again we would study physical education, become teachers, and make it possible for many boys to learn how to play and realize the benefits of a good program in physical education.

Most college students have studied the requirements and op-portunities of numerous vocations before entering college to start preparing for the careers they want to follow. If you entered college without a definite choice of vocation, or are dissatisfied with your original choice, you should thoroughly investigate any career in which you think you may be interested. Your final choice should be made only after a careful study of your possi-bilities for success, and personal assurance that your decision is a wise one.

Anyone who is undecided about a vocational choice or who has no decided preference will benefit from a study of vocations and the personal characteristics required for satisfaction and success as a professional worker. If you are sure of yourself and your selection, you are better qualified to concentrate on high achievement in your work. In addition, the purposes, standards, and requirements of your vocation become your personal goals.

If you are a transfer student from a community or junior college, or were enrolled in a school where the first two years were largely devoted to general education, you have undoubt-

edly encountered a number of problems. A student who changes
from one college or university to another, or from a general to a
major field, must often make up deficiencies in courses that are
prerequisite to advanced work. Some college credits are transferred only as elective hours in a major curriculum. A student
who selects a major field solely because in that field he can graduate in the customary four years has not necessarily selected
wisely. An extra term or year in college to complete requirements for a preferred career may be a worth-while investment,
and should be considered seriously.

An understanding of the basic purposes and nature of physical
education, health education, and recreation provides the foundation for a re-evaluation of your choice and a personal appraisal
of your qualifications as a prospective member of a profession.

THE NATURE OF PHYSICAL EDUCATION, HEALTH EDUCATION, AND RECREATION

Physical education, health education, and recreation are
closely related in many ways. All are important aspects of education and deal closely with human qualities. Education provides the knowledge by which people learn to do well the things
that are fundamental to daily living. Physical education, health
education, and recreation are essential to a well-rounded education, and contribute materially to the life of every person.

All education is concerned with giving people an opportunity
to develop their abilities. Vigorous and strong bodies, sound
health, mental alertness, and social and emotional balance are
desired for every person. Since each person differs from all
others, the task of educators is to help each one develop his own
potentialities. Physical education, health education, and recreation are indispensable areas of education since they contribute
to the health and to the social, emotional, and mental development of children and young people, as well as to physical and
recreational interests and skills. Leaders in these fields have important functions to fulfill if education is to accomplish its
purpose.

Physical education

Physical education is a vital part of American education. Its contribution to the general program of education includes among its purposes the development of health, physical welfare, and recreational interests. The educational significance of physical education in relation to these purposes has long been acknowledged. Active sports, games, dancing, aquatics, and camping and outing activities make up the program of physical education. The capable physical educator finds many opportunities to help children and young people develop capabilities for responsible, intelligent, and democratic behavior through their participation with others in the activities of the program. A well-conducted program of physical education provides equally for those who are physically handicapped, those of average ability, and those who are highly skilled. Intramural and interschool athletics as an outgrowth of the physical education program are widely accepted as an essential phase of school life.

Physical education is important in adult life. The tensions of modern living place great strain on man's physical and mental health. Interesting, stimulating physical activity is recognized as valuable to relaxation and in combating tensions. Freedom from tension in turn strengthens resistance to influences that threaten mental and physical health. Sports, games, hunting, fishing, camping, and outdoor activities interest entire families; contribute to relaxation, recreation, and health; and provide enjoyable pursuits that can be followed throughout life.

Health education

The importance of health education is unquestionable. Educators have long recognized their responsibility toward health, and all major statements of the purposes of education prepared by national groups in recent years have listed health as a primary function of education. As early as 1918, health was listed as the first objective of education.

Educators realize that attention must be given to the life of a child outside the school as well as in the school, and that mental and physical health are of utmost importance. They recognize that each child must develop health habits and attitudes as well as health knowledge. An adequate program of health education provides opportunity for boys and girls to understand themselves and the health problems affecting their everyday living.

It is unfortunate that health is sometimes misconstrued to mean merely the absence of disease. Good health is a combination of mental and emotional balance, physical well-being, and freedom from disease or illness. Some individuals who are physically handicapped are happy, well-adjusted people who maintain a high level of health within their limitations. All aspects of health are important in the health education program: public health and welfare; personal health—mental, physical, social, and emotional; and such hereditary, environmental, and behavior factors as affect health. Health education is of vital importance in the school program, in the family, in the community, and to the nation.

Recreation

Recreation reaches all people in some way. There is no limit to the extent of recreation, or to the form which it takes. Individuals use their leisure time in a variety of ways. It is of great importance that people learn to use their leisure time wisely; that they have an opportunity for recreation which is acceptable to the communities in which they live; and that leadership is available for those who desire help with recreational interests.

Many thousands of people take part in organized programs of recreation. Other thousands follow recreational interests on their own initiative. Recreation education is important in school and adult programs of education to help people plan and carry out self-organized and self-directed activities. The extent of recreation is limitless. Art, dramatics, music, literature, and active and spectator sports attract the interest of many people. Gardening, carpentry, model building, collecting, cooking, sewing, upholstering, and a wide variety of other hobbies afford enjoyment to individuals and groups. Photography, nature study, camping, travel, and radio and television programs, as well as various social activities, provide a wide range of leisure time pursuits for many persons. These activities represent only a few of the many recreational interests followed by people.

That recreation is important to the American way of life is demonstrated by the widespread development of private and public recreation areas and programs in the United States. Local, state, and national governmental agencies spend many thousands of dollars annually to promote and conduct recreation, and to increase recreational areas and opportunities. The provision of state and national parks, public picnic and camping grounds, and the development of botanical and zoological gardens, wild-life preserves, forest reserves, museums, libraries, municipal in-door and outdoor theaters, and stadiums have become accepted responsibilities of government.

The school camp movement and programs are recognized as important educational aspects of the modern school. Recreation education is carried out by both public and private agencies for in-school and out-of-school children and youth, and for adults. Industrial and business firms promote recreation programs. Private clubs, churches, and youth organizations often employ year-round leaders to conduct recreation activities. Recreation is unquestionably an important part of education, and essential to the American way of life.

QUALIFICATIONS

The qualifications for professional leaders in physical education, health education, and recreation vary according to the type of work to be done, the specialization selected, and the personal qualifications demanded in the area. You should compare your personal characteristics with the qualities desirable for professional workers in the field of your choice. You should also consider carefully the educational requirements that must be met to qualify for these professions.

Leaders in physical education and health education, recreation, coaching, camp counseling, and occupational and physical therapy need preparation similar to that for teachers. You should, therefore, secure as much information as possible about professional preparation for teaching. You should make a careful appraisal of your personal qualifications as a prospective leader, and plan to develop into the kind of a person who is successful in fields requiring ability to work well with people.

Personal standards for physical education and health education teachers and recreation leaders are high. The following characteristics are demanded of teachers and leaders in these fields.

Physical Health. Excellent health, abundant vitality, and physical stamina are basic requirements. Personal habits of good health are important. Physical education and recreation work require a great deal of physical energy, freedom from physical handicaps, and the ability to stand long hours of physical activity. The health educator should represent equally fine health qualities as an example of his field.

Mental Health. The teacher or leader must be a well-balanced person, able to maintain emotional control under trying circumstances and capable of relieving his own tensions through well-directed personal interests and leisure-time activities. Enthusiasm, cheerfulness, and a good sense of humor are important characteristics.

Intelligence and Scholarship. Students in these areas face a curriculum of difficult subjects in preparation for teaching or recreation leadership. Young men and women planning to enter these professions must have the intelligence and ability to undertake such studies as chemistry, physics, biology, anatomy, physiology, psychology, and sociology; technical aspects of teaching and learning physical and recreational activities; and the broad areas of general and professional education. Scholarship influences placement opportunities after graduation. The better positions are generally secured by students who have maintained acceptable scholastic standings.

Voice and Command of English. A well-modulated, distinct, and effective speaking voice is a necessary attribute. An excellent command of the English language is desirable; good spoken and written English is a necessity.

Leadership and Teaching Ability. An interest in helping others learn and the ability to teach others how to do things is imperative. Many opportunities are available to undergraduate students to develop their teaching skill by working with children and young people before their formal employment begins. Students may work as leaders on playgrounds, in summer camps, in youth organizations, in hospitals and welfare agencies, and with after-school activities. Successful leadership experience in high school is of value in preparing for professional leadership.

Courtesy of University of Illinois

Skill in Physical Activities. Good coordination, the ability to develop physical skills easily, and above average skills in a number of sports are significant only when associated with many of the other qualifications of a good teacher or leader. Proficiency in a number of recreational activities and familiarity with athletics, swimming, dancing, and camping are expected of the

Chart 1

SELF-APPRAISAL CHART [2]

(Continued on following pages)

HEALTH AND PHYSICAL FITNESS	Never	Seldom	Sometimes	Frequently	Always
1. Do you have good health?					
2. Can you participate in strenuous activities and do hard work?					
3. Do you become irritable and nervous when you are tired?					
4. Can you take part in all of the activities your friends and classmates engage in?					
5. Do you feel energetic and eager to start the day when you get up in the morning?					
6. Do you have a good appetite and enjoy your food?					
7. Do you give others the impression that you are healthy, vigorous, and vitally alive?					
8. Do you feel alert and ready to take part in sports or other activities after school?					
9. Do you find it necessary to miss school or avoid other activities because of colds or various minor illnesses?					
10. Do you plan your work so that you get sufficient sleep?					
PERSONAL APPEARANCE AND GROOMING					
1. Are you careful of your appearance? (Neatness; cleanliness; well-cared-for nails, hair, and skin)					
2. Do you try to stand, sit, and walk with good posture?					
3. Do you try to make the most of your good qualities through careful grooming and good posture?					
4. Are you "sloppy" in dress and manner?					
5. Do you give others the impression that you are well-groomed and attractive in appearance?					
6. Do you feel that you are properly dressed and well-groomed when you attend social affairs? (Good taste, simplicity, neatness)					

[2] Adapted with permission from E. E. Samuelson *et al., You'd Like Teaching* (Central Washington College of Education, Ellensburg, Washington. Seattle, Washington: Craftsman Press, 1946), pp. 31-35.

Chart I (Continued)

EMOTIONAL STABILITY AND CONTROL	Never	Seldom	Sometimes	Frequently	Always
1. Are generally even-tempered, cheerful, and happy?					
2. Can you take a joke or teasing without becoming angry or upset?					
3. Are you a good sport when you lose a game?					
4. Do you find something interesting to do when you feel low, depressed, or worried?					
5. Are you sympathetic, patient, tolerant of others?					
6. Does your sense of humor include situations that involve you?					
7. Can you meet obstacles without becoming discouraged and giving up?					
8. Do you resent criticism and find it difficult to acknowledge your errors?					
9. Are you often moody, depressed, or discouraged?					
INTELLECTUAL ABILITIES AND INTERESTS					
1. Are school subjects easy for you to understand?					
2. Do you take time to find out more about topics that have been discussed or assigned?					
3. Do you read articles and books on current topics?					
4. Do you like to investigate new ideas or ways of doing things for your own enjoyment and information?					
5. Do you make suggestions for new ideas or plans to be carried out by classes or other school groups?					
6. Are you interested in the scientific developments in industry, engineering, agriculture, and medicine?					
7. Do you enjoy hearing good music and seeing works of art?					

specialist, even though he cannot be an expert in all activities. Teachers and leaders should, moreover, understand and appreciate the values of the various activities in the total program.

A varsity letter in one or more sports may be of value to a man in securing a position, since an earned letter is custom-

Chart 1 (Continued)

SCHOLARSHIP	Never	Seldom	Sometimes	Frequently	Always
1. Are your high-school records above average?					
2. Do you feel it is worth while to maintain a high scholastic record?					
3. Are you interested in the subjects you have taken in high school, or are taking at present?					
4. Do you like to study and find it easy to concentrate when you are studying?					
5. Do you express yourself well before a class or other group?					
6. Do others understand you when you explain things?					
7. Is it easy for you to give directions so that others can follow them?					
SOCIAL ADJUSTMENT AND ASPIRATIONS					
1. Are you interested in other people, their problems, and their plans?					
2. Do you like to help people solve their problems?					
3. Do you like people - children in particular?					
4. Do you practice courteous behavior and try to improve your social assets?					
5. Do you set high social standards for yourself and try to meet those standards?					
6. Do you encourage your friends and groups with which you are associated to maintain acceptable social standards?					
7. Do you feel you cooperate well with others in socially desirable activities?					
8. Are you willing to make sacrifices and endure inconveniences to achieve worth-while goals?					

arily evidence of a high degree of skill. It is clear that few can be outstanding in all sports, but every professional student should aim for the highest possible level of skill. Women students who have been members of club teams representing highly skilled players, who have participated widely in intra-

Chart 1 (Continued)

LEADERSHIP ABILITY	Never	Seldom	Sometimes	Frequently	Always
1. Have you been a leader in student groups, held offices, taken part in programs, been a committee member or chairman?					
2. Are you considered a leader by others?					
3. Have you been active in clubs and organizations other than athletic groups?					
4. Do teachers seem to feel you are a good leader in classes, other school groups, and athletics?					
5. Do other students respect your opinion, ask your advice, talk over problems with you?					
6. Do you respect the opinions of other people?					
7. Are you sensitive to the feelings of others?					
8. Do you cooperate with others when working with a group rather than trying to "run" affairs?					
9. Do you take advantage of your athletic reputation?					
10. Do you insist on your point of view even when you realize it is not the best solution to a problem?					
11. Do you think through a problem before discussing it or expressing an opinion before a group?					
12. Are you able to get others to follow your suggestions without insisting or causing unpleasantness?					
13. Do you make an effort to be friendly and courteous, and show willingness to listen to others?					
14. Do you enjoy helping others and trying to teach them things you have learned or skills you have mastered?					
15. Are you patient and helpful with others who do not learn as rapidly as you do?					

mural sports, or who have been members of dance groups are usually capable of demonstrating and teaching with confidence in their own skills.

Personal Attributes. All personal attributes represent factors to be considered in planning a career. Such qualities as initiative, self-control, good taste, and respect for social standards are

Chart 1 (Continued)

PERSONAL SKILLS	Never	Seldom	Sometimes	Frequently	Always
1. Are you considered an all-around athlete by others?					
2. Have you been active as a leader in an athletic club or association?					
3. Have you tried to learn better ways of performing sport skills?					
4. Do you feel that boys and girls who are not good athletes are less important to the school than the athletes?					
5. Do you feel that people who are not interested in sports and games have a superior attitude?					
6. Do you try to understand and appreciate the attitude of others who like activities that you do not particularly enjoy?					
7. Have you been considered outstanding in your physical education classes?					
8. Are you interested in learning new sports and games?					
9. Have you tried to develop ability in a number of recreational activities such as craft work, nature study, woodcraft, and hobbies?					
10. Are you considered a good dancer by your partners?					
11. Do you try to concentrate on becoming an expert performer in your favorite sport or in dance activities?					
12. Have you enjoyed teaching others to play games, or swim, or dance?					

important characteristics for every person; they are necessary qualities for teachers and other leaders. Cheerfulness, friendliness toward people, and enthusiastic enjoyment in professional work contribute immeasurably to successful leadership.

Personal qualifications that create favorable public relations, influence young people wisely, and inspire the trust of children and parents are highly desirable characteristics. That these attributes are basically of as much importance as scholarship has been demonstrated by numerous leaders whose academic records have been unimpressive but who have made outstanding contributions through their practical leadership.

Chart 2

SELF-APPRAISAL

SUMMARY OF RATINGS					
HOW DO YOU RATE?	Excellent	Good	Average	Fair	Poor
1. Health and physical fitness					
2. Personal appearance and grooming					
3. Emotional stability and control					
4. Intellectual abilities and interests					
5. Scholarship					
6. Social adjustment and aspirations					
7. Leadership ability					
8. Personal skills					
HOW DO YOU RATE YOURSELF?					

SELF-APPRAISAL

The foregoing statement of personal standards and qualities serves to summarize some of the more important qualifications you should possess to be successful as a physical educator, a health educator, or a recreation leader. Although no personal rating is entirely accurate, some form of personal appraisal should be made by every person planning to enter a profession with established requirements for the personal qualifications of its members. Such an evaluation serves to indicate traits that need improvement, habits that need correction, and qualities that are outstanding. A comparison of self-appraisal ratings with the requirements of a career helps to indicate potentialities for outstanding professional leadership as well as qualities which may be detrimental to success.

Chart 1 (pp. 14-18) can help you assess your personal characteristics. The opinions of parents, teachers, and friends should also be secured on the items appearing on the rating chart.

After you have completed rating yourself, summarize your capabilities and qualifications on the scale given in Chart 2. The summary should give you an over-all picture of your strengths and weaknesses. You will undoubtedly be interested in making a reappraisal of your qualities sometime in the future to determine whether you have improved your weak points and maintained your stronger characteristics.

When you have rated yourself on each of the items, look over the results. How do you rate? Remember that very few people will have accomplished the greatest development of which they are capable. The majority have to learn to get along with others, to acknowledge their own shortcomings and try to correct them, and to develop interests which will contribute to a well-rounded personality. Study your answers and estimate how you stand in each of the areas you have appraised. Then try summarizing your ratings with Chart 2.

Your rating should give you a fair example of how you compare at the present time with the qualifications expected of professional leaders. Your four years of college offer you the opportunity to meet the requirements of your career, to learn the necessary personal skills, and to become a well-rounded and well-educated person. The following chapters discuss the nature of the professions of physical education, health education, and recreation, and allied fields of work; the curriculums of professional preparation; and opportunities to develop the skills necessary for leadership in your career.

SUMMARY

Intelligent planning is essential to progress toward a vocation in which a lifetime may be spent. You should carefully evaluate your interests to determine whether they are vocational or avocational in nature. If you have already chosen a career, you should re-examine your choice. You will need to study the nature and content of physical education, health education, recreation, and related fields. You should investigate and analyze the personal characteristics needed for success in the field, the required standards of preparation, and the future possibilities for a permanent career. It is particularly important to appraise your personal attributes, interests, and abilities on the basis of requirements for prospective professional workers in physical education, health, or recreation.

At least four years of college are ahead of you. This is the normal requirement for certification to teach in the majority of states, or for employment in recreation. Since curriculums differ among schools, you should study the major program, scholastic regulations, and course requirements in your own college.

Your college life should provide an opportunity to become a well-educated person in every respect. An intelligent and well-rounded college student makes and values close personal friends and a wide range of acquaintances; learns to understand differing viewpoints and beliefs; participates in many social, cultural, and recreational activities of campus life; and benefits from studying under outstanding educational leaders on the faculty of his college.

SUGGESTED PROBLEMS

1. List your reasons for interest in physical education, or health education, or recreation as a career. Are these reasons a sound basis for a future career? Why?

2. List the characteristics you have admired most in teachers or recreation leaders. Select the teacher or leader you have liked best and state the reasons for your opinion. What effect have your teachers or recreation leaders had on your selection of a career?

3. List the characteristics you like least in teachers or recreation leaders. What can you do to avoid such characteristics in your own personality or in your relations with other people?

4. Answer the questions on the self-appraisal chart. Ask friends and teachers to rate you on the same qualities. In what ways can you improve? What are your greatest strengths? Your greatest weaknesses?

5. Compare the qualities you possess with those you have listed for the best- and least-liked teachers, and decide what personal characteristics you need to possess as a future teacher or recreation leader.

6. List the benefits you believe to be associated with a college education.

REFERENCES

Allen, Ross L., "Health Education as Your Career," *Journal of the American Association for Health, Physical Education and Recreation,* 24:19, October 1953.

Evans, Eva Knox, *So You're Going to Teach!* Chicago: Julius Rosenwald Fund, 1943.

Fitzgerald, Gerald B., "Recreation as Your Career," *Journal of the American Association for Health, Physical Education and Recreation,* 23:27, November 1952.

Houle, Cyril O., *Teaching as a Career,* Occupational Monograph No. 5. Chicago: Science Research Associates, 1940.

The Job of the Physical Education Teacher. Prepared for the War Department by the National Roster. Washington, D. C.: Government Printing Office, 1945.

Lee, Edwin A., ed., *Teaching as a Man's Job.* Homewood, Illinois: Phi Delta Kappa, 1938.

Makechnie, George K., *Physical Education,* Vocational and Professional Monographs, No. 68. Boston: Bellman Publishing Company, Inc., 1946.

Nash, Jay B., *Opportunities in Physical Education, Health and Recreation.* New York: Vocational Guidance Manuals, Inc., 1953.

Palmer, Chester L., "Physical Education as Your Career," *Journal of the American Association for Health, Physical Education and Recreation,* 24:17, March 1953.

Samuelson, E. E., *et al., You'd Like Teaching.* Central Washington College of Education, Ellensburg, Washington. Seattle: Craftsman Press, 1946.

SOURCES OF INFORMATION

State Departments of Education. Information may be secured free of charge concerning state-approved institutions and requirements for certification of teachers.

United States Office of Education, Washington, D. C. Special lists of accredited colleges and universities, requirements for certification, and placement information are available on request.

American Association for Health, Physical Education and Recreation, 1201 Sixteenth Street, N.W., Washington 6, D. C. Vocational guidance pamphlets are available at a cost of 5 cents each on physical education, health education, and recreation as careers.

National Education Association, 1201 Sixteenth Street, N.W., Washington 6, D. C. Information concerning the national organization for prospective teachers (Future Teachers of America) and other written material related to teachings may be secured on request.

Public and Private Colleges and Universities. Information concerning admission requirements, fees, estimated living expenses, and the curriculum is available to prospective students on request. Inquiries to the Director of Admissions receive prompt replies from most institutions.

National Recreation Association, 314 Fourth Avenue, New York 10, New York. Information on recreation as a career may be secured on request.

American Public Health Association, 1790 Broadway, New York 19, New York. Information on preparation of public health specialists and requirements for placement may be secured on request.

Courtesy of University of Illinois

Physical education
health education
and recreation
as careers

The personal aspects of career planning, a brief statement of the nature of physical education, health education, and recreation qualifications, the importance of self-appraisal, and the general requirements have been presented. A thorough knowledge of a vocation, the requirements for preparation, and future opportunities represents an investment in a career and increases probabilities of success.

The importance of physical education, health education, and recreation should be understood by every prospective member of these professions. Specific requirements for preparation and employment; opportunities for advancement; provisions for salary, tenure, and retirement; and the nature of the work should be studied as the background for professional preparation. Teachers of physical education and health education, recreation leaders, vocational counselors, parents, and friends may offer valuable assistance in making plans for additional specialization.

Physical education, health education, and recreation offer wide opportunities to the young men and women who select one of these fields, or a combination of them, as careers. Each profession must be investigated separately to be fully understood. Similarities, as well as differences, will be found in requirements for preparation and in opportunities for employment.

The opportunities in any career should be evaluated from the standpoint of personal happiness and satisfaction as well as for the immediate or long-range prospects for employment. Happiness in a vocation is essential to effective and creative work. Enthusiasm for the work is reflected in enjoyment of daily living and pride in achievement. Opportunities to be found in a career are, necessarily, a realistic consideration. The possibilities for satisfaction in one's work are limited if the future offers little hope for improvement in working conditions, salary, or promotion.

While physical education, health education, and recreation are closely allied professions, each profession has specific opportunities of its own. Professional workers in each of these fields must meet qualifications identified with their particular area of work. Opportunities in the three fields are comparable for men and women. All three professions represent significant careers of service.

PHYSICAL EDUCATION AS A PROFESSION

Although the profession of physical education offers excellent career possibilities for both women and men, the nature of professional work in physical education has resulted in certain well-justified questions regarding the advisability of choosing this field as a career. The specific nature of physical education as a profession for women and for men is discussed separately.

Physical education as a profession for women

The woman who plans a career in physical education must meet high standards of personal character, appearance, conduct, and femininity. Good health, freedom from physical defects, and the ability to develop skill in the activities of the physical education program are essential. The woman physical educator is expected to meet the same standards of personal qualifications, scholarship, and professional competency required of other teachers.

Parents sometimes object to having their daughters select physical education as a career in the fear that they will become mannish and muscular, and represent the undesirable characteristics of the so-called "typical" woman athlete. It should be reassuring to parents to know that only a few women engaging in competitive sports have received unfavorable publicity. In contrast, thousands of women who teach physical education, who are well-skilled in sports, or who engage in competitive sports are consistently granted tribute for the high standards of conduct they display, and for the leadership they give to children and youth. In addition, it is possible for a woman who is particularly interested in dance to specialize in this area of physical education and plan a career as a teacher of dance activities.

Women who like physical activities, who enjoy working with boys and girls, and who realize the significance of physical education find that this field offers an exceptionally fine career for a woman. As a teacher, the physical educator has outstanding opportunities for leadership. As a person, she is able to maintain recreational interests in physical activities. As a homemaker and mother, she is well prepared to create an environment favorable to health and happy home relationships in which parents and children work and play together with mutual understanding and cooperation.

The woman who has prepared for a professional career in physical education understands the importance of sound mental and physical health, the ways in which a child grows and develops, and the values of healthy, happy play in the lives of children. She is capable of directing children's play, of planning parties, and of assisting with the development of community programs of recreation for young people. As a member of a community, she is qualified to take an active part in the work of the Parent-Teacher Association, to become an influential member of civic groups, and to contribute leadership to community undertakings.

Physical education as a career for women offers possibilities for a lifetime profession, for a vocation of a professional nature until marriage, and for an excellent preparation for home life and community service if teaching is supplanted by marriage as a career.

Physical education as a profession for men

The man who plans a career in physical education must meet the same high standards of personal qualifications and scholastic competence that are established for all prospective teachers. The same qualifications are expected of the man who is primarily interested in specializing in coaching. Although a high degree of skill in sports and other physical activities is of value, it is possible for men who are not outstanding athletes to become successful teachers of physical education. Skill in physical activities, sincere interest in teaching, a real enjoyment in working with children and young people, and an understanding of the importance of physical education combine to produce effective physical educators.

The favorable attitude of the public is encouraging to men who consider physical education as a prospective career. The average community looks on the physical educator as a leader of youth and an important influence within and outside the school. The fine quality of teaching and coaching provided by most men in physical education represents an example to be followed.

A majority of positions in physical education for men involve coaching responsibilities as well as teaching physical education. The coach must be a regular member of the school faculty in most cases and must participate in a variety of school activities. The profession of physical education offers a career for men in a field that contributes to total education, physical development, recreation, and health. It provides a constant challenge to each member of the profession and offers great opportunities for a satisfying and rewarding life's work.

Possibilities for employment

The demand for qualified men and women teachers of physical education has been constant for many years. At the present time the demand is greater than ever before, and is accompanied by a serious shortage of men and women who are prepared to teach physical education. A nationwide survey made in 1953 revealed that there were fewer men and women qualifying for certification in physical education than in previous years. Table 1 clearly illustrates the decrease in college enrollment.

TABLE 1 [1]

TOTAL NUMBER OF COLLEGE AND UNIVERSITY GRADUATES TO QUALIFY FOR STANDARD
TEACHING CERTIFICATE; NUMBER IN MEN'S PHYSICAL EDUCATION; NUMBER IN WOMEN'S
PHYSICAL EDUCATION; WITH PERCENT OF TOTAL

Year	Total College Graduates Eligible for Teaching Certificates	College Graduates Prepared to Teach					
		Men's Physical Education		Women's Physical Education		Men and Women	
		Number	Percent of Total	Number	Percent of Total	Number	Percent of Total
1949	86,447	7,548	8.73%	2,402	2.78%	9,950	11.51%
1950	115,477	10,614	9.19	3,178	2.75	13,792	11.94
1951	106,797	8,179	7.66	2,562	2.40	10,741	10.06
1952	99,159	6,546	6.60	2,607	2.63	9,153	9.23
1953	91,104	5,680	6.23	2,586	2.84	8,266	9.07

1 Ray C. Maul, "Wanted: Physical Education Teachers," *Journal of the American Association for Health, Physical Education and Recreation,* 24:12, May 1953. (Reprinted by permission.)

The reasons given for the decrease in certification and the resulting teacher shortage include several factors. First, there was a decrease in college graduates after 1950. Second, in a period of high employment college graduates found many work opportunities outside of teaching. Third, the national defense effort absorbed many men and women in industrial employment. Fourth, the armed forces claimed many men soon after graduation. Fifth, with a trend toward earlier marriages, many more young women were married before completing college work or within a short time after entering the teaching profession.

The demand for teachers is directly related to school enrollments. The number of children in elementary and secondary schools in 1947 was estimated at more than 30 million.[2] That number had increased by four million in 1953, and further estimates indicate an expected increase of an additional six million children by 1960.[3] The 1950 census and vital statistics report of the federal government revealed that the expected decrease in birth rate following World War II had not materialized, and that there has actually been an extensive increase in elementary school enrollments. The children born during the early war years began to reach high-school age in 1954 and, in a few years, will create a demand for large numbers of teachers to fill new positions. The first group of these boys and girls to enter junior high school created a need for many additional teachers.

Not only is there a demand for teachers to fill new positions, but many vacancies arise each year in established positions. Retirement and death among older teachers create vacancies. Women teachers marry and leave teaching for careers as homemakers. A number of teachers change from one school to another, and some enter business or other professions. Other teachers resign or take leaves to study for advanced degrees. These positions must be filled if the school program is to be carried out.

Clearly an encouraging view of employment opportunities may be taken by physical education students. Approximately one out of twelve teachers was devoting all or part of his time to physical education or related areas, such as health education

2 Benjamin W. Frazier, *Teaching as a Career*, Bulletin 1947, No. 11, Federal Security Agency, Office of Education (Washington, D. C.: Government Printing Office, 1947), p. 9.

3 Maul, *op. cit.*, p. 12.

or recreation, in 1950.[4] The demand for teachers and coaches varies in different parts of the country and is dependent on both school population and the extent of the school programs. There is a consistently increasing need for more men teachers of physical education for elementary and junior high school positions. Youth-serving agencies such as the YMCA, the YWCA, and others employ a number of well-qualified men and women each year to conduct programs of health and physical education. Widespread recognition of the need for more adequate programs of physical education is creating favorable opportunities for placement as better programs are developed. A recent survey showed that in 873 schools in towns over 2500 in population, 160,000 boys and girls were not enrolled in physical education courses.[5] Many more teachers are needed to prevent a continuation of this condition.

The goal of physical education as expressed by leaders in the field today is to provide an adequate program for all children in every school throughout the country. Such a program would include health services and instruction, physical education classes, and opportunities for participation in a variety of recreational and competitive activities, including intramural and interschool sports. In the area of physical education instruction alone if there were adequate teaching staffs provided for instruction on the basis of the accepted standard of one period a day, there would be many more opportunities for teachers in this field than now exist. For example, using a pupil load of 300 students for each teacher of physical education, 100,000 teachers would be required for the daily instruction of all school children. This figure provides only for the daily class, and not for any of the extra programs and services that are ordinarily included in the physical educator's job.

4 Jay B. Nash, *Opportunities in Physical Education, Health and Recreation* (New York: Vocational Guidance Manuals, Inc., 1953), p. 5.

5 "Personnel and Relationships in School Health, Physical Education, and Recreation," *Research Bulletin of the National Education Association,* 28:108, October 1950.

Types of positions

Positions in physical education represent a wide choice. Successful experience, advanced specialization, and the possession of a Master's or Doctor's degree are often required for positions of an administrative or supervisory nature. Inexperienced persons are seldom employed as specialists unless they are highly qualified for a particular position, although they may receive appointments as assistants to specialists. Positions generally available to inexperienced teachers are indicated on the accompanying list.

PHYSICAL EDUCATION

ELEMENTARY SCHOOL

Teacher of physical education
    Lower grades—boys and girls
    Upper grades—boys only or girls only
Teacher of physical education and athletic coach
    Upper grades—boys
Teacher of physical education and director of recreation
    Lower grades—boys and girls
    Upper grades—boys only or girls only
    All grades—boys and girls (recreation program)
Teacher of physical education, health coordinator, safety education director, and other school responsibilities

SECONDARY SCHOOL: JUNIOR AND SENIOR HIGH SCHOOL

Teacher of physical education
Teacher of physical education and athletic coach—boys
Teacher of physical education, health education, and safety education
Teacher of physical education, health education, and recreation
Teacher of physical education and health education, and athletic coach
Teacher of physical education in combination with other subjects
Athletic coach

COLLEGE

Part-time or full-time assistant or instructor
    Graduate assistant

Research assistant
Instructor
Private college teacher of dance or sports

COMMUNITY AND AGENCY

Recreation leader or instructor on summer playground
Recreation leader of physical activities in centers
Physical education teacher and recreation leader or assistant director
    YMCA, YWCA, and similar organizations such as Boy Scouts,
    Girl Scouts, and Camp Fire Girls
    Social, business, industrial, and church groups
Counselor for private, organization, or public camps
Rural extension recreation director

SPECIAL FIELDS

Assistant specialist in physical education and recreation
    Hospital recreation assistant
    Physical therapy or occupational therapy assistant
    Rehabilitation or physically-handicapped assistant

The working environment and duties

Teachers of physical education have an opportunity to work with boys and girls in surroundings that contribute to friendly and congenial relationships. Few people have greater opportunity for guiding and counseling young people and for securing their respect. The playground, gymnasium, pool, and athletic field are the classrooms for physical education. Physical education activities interest young people and encourage their spontaneous enjoyment and wholehearted participation.

The wide variety of activities of the physical education program challenge the initiative of the physical education teacher and require that he be well-informed and efficient. Teaching physical education requires skill and imagination, patience and humor. Planning and improving a program is a continuous responsibility and involves many duties. Intramural and extramural programs often extend the school day beyond the time that other teachers spend in the school. The physical educator frequently finds it necessary to return to the school in the eve-

TABLE 2 [6]

DUTIES ENGAGED IN BY 538 MEN TEACHERS OF PHYSICAL EDUCATION IN 436 SCHOOLS

School Groupings:	A	B	C	D	E	F	G	Tots.
Number responding	60	90	149	65	30	24	18	436
Percent of return	25	39	53	70	61	72	36	45
Administration and Supervision								
Coach	34	78	133	60	38	41	71	455
Teacher P. E.	24	61	123	63	37	41	84	433
Director of athletics	19	49	83	45	16	22	22	256
Teacher academic subjects	30	76	19	64	28	11	12	240
Director P. E.	17	33	46	35	23	21	19	194
Director intramurals	4	29	50	39	22	24	22	190
Supervisor P. E.	16	28	44	19	10	9	5	131
Director recreation	8	18	27	19	8	11	6	97
Supervisor of:								
Athletic field	14	43	62	34	17	22	37	329
Gymnasium	18	45	83	42	23	29	20	260
Equipment	18	49	81	39	17	20	14	238
Playground	11	19	31	10	5	13	13	102
Tennis courts	3	11	20	8	6	11	9	68
Pool	0	0	3	9	6	10	34	60
Miscellaneous	0	3	3	10	2	2	21	41
Health Service								
First aid	30	71	103	62	33	41	66	406
Keep team in condition	28	72	116	61	30	29	56	392
Improve community health	18	40	52	40	25	24	50	249
Organize and assist in med. exams...	22	39	65	31	23	17	35	232
Prescribe exercises	3	23	38	33	20	24	35	176
Keep follow-up records	13	32	46	27	14	17	23	172
Give other exams	2	2	16	19	7	13	20	79
Miscellaneous	0	1	2	2	1	1	5	12
Promotion of Program								
Promote intramurals	16	52	96	8	36	32	46	286
Athletic publicity	22	37	76	33	16	21	48	253
Officiate games	13	33	65	46	25	30	33	245
Stage exhibitions	5	9	31	30	20	24	34	153
Direct athletic association	8	17	39	19	13	18	20	134
Promote recreation faculty—adults...	7	13	34	18	12	13	12	109
Promote health campaigns	6	10	15	10	9	6	24	80
Miscellaneous	0	0	0	1	0	1	1	3
Testing and Measuring in Physical Education								
Achievement tests	1	20	32	35	18	24	42	172
Knowledge tests	2	11	29	43	18	17	28	148
Classification tests	0	7	11	22	11	16	19	86
Motor ability tests	1	8	14	14	7	16	17	77
Strength tests	0	0	9	2	1	7	13	32
Miscellaneous	0	0	0	1	0	1	1	3
Financial Duties								
Purchase equipment—P. E.	23	55	89	45	27	23	32	294
Manage athletic finances	14	32	41	14	8	15	23	147
Make out athletic budget	10	19	26	19	11	17	16	118
Make out P. E. budget	2	10	14	13	14	16	12	81
Miscellaneous Duties								
Church work	20	46	80	35	18	22	14	265
Make speeches	8	14	26	22	20	26	32	148
Miscellaneous	3	19	19	7	7	9	12	75
Direct clubs	4	13	16	17	4	8	12	74

[6] C. O. Jackson, "Activities Engaged in by Teachers of Physical Education in the High Schools of Illinois," *Research Quarterly of the American Association for Health, Physical Education and Recreation,* 13:242, May 1942. (Reprinted by Permission.)

TABLE 3 [7]

DUTIES ENGAGED IN BY 467 WOMEN TEACHERS OF PHYSICAL EDUCATION IN 436 SCHOOLS

School Groupings:	A	B	C	D	E	F	G	Tots.
Number responding	60	90	149	65	30	24	18	436
Percent of return	25	39	53	70	61	72	36	45
Administration and Supervision								
Teacher P. E.	23	61	110	55	33	37	56	375
Teacher academic subjects	23	59	106	43	11	2	43	287
Supervisor gymnasium	5	9	22	21	11	17	10	95
Supervisor equipment	4	8	19	12	9	16	7	75
Director P. E.	1	9	16	11	3	15	14	69
Supervisor athletic field	0	3	10	10	6	9	20	58
Director intramurals	0	1	13	10	9	9	7	49
Supervisor playgrounds	7	4	14	10	5	4	2	46
Supervisor P. E.	2	10	13	9	3	2	1	40
Supervisor pool	0	2	3	6	1	9	18	39
Supervisor tennis courts	1	5	12	9	2	6	0	35
Director athletics	4	5	6	7	3	5	3	33
Coach athletic teams	2	6	5	3	2	9	3	30
Director of recreation	4	3	5	9	2	4	2	29
Miscellaneous	1	2	3	5	0	2	11	24
Health Service								
Render first aid	7	31	53	45	26	34	56	252
Prescribe exercises	1	23	36	29	23	22	37	171
Give orthopedic exams	1	14	24	29	20	28	39	155
Improve community health	10	21	33	20	12	13	44	153
Keep follow-up records	5	11	17	17	11	26	37	124
Organize and assist in medical exams	2	10	18	20	11	16	40	117
Give other exams	1	3	7	9	7	9	27	63
Keep team in condition	1	2	10	8	6	7	8	42
Miscellaneous	0	3	2	4	2	7	4	21
Promotion of Program								
Stage exhibitions	5	17	44	38	29	36	38	207
Promote intramurals	5	15	51	6	32	33	57	199
Direct athletic association	6	14	46	39	24	25	27	181
Officiate	2	10	30	22	15	26	41	146
Promote health campaigns	3	4	9	15	8	11	35	85
Carry on publicity	1	5	10	7	8	9	17	57
Promote recreation	1	6	8	12	6	5	13	51
Miscellaneous	3	2	2	3	2	3	3	18
Testing and Measuring								
Achievement tests	5	17	48	40	24	32	48	214
Knowledge tests	2	17	34	35	21	34	30	173
Motor ability tests	1	3	12	19	13	12	40	100
Classification tests	1	4	8	9	8	14	22	66
Strength tests	0	1	1	1	1	2	6	12
Miscellaneous	0	0	1	0	1	5	2	9
Financial Duties								
Purchase equipment and supplies	2	9	25	18	6	17	23	110
Manage finances	1	4	8	6	5	5	15	44
Make out budget, interscholastic	0	2	5	7	8	9	8	39
Miscellaneous	1	2	1	0	3	2	6	15
Make out budget P. E. only	0	0	1	0	0	0	1	2
Miscellaneous Duties								
Church work	14	36	62	24	6	8	7	157
Speeches	2	7	14	10	4	5	4	46
Direct clubs	3	8	8	7	7	4	3	40

[7] C. O. Jackson, "Activities Engaged in by Teachers of Physical Education in the High Schools of Illinois," *Research Quarterly of the American Association for Health, Physical Education and Recreation*, 13:242, May 1942. (Reprinted by Permission.)

ning to conduct recreational and athletic events and assist with
community programs. The numerous duties of the teacher and
coach are indicated in Tables 2 and 3.

In addition to regularly assigned duties, activities such as
those indicated by a young woman teacher are common:

> I teach physical education in a senior high school. The activities
> I teach include archery, badminton, bowling, first aid, golf, mod-
> ern dance, and swimming. We are required to attend all teachers'
> meetings, preschool meetings, and assemblies, and the district
> meeting of the state teacher's association. Attendance at these
> meetings is on school time.

My duties in connection with teaching but not on actual teaching time include:

1. Sponsor of a swim club, which meets one night a week for
   one semester. The club presents an annual swimming show.
2. GAA activities on one or two nights a week depending on
   the time of year.
3. Spring festival of sports, which is compulsory. I must contribute about 20 minutes or more of activities.
4. P.T.A. meetings which are held once a month at night.
5. Lunchroom duty for about two weeks a year, when I have to
   stay and watch the students eat their lunches.
6. Sponsor for the Spring Formal (similar to a Prom).

In addition:

1. I have charge of a free swim during fun nights, which are
   held once a month.
2. I take or sell tickets at sports events—we are lucky, we get
   paid for this.
3. Last year I was sponsor for a junior Orchesis group in modern dance. This activity was dropped this year because there
   was no space available for practice.
4. I attend the potluck dinner held once a month by the faculty
   women.
5. The faculty of the entire school district have a potluck and
   square dance once a month. You can bring your family to
   this one.
6. Last year I refereed basketball games at the YWCA.
7. Among some of the social activities which faculty are expected to assist with are such events as exhibition basketball games, stunt shows, senior parties, and chaperonage at
   dances.

The extent of the duties of a man physical educator and coach is illustrated in this statement by a three-year teacher:

1. Teach five freshman physical education classes.
2. Head freshman football coach (three assistants)
3. Head freshman basketball coach (two assistants)
4. Run faculty recreation program twice a month from 7:30 to 9:30 P.M. (square dancing, badminton, table tennis, and volleyball)
5. Scouting assignments in 8 football games and 4 basketball games

Day's Agenda:

8:15	Arrive at school
8:15-8:30	Pick up mail, read daily bulletin
8:30-8:52	Prepare for 1st-period class—get dressed, check teaching to be done, get equipment ready
8:52-10:30	Teach two physical education classes
10:30-12:00	Free periods—answer mail, plan daily practice for after-school sports, work on scouting report, plan lessons for the next day. (Use "curriculum" as a guide for teaching skills.) Interviews with pupils.
12:00-12:30	Lunch
12:40-3:04	Teach three more physical education classes
3:04-5:30	After-school sports coaching assignment
5:30-5:50	Shower and talk with other coaches about day's practice
6:00	Arrive home for dinner

The duties of the coach include not only teaching the skills of the sport effectively but also many other related activities. He must be the kind of a person who inspires respect and loyalty from squad members and who emphasizes the importance of team cooperation and sportsmanship. The coach should be prepared to assist in educating the public and the student body to desirable ethical procedures in sports competition and to maintain a high level of personal conduct. He should respect the rules, avoid overemphasis on the professional and commercial aspects of the sport, coordinate the competitive program with other school activities, and broaden the sports offerings to include greater numbers of participants.

A coach must be familiar with good conditioning methods

and with effective training practices. He must be capable of understanding strategy and team play, and must be able to analyze and plan offense and defense according to the abilities of opponents. Since this type of planning is dependent on interpreting his own and other scouting reports, he must be competent as a scout and in using scouting reports. The coach must have a knowledge of business details, including purchasing, budgets, and supplies, and must be able to handle the many details involved in a home game or team travel.

The coach must develop signals and work out special plays. He must plan and carry out training procedures, diets, health habits, and similar controls for the boys. Planning schedules, hiring officials, and cooperating with the school board, school administration, and faculty members all require the attention of the coach. Most high school coaches are also teachers of physical education and other subjects and must be bona fide members of the faculty. Even in college, most coaches are members of the teaching faculty and are expected to perform teaching duties in addition to coaching responsibilities. There are very few jobs in the coaching field which involve only sports coaching.

An example of the sort of student who has a real potential for success in both teaching and coaching is found in the actual history of a student in a midwestern university. This man was an outstanding varsity football player. He was a good but not highly skilled basketball and baseball player, and he played intramural basketball very capably. He participated in as many sports activities as possible and was a good swimmer and an adequate gymnast. He avoided specialization in one area to the exclusion of others and achieved a good record in his professional work. In addition to his varsity and intramural sports participation, he compiled a four-year scholastic average of only slightly below an A. At the time of his graduation, placement opportunities were not favorable but he secured a position without difficulty. After one year in this position he accepted an appointment in one of the finest educational systems of the midwest. His present salary, after four years of teaching physical education and coaching, compares favorably with those of other graduates who have been in the field for eight or ten years.

HEALTH EDUCATION AS A PROFESSION

Young men and women who plan careers in health education have chosen a profession with high standards and wide opportunities for service to many people. The health educator should be interested in and familiar with social progress and advancements in science and medicine. He should be able to work cooperatively with others. He should represent fine personal health, excellent social, mental, and emotional adjustment, and an intelligent understanding of the extensive field of health education.

The need for teachers who are prepared to teach health education has become urgent since state laws have authorized health instruction in the public schools. An increasing number of colleges and universities offer preparation in health education to meet the demand for teachers. National, state, and local groups are cooperating actively with school groups to improve health instruction for all school levels as the importance of competent health education teachers becomes increasingly apparent. In addition to health work in schools, there is an increasing demand for health education specialists in health agencies and foundations such as the National Tuberculosis Association.

It is essential that teachers develop an interest in the health of the children in their classes. All teachers should understand the health problems of children and do their best to help individual children meet their problems. Schools also need specialists in health education. The health specialist possesses a thorough knowledge of the latest and most reliable information and methods. He is responsible for making health habits and attitudes an effective part of each child's life, and must plan and carry out experiences which help children understand the personal importance of health.

The health educator is associated with a vast movement to

promote the health of the nation. Whether he works in a school program, in a community health unit, or with an organization, the health educator has an opportunity to associate with leaders in all fields. Health education is a relatively new profession. The health educator is a part of a growing, vitally important undertaking. Participation in such a profession is a constant satisfaction to its members.

The profession of health education offers a worth-while career for capable young men and women. Health educators work closely with other health leaders and medical authorities, with public officials, and with members of the community to promote health and to develop programs important to the entire nation. Health education offers an excellent career for physical education teachers who find that they prefer a less physically active vocation after a number of years, or who are unable to continue teaching vigorous activities. Those who decide to change careers may specialize in health education through graduate study and qualify for a related field of professional opportunity.

Possibilities for employment

Health education, as a relatively new teaching field, offers fewer teaching opportunities than are found in physical education. The number of teaching positions is, however, increasing rapidly. Public schools and colleges employ health instructors who are capable of coordinating health programs and services. Openings are available in both private and public health agencies for competent health education specialists. The emphasis on the importance of health to everyone and on the need for leaders who are capable, intelligent, professionally-minded persons creates a favorable outlook for adequately prepared health educators. The increasing demand for teachers to provide for the numbers of children entering school may be expected to create many new positions for health educators.

Many physical education teachers will continue to give instruction in health and safety, since a great many schools cannot employ a full-time teacher of either physical education or health education. It is important that physical education teachers become competent to teach health and safety. It is equally important that adequate time be provided for health instruction in the school program, and that teachers give emphasis to the significance of health instruction.

Opportunities for employment are indicated by the placement figures for 957 health education majors in the period 1947-1952.

TABLE 4

PLACEMENT OF ALL HEALTH EDUCATION MAJORS,
FIVE-SCHOOL-YEAR PERIOD, 1947-1952, UNITED STATES [8]

Rank Order	Type of Placement	Number	Per Cent
1	Senior High School	235	24.6
2	College or University	96	10.0
3	Voluntary Health Agency	88	9.3
4	Graduate Work	74	7.8
5	Public Health Department	62	6.5
6	Unaccounted for	58	6.1
7	Military Service	54	5.6
8	Junior High School	51	5.3
9	Nursing and Health Education	50	5.2
10	Elementary School	46	4.8
11	Housewife	33	3.4
12	Health Coordinator	32	3.3
13	Physical Education and Recreation	30	3.1
14	Industrial and Commercial Health Education	10	1.0
15	Physical Therapy	9	0.9
16	Unemployed	8	0.8
17	Public Welfare	4	0.4
18	Public Health Apprentice	3	0.3
19	Y.M.C.A.	2	0.2
20	Miscellaneous Placement *	12	1.3 *
	Total	957	100.0%

* *These 12 positions were distributed as follows:* Department of Public Welfare, 1; Civilian Director of Health, Air Base, 1; Research Chemist, 1; Dental Hygienist, 2; Club Work, 1; Business, 1; Credit Agency, 1; State Health Council, 1; Hospital Attendant, 2; and Juggler on the Stage, 1.

Types of positions

Specialized positions in health education usually require advanced study and preparation. The college graduate with a

[8] "Recruitment and Placement of Health Education Majors," *Journal of School Health*, January 1954, p. 12.

Bachelor's degree and no experience may find positions such as those listed here.

HEALTH EDUCATION

ELEMENTARY SCHOOL

Health coordinator for school, teacher of physical education, recreation director
Assistant to public school health coordinator in one or more schools

SECONDARY SCHOOL: JUNIOR AND SENIOR HIGH SCHOOL

Teacher of health education
Teacher of health education and physical education
Teacher of health education, physical education, and safety education
Teacher of health education, athletic coach, recreation director
Health coordinator and teacher of health education
Assistant health coordinator, teacher of health education and physical education, athletic coach
Teacher of health education and one or more other subjects

COLLEGE

Part-time or full-time assistant or instructor
Instructor of health education
Instructor of health education and physical education, and assistant coach
Instructor of health education, assistant director or counselor in college dormitory

SPECIAL FIELDS

Health education assistant in organizations and foundations
Assistant to specialist in hospitals and special schools
    State and federal rehabilitation programs
    Physical therapy and occupational therapy programs
    Physically-handicapped programs

The working environment and duties

Health education utilizes classrooms, laboratories, and all available resources of the school and the community. Public water and sanitation systems, hospitals, dairies, and other areas and facilities affecting health offer opportunity for exploration. The work of the health educator extends beyond the school. It involves arranging field trips and tours of water purification plants, sewage disposal units, canneries and other food preparation centers, and other areas of importance to health. The health education classroom becomes a laboratory for learning about and understanding health and its importance to daily living.

The program of health education includes instruction, health inspection and care, and supervision of the school environment to provide a healthful, safe place for boys and girls. An adequate health program is planned to acquaint pupils, parents, teachers, and members of the community with the importance of health and with practical health attitudes and habits. The health educator coordinates public health services with the school program; provides for cooperation between the school and medical and dental health programs; and encourages community interest in solving health problems. The work of the health educator involves close working relationships with community health authorities. The health educator spends many hours outside his classroom planning class work, conferring with community leaders, and contributing time and leadership to community and professional groups. The duties of health educators are indicated in the following report of a professional worker's schedule.

My duties include the following responsibilities in the school:

1. Cooperate with doctors, nurses, and school administrators in medical and physical examinations.
2. Organize school health services.
3. Coordinate health instruction throughout the school system.
4. Teach high school health classes.
5. Coordinate the planning of the health education curriculum for the city schools.
6. Supervise health teaching in the elementary schools.
7. Plan and conduct in-service programs for all teachers.
8. Select, secure, and distribute audio-visual and other educational aids for the health program.
9. Serve on the community health council.

10. Make speeches to P.T.A. and other organizations in support of the health program.

11. Plan publicity and the public relations program for school health programs.

RECREATION AS A PROFESSION

The recreation field needs leaders who are able to meet high personal and professional standards. Young men and women who are interested in recreation as a career should develop a

Courtesy of Chicago Park District

variety of recreational interests of their own. They should also become familiar with activities which are of recreational interest to others. The ability to organize programs, to conduct activities, and to work cooperatively with other people is expected of recreation leaders. An attractive appearance, enthusiasm, and friendliness are assets to any leader and combined with a sincere liking for people, are among the requirements that recreation leaders must meet. A recreation leader must impress others with his wholehearted interest in the personal enjoyment of each person with whom he comes in contact.

Recreation is a profession devoted to the leisure-time interests of the population. Recreation as a career means an opportunity for personal and professional satisfaction from helping to provide greater happiness for others. Young men and women who choose recreation as their future profession select a career with many possibilities for service to people of all ages—a career which helps people live fully and keeps the leader youthful and enthusiastic in spirit. Recreation as a profession brings many challenges and satisfactions to the leader.

Possibilities for employment

It is estimated that approximately 20,000 full-time, year-round recreation leaders are employed in public and voluntary agencies. Many more are engaged in conducting recreation as a part of their regular duties in a program of school physical education and recreation. Approximately 52,000 people are employed on a part-time or seasonal basis, and over 100,000 volunteer workers contribute time to recreation programs.[9] Positions are available with municipal, county, and state recreation departments, and with youth-serving agencies such as the YMCA and YWCA, Boy Scouts, Girl Scouts, Camp Fire Girls, 4-H Clubs, and teen-age centers. Business and industrial firms employ recreation directors; the armed forces require civilian recreation leaders; hospitals provide recreation programs conducted by qualified leaders. Opportunities include administrative positions as well as leadership in music, crafts, dramatics, and nature activities.

Qualifications for available positions vary. Minimum requirements usually include undergraduate preparation in physical education and recreation and a Bachelor's degree. Persons with

[9] *Recreation: A New Profession in a Changing World* (New York: National Recreation Association, 1952).

a major in recreation generally command the better positions, although many fine opportunities are available to other well-qualified leaders.

Types of positions

A great variety of positions is available for the graduate with a major in recreation. The following list indicates some of the many positions in which the leader can find employment immediately following graduation.

RECREATION

PUBLIC SCHOOLS

Assistant director or director of summer recreation and teacher of physical education

Coordinator of school recreation and teacher of physical education

Recreation director, teacher of physical education and health education, and athletic coach

Recreation director, teacher of physical education and one or more school subjects, and athletic coach

COLLEGE

Assistant to director of Student Union

Assistant program director in residence halls

Assistant to intramural director for men and women

Assistant or instructor in physical education and assistant in recreation

PUBLIC RECREATION

Recreation leader in center or on playgrounds

Director of center, swimming pool, or camp

Assistant specialist or assistant supervisor

    Athletics

    Music, dramatics, arts and crafts, dancing

    Nature activities

    Girls' and women's activities

CIVILIAN POSITIONS WITH ARMED FORCES

Recreation assistants

Assistant specialists

Music, crafts, hobbies
Entertainment, library, dramatics
Assistant program director

YOUTH ORGANIZATIONS AND OTHER PRIVATE AGENCIES

Assistant program director
Assistant camp director or camp counselor
Assistant or director of physical education program
Assistant or director of social recreation club work, and special
    services

SPECIAL FIELDS

Assistant to occupational and recreational therapists
Assistant to director of hospital recreation
Leader of recreational activities in hospitals
Assistant to recreation specialists in hospitals

Many positions in public recreation require that candidates
become certified through civil service examinations. It is not
unusual for employing agencies to stipulate that eligibility for
employment is dependent upon legal residence in the community. Residence and civil service certification may be required of summer recreation workers by municipal recreation
departments. Positions with state and federal agencies customarily require civil service status.

The working environment and duties

Recreation programs use facilities similar to or identical with
those of physical education. In addition, the work of the recreation leader is carried on in craft shops, libraries, museums,
parks, and camping areas. The informal nature of recreational
activities, combined with the pleasant and friendly characteristics of people who are participating in voluntarily selected
activities, creates a congenial working environment.

The recreation program includes an even wider variety of
activities than the physical education program. Many of the
activities require instruction such as that given in schools, and

involve class organization and skillful teaching. Other activities need only guidance and supervision. Adult groups and clubs are often self-directed, and carry on their activities with the assistance of leaders in planning, scheduling facilities, and organizing programs. A good recreation leader develops leadership qualities in the people participating in the program.

Recreation programs are conducted to satisfy the interests of people of all ages, and planned for the time of day various groups have leisure time. Late afternoon and evening hours are popular with many adults since the majority of employed people have free time during those periods. Programs are provided at other hours for homemakers who often have free time only during the middle of the morning or early in the afternoon. Children take advantage of recreation centers and playgrounds after school hours and during vacations.

The recreation leader may find his day divided between morning and evening work, or afternoon and evening hours. Fortunately, the working day for recreation leaders has been adjusted so that their working hours are approximately the same as in other vocations, even though the arrangement may be less favorable for their personal lives. Vacations must often be taken in the fall, since summer duties are customarily heavy. The majority of recreation leaders are enthusiastic about their profession and feel that their work is well worth the variation in working hours and the additional time spent in planning and organization work. A new recreation leader expresses this feeling as follows:

> My enthusiasm for recreation has not declined since graduation in that field. Extensive hours, average salary, and everyday hard work have, if anything, made me more cognizant of the needs of the people. The chance to see the enjoyment of the participants, to recognize the opportunities that recreation provides, and to feel important to the community outweigh the disadvantages a hundred fold. True, at times I have felt like a boxer who has just taken a count of nine, but in each case I have come back to win over my invisible opponent.

Perhaps the biggest disadvantage of this field is trying to satisfy everyone. You cannot do it. Please the majority and you do all right. A typical day:

8:30-9:00	Read and answer mail
9:00-10:00	Get publicity ready and distribute to all outlets
10:00-10:10	Coffee time
10:10-11:00	Get center ready for evening operation or visit outdoor facilities and observe activity
11:00-12:00	Program planning for future activity
12:00-1:00	Lunch
1:00-2:00	Prepare for evening activity, outline program
2:00-3:00	Committee meetings
3:00-4:00	Grade-school activity (football, basketball, and so on)
4:00-5:00	Contact officials for evening athletic leagues Instruct supervisors of gyms about duties Get keys to school centers
7:30-10:00	Call square dance, or lead other social activity

Work days for recreation people are not typical, for every day is a new experience in itself. Evening and afternoon work hours are customarily alternated.

EDUCATIONAL PREPARATION

A four-year college education is the minimum requirement for the professions of physical education, health education, and recreation. Any accredited college or university offering a curriculum meeting state standards for the certification of teachers of physical education and health education and for athletic coaches may recommend graduates for certification in their major fields. National organizations have recommended standards for recreation leaders similar to those for teachers as a basis for future certification requirements. The basic curriculum is similar for all three fields. Areas of specialization differ in emphasis on specific studies, activities, and practical experiences in teaching and leadership.

The curriculum

The curriculum is based largely on the certification requirements within each state. Certification standards represent educational qualifications teachers should possess. All states require certification of teachers of physical education and health education, and a large proportion of the states require that athletic coaches hold teaching certificates.[10]

The curriculum is usually planned for a four-year course with a minimum of 120 hours of semester credit required for graduation. Areas of study are divided into four broad fields: general education, science, professional education, and professional courses in the major field. The credit hours and courses and the arrangement of the curriculum vary widely among different institutions.

General Education. The curriculum in general education forms a background of cultural education essential to the understanding of people, society, and government; an appreciation for the arts and sciences affecting daily living; and the development of skill in written and spoken English. The natural sciences may be coordinated with other courses, offered as survey courses, or listed as separate requirements.

Science. Sciences represent an area of study of particular significance to teachers of physical education and health education. An understanding of the human body, its structure and functions, and the knowledge of physiological effects of activity are required in teaching physical education and health education. Chemistry, bacteriology, and nutrition are additional requirements for health education majors. A sound background in biological science is essential to the teacher who plans graduate study and further specialization in physical education and health education. Biological science is also of importance to the recreation major in preparation for nature study activities. The recreation student also needs additional specialization in sociology and group work.

Professional Education. Professional education is designed to

---

[10] Frank S. Stafford, *State Certification Standards for Secondary School Teachers of Health Education and Physical Education and for Athletic Coaches,* Bulletin 1949, No. 16 (Washington, D. C.: Federal Security Agency, Office of Education, 1949), p. 30.

provide prospective specialists with the understandings and skills necessary for effective teaching. Through this curriculum the student gains familiarity with the ways in which learning takes place, the significance and characteristics of growth and development, the role of the teacher or leader, and the functions of education. In addition, students gain practical experience by working with children under the guidance of experienced teachers and supervisors.

Professional Courses in Physical Education. The physical education curriculum is made up of a wide variety of activity and theory courses. Laboratory courses in physical education activities, corrective and remedial work, first aid, and athletic training familiarize students with these aspects of physical education. Recreation leadership and camp counseling courses provide the student with theory and practical work in social recreation, outing activities, outdoor cookery, arts and crafts, and other recreational pursuits. Theory courses provide students with a background of the history and principles of physical education. Special methods of teaching adapted to physical education, program planning and instruction, and a knowledge of administration develop ability to organize and conduct programs of physical education.

Professional Courses in Health Education. The program of the health education major provides special courses in personal and community hygiene; instruction in the conduct of school, home, and community health programs; and work involving participation in actual health teaching situations. The graduate of a professional program must be able to organize health education programs for the whole community and work with other health agencies and local groups. The health educator must be able to plan school programs, coordinate school health services, promote a healthful school environment, and present instruction in health and related safety education. He must have adequate preparation so that he may study the success of his program and plan changes. He must be able to work at all levels of the school program. The teaching of health classes in the secondary school and the coordination of all health activities for student and faculty are among the duties of the specialist.

Professional Courses in Recreation. The recreation major must be particularly well qualified in speaking and writing and must have an understanding of government and human relations. His major preparation should provide skills in many recreational sports, music, dramatics, crafts, nature activities, camping and outdoor education, and dancing. Professional theory courses should prepare him to organize and administer programs and to work effectively with the problems of facilities and equipment. He must be able to work well with others in his program and in the community.

SUMMARY OF REQUIREMENTS

A study of the requirements of different institutions indicates that a major field is planned for as few as 24 or as many as 50 semester hours of credit, and that one, two, or three minor fields are recommended in conjunction with the major. The following summary of the requirements listed in the four areas of study and the range of semester hours in each indicates the general nature of the curriculum.[11]

GENERAL EDUCATION

12 to 60 semester hours

English	Mathematics	Sociology
Literature	Psychology	Art
Speech	Social Studies	Music
Modern Languages		

SCIENCE

6 to 18 semester hours

Anatomy	Zoology	Bacteriology
Physiology	Chemistry	Genetics
Biology	Physics	Nutrition

11 Stafford, *State Certification Standards*, pp. 1-33; and T. Erwin Blesh, "Evaluative Criteria in Physical Education," *Research Quarterly of the American Association for Health, Physical Education and Recreation*, 17:114-126, May 1946.

PROFESSIONAL EDUCATION

14 to 32 semester hours

Introduction, History, Principles
Philosophy of Education
Educational Psychology
Child and Adolescent Psychology
Mental Health for Teachers

Elementary and Secondary
    Education
Educational Guidance
Mental Hygiene
Educational Administration
Student Teaching or Field Work

PROFESSIONAL COURSES IN PHYSICAL EDUCATION

24 to 50 semester hours

Introduction or Orientation
History and Principles
Methods of Teaching and
    Coaching
Physical Education Activities
Applied Anatomy and Physiology
Kinesiology and Correctives
Physical Education Programs

First Aid and Safety Education
Health Education
Recreation and Camp Leadership
Evaluation in Physical Education
Administration of Physical Education, Health Education, and
    Recreation

Major students of physical education and recreation learn
many activities such as those included in the accompanying list.

Games, relays, individual and group contests

Gymnastics and calisthenics

Individual and dual sports:

Archery	Fencing	Tennis
Badminton	Golf	Track and field
Boating-Canoeing	Skiing	Wrestling

Team sports:

Baseball	Football	Speedball
Basketball	Soccer	Touch football
Fieldball	Softball	Volleyball
Field hockey		

Recreational games:

Aerial darts	Shuffleboard
Deck tennis	Table tennis

Rhythms and dancing:
    Folk   Rhythms   Social
    Modern   Tap   Square

Stunts and tumbling

Swimming, diving, life-saving, and other water sports

Camping and outing:
    Campcraft   Fishing   Nature lore
    Scouting   Hunting   Woodcraft

Courtesy of Androscoggin Camps

Students who are specializing in dance activities follow a major program similar to that for physical education, with the exception that emphasis is placed upon various forms of the dance. It is advisable for dance majors to become familiar with sport activities since many positions require ability to teach both sports and dancing. Courses in general education, science, and professional education are customarily identical with those required for majors in physical education.

PROFESSIONAL COURSES IN DANCE

24 to 30 semester hours

Introduction or Orientation
History and Principles
Team and Individual Sports
Fundamentals of Rhythm
Folk, Social, and Square Dance
Applied Anatomy and Physiology
Kinesiology and Correctives
Dance in Elementary and Secondary Schools

Health Education
Social Recreation
Dance Composition
Accompaniment for Dance
Dramatics and Stagecraft
Dance Production
Theory of the Dance
Administration of Physical Education, Health Education, and Recreation

PROFESSIONAL COURSES IN HEALTH EDUCATION

24 to 50 semester hours

Personal and Community Hygiene
Introduction to Health Education
Programs of School Health
Public Health and Sanitation
Physical Education Activities
Principles of Health Education

Physical Inspection
Family Relations and Health
Health Counseling
School Health Inspection
Social Health Problems
Administration of Health Education
Field Work Courses

PROFESSIONAL COURSES IN RECREATION

24 to 50 semester hours

Introduction to Community Recreation
Recreational Leadership
Physical Education Activities [12]

Recreational Dramatics
Social Recreation
Community Music
Camping and Nature Education

[12] Recreation majors learn many of the activities listed under professional courses in physical education.

First Aid and Safety Education
Health Education
Arts and Crafts for Recreation

Club Organization and Leadership
Administration of Recreation [13]

[13] A single course in Administration of Physical Education, Health Education, and Recreation may be offered for undergraduates.

Major and minor combinations

It is advisable to plan a program of study that will result in meeting requirements for two major fields, or for a major and two minors. The professional curriculum usually provides for at least one major and one minor field of study. Two majors, or a major and a minor, may be secured in the same department in some colleges and universities. Choices may be possible for preparation in physical education, health education, recreation, dance, and physical therapy in various major and minor combinations. Regardless of the combination, care should be taken that certification requirements are met in all fields elected as majors and minors.

Recommended combinations

Suitable combinations vary in different localities according to the demand. Information regarding combinations should be secured from major advisers when planning an undergraduate program of study. In general, the following combinations have proved valuable in terms of placement opportunities.

1. *Physical education and health education.* Increasing emphasis on health education has created a demand for teachers who are qualified to teach both physical education and health education, and to act as coordinators for the school health program.

2. *Physical education and recreation.* The trend toward including outdoor education, camping, and expanded programs of recreation in the school curriculum indicates that there will be a demand for teachers who are prepared to conduct a wide variety of recreational activities. In addition, the teacher who is prepared as a recreation leader or camp counselor finds opportunities for enjoyable and remunerative summer employment.

3. *Coaching, physical education, and other subjects.* Men physical education teachers in many high schools are expected to assume coaching duties as well as to teach academic subjects. This is particularly true in the smaller high schools and in

junior high schools. An increase in the number of interschool sports has increased the necessity of developing a variety of combinations of physical education and coaching. Since the opportunities to work as a coach of a single sport are very limited, men should be prepared to teach and coach in several sport areas.

4. *Dance and physical education.* Numerous positions in high schools require the ability to teach modern dance as well as sports activities. College positions often combine the teaching of one or more sport activities and modern dance, and many require some degree of specialization in dance.

5. *Physical education or health education, and science.* Majors in physical education and health education meet many of the requirements for a science major. It is generally possible to complete a minor or major in science with relatively few semester hours in addition to those in the required curriculum. General science is a frequent combination with physical education and health education.

6. *Physical education or recreation, and art or dramatics.* A combination of art or dramatics with physical education and recreation is necessarily dependent upon some talent or ability in the field selected. Qualification as an art or dramatics teacher is an advantage to the physical educator in schools where enrollment does not warrant employing full-time teachers for special subjects. Recreation leaders who are prepared to supervise art and dramatic activities find increased opportunities for advancement to supervisory positions.

7. *Physical education, health education, and recreation.* Combined preparation in the three fields provides excellent background for placement. Knowledge of three closely related areas of education forms a sound basis for determining the choice of a field of specialization on the graduate level.

8. *Physical education or health education or recreation and physical or occupational therapy.* The combination of another field with the highly specialized fields of physical or occupational therapy may require additional time spent on under-

graduate preparation. Preparation in such combinations opens many possibilities for employment. Qualified civilian workers are in demand for military hospitals. Schools for atypical children require highly trained specialists to conduct physical education and recreation and work with physical therapists in correctional programs. Institutions of various kinds employ specialists who are competent as health and recreation directors.

9. *Physical education or health education and safety education (including driver education).* The teacher of physical education is often required to teach safety and driver education. Whether or not a combined major and minor is possible, it is advisable to plan to include courses in safety education if they are not required as a part of the professional curriculum.

10. *Other combinations.* Combinations with subjects such as home economics, mathematics, industrial arts, and music may prove practical for students with abilities and talents in these areas of education. English and social studies are frequently listed as combinations with physical education in description of vacancies. Requirements should be studied carefully. A program should be planned early in college to determine whether it will be possible to complete the courses of study with a major or minor. The demand for teachers in the minor field should be determined with the assistance of a counselor.

Job combinations are illustrated in Tables 5 and 6. Table 5 was prepared from vacancies reported to a teachers college placement bureau in 1953. The positions described were taken at random from those reported during a one-month period and represent typical combinations. Table 6 summarizes the teaching and coaching vacancies listed with the placement office of a large state university during 1952. The positions involving physical education, health education, and recreation alone listed during the same periods with these placement offices indicate the demand for qualified personnel in these areas.

The shortage of qualified teachers and leaders in physical education, health education, and recreation is further emphasized by the needs of schools requiring capable teachers who are

TABLE 5

TEACHING COMBINATIONS REPORTED TO TEACHERS COLLEGE PLACEMENT OFFICE

MEN Combined with Physical Education and Coaching		WOMEN Combined with Physical Education	
Administration	2	Biology	2
Biology	3	Commerce	5
Commerce	3	English	7
Driver Education	3	General Science	3
English	4	Home Economics	2
General Science	6	Mathematics	1
Industrial Arts	9	Music	3
Mathematics	5	Social Studies	7
Social Studies	8	Elementary School Grade Subjects	5
Total	43	Total	33

Physical Education

Elementary Physical Education	6	Elementary Physical Education	6
Physical Education and Coaching (Secondary)	14	Secondary Physical Education	43
Total	20	Total	49

TABLE 6

TEACHING COMBINATIONS REPORTED TO UNIVERSITY PLACEMENT OFFICE

MEN Combined with Physical Education		WOMEN Combined with Physical Education	
Mathematics	4	Commerce	5
Science	4	English	17
All others	6	Mathematics	5
Combined with Coaching		Science	18
Driver Education	13	Social Studies	8
Mathematics	16	All others	15
Science	26		
Social Studies	30		
All others	12		
Total	111	Total	68

Physical Education

Physical Education and Coaching	81	Health and Recreation	7
Elementary Physical Education	15	Elementary Physical Education	25
Secondary Physical Education	8	Secondary Physical Education	130
		Secondary Physical Education and Swimming	11
Total	104	Total	173

also able to teach other school subjects. Many schools in small communities require that teachers be competent to teach several subjects since they are unable to employ a sufficient number of teachers to warrant specialists. Despite the trend toward consolidation of school districts and the resulting employment of a greater number of teachers for separate areas of study and for individual grades, many hundreds of small schools still require multiple-subject teachers.

The following descriptions of teaching positions listed with placement agencies illustrate the actual teaching combinations for which teachers are employed.

MEN

1. English (10 hours in Library Science); if possible teach Boys' Physical Education and handle Dramatics.
2. Junior High School Mathematics, Science, Boys' Physical Education; coach.
3. Biology, American History, Problems in American Democracy, Boys' Physical Education; coach Basketball and Baseball.
4. Social Studies, American and World History, Civics, Economics, Boys' Physical Education; coach Athletics.
5. Physical Education for Upper-Grade Boys; teach one other subject such as English or History.

WOMEN

1. English, Health, Safety, and Physical Education.
2. Science, Biology, Chemistry, Girls' Physical Education.
3. Girls' Physical Education; conduct Band and Chorus.
4. Girls' Physical Education; if possible teach one or two classes in Home Economics.

OPPORTUNITIES IN PHYSICAL EDUCATION, HEALTH EDUCATION, AND RECREATION

The physical educator, health educator, and recreation leader are members of a large professional group. The nature of their work requires close working relationships with other professional persons and with numerous community leaders. Favorable conditions for an enjoyable and satisfying career are associated with the majority of positions in physical education, health education, and recreation. Teaching and recreation work, like other professions, do have some unfavorable aspects. All professional workers should be aware of the various conditions affecting their work and their future.

Professional status

Members of the professions of physical education, health, and recreation are represented by strong national organizations. The American Association for Health, Physical Education and Recreation is a department of the National Education Association and is one of the largest and most influential of professional organizations. Among the members of this organization are outstanding leaders in physical education, health education, public health, medicine, nursing, and therapeutics. Many other national organizations concerned with physical education, health, and recreation are affiliated with the Association. Membership is open to students majoring in physical education, health education, and recreation, and to student physical education clubs. Many clubs have affiliated with the Association, and hundreds of professional students are active members. The National Recreation Association and the American Recreation Society play important parts in the promotion of recreation programs and activities. The American Public Health Association is among the numerous professional organizations directly concerned with health programs.

Community relationships

All teachers and leaders are expected to participate in community undertakings and to become active members of the communities in which they work. The leaders of civic recreation, social welfare, and education programs seek the support of teachers and recreation workers who are accustomed to working with large groups; who have a recreational point of view; and who understand the needs of children, young people, and adults for wholesome recreational activity. Teachers and leaders become acquainted with members of a community through professional contacts. A person who is friendly and sincere, and who contributes time and energy to community-wide undertakings, becomes a part of the community and is accepted wholeheartedly, socially and professionally.

Teachers and youth leaders are expected to represent the highest standards of conduct and to accept the role of models of behavior for young people. Hence their lives may be restricted to some extent. A person who wishes to be respected in the community should be willing to conform to local conventions. Anyone who finds that restrictions are more demanding than seems justifiable should nevertheless attempt to meet the established standards until he can secure a position in another location.

Economic status

The income from teaching or leadership in physical education, health education, and recreation usually provides for a comfortable standard of living. Teachers who accept positions in localities where salaries are below average may find it necessary to supplement their salaries in some manner to provide for emergencies, or to increase retirement incomes from their own savings and investments. Some teachers and leaders have changed to occupations offering greater financial opportunity; others have secured positions in areas where salaries are higher. The statement of a young married woman teacher illustrates adjustments teachers have made in one community. Her statement also emphasizes a definite advantage found in teaching—that of freedom to move to more favorable localities and better positions.

> The starting salary in the community where my husband and I teach is below average. It was all right when I lived alone, but it is hardly possible for two to live on one person's salary. It would be impossible to raise a family and maintain the living standard expected of teachers on present salary levels. All of the married men on the faculty have other jobs or incomes in addition to teach-

ing. Both of us have to work until my husband can get another job. To alter this situation, we could move to another town, and this we will do in the near future.

Although incomes have improved and show indications of further improvement in the future, teaching and recreation work will probably not be among the most highly paid professions for many years to come. The physical education teacher and coach is particularly fortunate, since his preparation qualifies him for enjoyable and remunerative work during summer vacations and makes it possible for him to supplement his income during the school year. Opportunities are available to men to play and coach in professional sports, and to coach and officiate during the school year in addition to their regular teaching and coaching responsibilities. Summer camps and recreation positions are available to both men and women physical educators. Women teachers may earn additional income by coaching and officiating for women's teams in some localities. Other opportunities are found for additional income through teaching adult groups during the evening and on weekends. Adult education classes in recreational activities such as square dancing, golf, tennis, and social recreation require the paid services of competent teachers.

It is natural to be interested in the amount of income that can be expected from a vocation. Provisions for job security and retirement protection are problems that concern everyone. Present conditions emphasize the necessity for planning for a future which seems to assure a reasonable income and security on the job and after retirement.

Salary. The salary of a beginning teacher or leader with four years of college preparation compares favorably with the income of other college graduates starting out in professional work. Recreation leaders and professional workers in public and private agencies start at salaries comparable to those for beginning teachers. Salaries vary widely in different states and localities; large cities generally pay higher salaries than do small communities. Almost all states provide for annual increments through a statewide salary schedule for teachers. Additional salary increases are customarily granted to teachers who have completed five or more years of preparation.

Inexperienced teachers usually start at minimum salaries, which often vary according to the size of the school and the location. The maximum salary range quoted in 1951 was $3100 to approximately $5600, according to experience, preparation, and the size of the school.[14] There has been a consistent upward trend in salaries during the past few years. Coaches responsible for several sports in addition to teaching duties often receive additional compensation. Highly paid coaching, supervisory, and administrative positions commanding salaries of $10,000 and above are relatively few in number, and require outstanding qualifications.

Salaries of teachers, leaders, and other professional workers in physical education, health education, and recreation vary according to the nature of the work. In general, salaries are comparable in teaching, organization work, and public and private agency positions in these fields. Positions with industrial and business firms may command slightly higher salaries.

Security. Provisions for security in a position are made through tenure regulations. Teachers who are newly employed in a school system are usually appointed for a period of one year. A probationary period of from one to three years may be required before the teacher receives his contract on a continuing basis or is placed on permanent tenure. Following the attainment of tenure a teacher is seldom dismissed without good cause and the privilege of defending himself against the charges that have led to the contemplated dismissal. Recreation

14 Frank W. Hubbard, "Salaries Lag in City-School Systems," *Journal of the National Education Association,* 40:399, September 1951.

Committee on Vocational Guidance, "Placement Trends: A Two-Year Study," *Journal of the American Association for Health, Physical Education and Recreation,* 22:50-51, September 1951.

"Salaries and Salary Schedules for City-School Employees," *Research Bulletin of the National Education Association,* 29:55-83, April 1951.

workers are frequently employed on civil service status and enjoy the security of such programs.

Additional security is customarily provided through retirement programs which operate on the principle of retirement insurance. The usual plan for teachers involves the payment of a small percentage of the monthly salary by the employee. This sum is matched with an equal or greater amount of school funds, and the combined deposit is held at interest until the specified retirement age. Following retirement the teacher is assured of a definite income from the accumulated investment. When a teacher leaves the employ of the public schools, the amount deposited in the retirement program is usually returned with interest and represents savings during the period of employment. Retirement programs are in use by agencies, business, and industry to protect professional workers.

Possibilities for advancement

Advancement is possible in a number of ways. Better positions or better salaries usually result from successful work. Changing from a position to a better one, doing graduate study, earning advanced degrees, conducting outstanding research, and writing for publication are often steppingstones to advancement. Service to local, state, and national organizations is rewarding personally, and may result in opportunities for a better position and salary.

Future prospects

The question of what the future holds for the physical educator, health educator, and recreation leader is a natural concern of every person considering a career in these professions. Everyone who chooses one of these careers should be aware of the possibilities that limit the extent of time he will be able to continue active work in a field that demands excellent health and physical vigor. The necessity for maintaining physical vigor is particularly important to the physical educator and to the athletic coach.

The high standards for health and physical fitness mean that some apparently minor defects that would not obstruct success in other professions, or in classroom teaching, may prove serious disabilities to the person who would like to teach physical education. The necessity for continuing active participation may become a limitation with increasing age. Many people cannot maintain an active life after middle age and must make a choice between either qualifying for a supervisory or administrative position or changing to another profession.

Graduate work and the possession of advanced degrees are required for many supervisory and administrative positions. A

Courtesy of MacMurray College

person who is not interested in a career requiring extensive study will find that this factor is a definite disadvantage in considering physical education, health education, or recreation as a profession. On the other hand, thousands of men and women past middle age are successfully engaged in teaching physical education and health education, coaching athletic teams, conducting recreational programs, or acting as supervisors and administrators. This should be considered as evidence that for these persons their professions have proved worthy of constant work and study. The number of leaders who have continued professional careers until retirement age and have contributed consistently to the profession through writing and research bears tribute to the opportunities for constructive and rewarding lifetime careers.

The future of a profession is determined by the people who carry on the work of that profession. The career opportunities, responsibilities, advantages and disadvantages, and possibilities for advancement are best interpreted by people who are actively working in the field. Young men and women who are planning careers should know what professional workers do and what they think about their work; what they dislike as well as what they like in their work. The following statements represent comments made by professional workers who are new to the field, by those who have been engaged in this work several years, and by others who have been members of the profession for ten or more years. These are the people who build the future of a profession.

An experienced teacher

The exact nature of my duties is varied. They represent an example of the possibilities that exist for those who are interested in school administration as a future goal. I have duties in three fields, namely administrative duties as Assistant Principal, physical education work, and guidance work as Educational and Vocational Guidance Director. My other activities include the coaching of soccer and baseball.

On the surface, this set-up probably appears as a jumbled assortment of varied responsibilities. But I like it. I still have a hand in coaching and physical education; the guidance work is challenging and rewarding in that I am actually assisting young people with their educational and vocational problems; and the administrative work offers the greatest future.

A new teacher

My work at the present time is very pleasant. I enjoy all the subjects I am teaching. The faculty here are all young and aggressive. The town is ideal from my point of view.

At the present time I am teaching driver education and woodshop and coaching all sports. This semester we are a little overcrowded in driver education, but we are trying to give every junior and senior a chance to take the course. Then we are going to offer the course at the sophomore level to catch the younger students before they start driving.

Woodworking is offered to the seventh and eighth grades and the senior boys in agriculture as a unit in that subject.

A typical day's schedule is as follows: driver education the first two periods, woodworking until noon, grade-school physical education first period after lunch, then driving, then high-school physical education, and the last period is varsity athletic period.

In answer to the question "How do you like what you are doing?," I would say it couldn't be much better. I am only teaching those subjects in which I am definitely interested. The physical education here has never amounted to anything. We now have two regular periods during each day, and are working for more. The equipment that was here was fair but there was no variety. Now we have a 20' by 20' wrestling mat, archery equipment, paddle tennis, and tennis, plus the activities that were offered previously.

So you see I have the advantage of starting in a place that is not accustomed to a great deal. Anything I do is an improvement. There is no pressure as to winning or losing a game. The school board is interested in reaching every boy and girl in school with athletics and physical education.

A three-year teacher

I like what I am doing very much. I enjoy getting up in the morning and going to my job. My day flies by and minutes are not counted. I have fun on my job; it is not monotonous and I am not an automaton. By other standards I am underpaid, but my job is interesting and joyful. I may gripe about the pay, but I am not disgruntled. There is no pressure to win, so I can run my program as I think best. I like my profession and will work continuously to improve it and myself.

An experienced teacher

I am athletic director and as such it is my job to purchase and care for all the athletic equipment used in the high school. I arrange all the athletic schedules, and obtain all the athletic officials. It is also my job to oversee the athletic facilities, and see that they are kept up. I handle most of the publicity connected with the athletic department or see that it is taken care of. These things along with a bushel of others make this a full-time job.

I am head football coach and have a line coach to assist me. We have two men working with our freshmen-sophomore team and also have an 8th-grade coach and a 7th-grade coach. We all use the same system as much as possible. I am also head basketball coach at the present time, and have two assistants in the high school; one of them handles the sophomores, and one handles the freshmen. We also have an 8th-grade coach and a 7th-grade coach.

As head track coach it is my job to oversee the entire track program, but personally I just handle the sprinters, the hurdlers, the high jumpers, and the broad jumpers in all four classes. One of my assistants handles the shot putters, discus throwers, and pole vaulters in all four classes, and the other assistant handles the quarter-milers, half-milers, and milers in all four classes.

There are two of us teaching boys' physical education at the present time. I handle the seniors, juniors, and sophomores and another man handles the freshmen and the 8th-graders. We individually plan our programs and try to make them as progressive as possible and try to link them together.

This year I am helping out in the industrial arts department and handle one 8th-grade woodworking class, two periods a week. I also have a study hall. This takes care of my duties at the high school except for such miscellaneous things as chaperoning school dances and parties.

Aside from my school activities, I am the swimming instructor at the pool in the summer and have coached a softball team of high-school-age boys that played during the evening. I have in the past been a Red Cross first aid instructor, and I expect that job will be coming up again. I have also been a Boy Scout counselor, which means passing the merit badge test for swimming and first aid, although I am not as active in that as I have been in the past. I have quite a full schedule of football games to officiate on Saturdays in the fall of the year. I am a member of the Recreational Council here, a member of the Civic Club, a member of the Baseball Association, and a member of the First Methodist Church, although I am not as active as I would be if my two boys were older.

I like my type of work very much with but few exceptions. The athletic coaching is my prime interest and it is very stimulating and challenging work. In working with the high-school boys in athletics we get very close contact with the boys, and I have found through nine years of this work that a high-school boy can be a very unpredictable subject. There is a great deal of satisfaction derived from seeing boys reach the goals they have set for themselves, and also in seeing them overcome bitter disappointment and make up their failures with fine performances at another time. The one bad feature of the athletic coaching set-up is the overwhelming desire on the part of the spectators or townspeople to win. I believe that this is greatly overemphasized in our high-school athletic program. Don't get me wrong. I like to win as much as the next fellow, but I do think that it is easy to forget the lessons that may be learned through athletic competition because of this tremendous desire to win.

The work in physical education is also interesting and stimulating, because we are dealing with an entirely different type than we are in the athletics. It is quite a thrill to witness a high-school boy perform a feat that previously he had not been able to do, no matter how simple it may be. In this type of work that old saying goes: there is never a dull moment. One does not wake up in the morning with the feeling that he has to go back to the same old grind, because every day presents new problems and new challenges.

A recreation director

I enjoy my work in recreation very much. There is always something different happening, and in my particular case there is no boredom or dead routine work. My association with the schools and township park board has been a great aid in starting the recreation program here. In particular, it has provided me with many personal contacts with children and their parents that I might not have had otherwise. When I pause and look back over the things that have happened in the past two and a half years, I feel that this recreation program is on the right track. Indications of our success are apparent in attendance figures as well as the number of inquiries that are made daily about the program.

All in all, it's a very satisfying type of work. The people you meet, the children that are helped by the program, and the direct personal relationships all go to give me a certain inner satisfaction that makes this work very enjoyable.

The main drawback or difficulty that I have encountered is that of making people aware that a program is being conducted and that it is planned to meet their interests, needs, and desires.

Some of the other problems, and I feel that all of us face them in one way or another, are those of cooperation and coordination of efforts of various civic and social groups, public relations, reports and informative articles, and so forth.

My daily schedule naturally depends upon the season of the year. When school is in session, I spend the mornings primarily on recreation work. The classes that I teach are junior-high physical education classes that meet from 1:30 to 3:30 daily except Friday. Most of the adult meetings, planning sessions, and board meetings are held during the evening hours. Saturdays and school vacations during the school year I usually spend doing maintenance work, since that is the time when it is easiest to get maintenance help. From the time school is out in June until the latter part of August, I spend my time planning, organizing, and conducting a summer recreation program.

I arrive at the office at 9:00 in the morning, take care of correspondence and do the planning of the program, check equipment, make arrangements for dances, and check on materials and activities. Also I pay calls on or receive visits from the Mayor, workers in allied fields, board members, and others interested in the recreation program.

A married woman teacher

My job is a very good one, and I enjoy it. Good facilities indoors and terrible ones outdoors make the job more challenging than a perfect situation would be. I have had some success in improving the situation, such as starting the block-of-time system of teaching and improving the method of requisitioning. I enjoy teaching and get a personal satisfaction from my work.

Some of the problems I have had to face are those associated with my work, adjustment to a new kind of social life and way of living, and limitations on the recreational opportunities in the community. I have found that suggestions are hard to put over, and must be made tactfully and slowly. Things I thought were accepted are really not. A change in the time arrangements for classes had to be presented diplomatically. Many educators have their own dogmatic opinions and refuse to listen to the advantages of the new way; they know only the disadvantages. Even people in physical education are slow to try new things.

The recreational facilities of the community are limited. During the winter a movie seems to be the basic entertainment offered. I bowl once a week. We attend high-school basketball games. In the spring, there is a public golf course and park.

My time for personal life is restricted. Housework is necessarily kept at a minimum. I don't mind this too much except when something unexpected takes up the weekend—then I am behind for about two weeks until I can catch up. This is my fault, I suppose, since I could refuse more extra duties than I do. I have little time for social affairs except on weekends and I still miss the companionship that I had in college.

Three major changes came simultaneously—moving to a new town, starting a new job with lots of responsibility, and being without friends. There is a certain satisfaction one gets from adjusting to a new situation, after the adjusting is under way. The restrictions of teachers were all known to me beforehand but as they became obvious, I felt like rebelling. Now I realize that even if I were not in teaching, I would live according to the same standards.

SUMMARY

The advantages that may be expected from careers in physical education, health education, and recreation include personal and professional rewards from:

1. A profession of significance to people of all ages
2. A satisfying and enjoyable life's work
3. A profession with opportunities for both men and women
4. An adequate income with future possibilities for improvement
5. Opportunities for advancement
6. Freedom and opportunity to change locality of employment
7. Security and retirement provisions
8. Vacations for study, work, and recreation
9. Possibilities for satisfactory community relationships
10. Continued stimulation and professional growth

Young men and women who choose physical education, health education, and recreation as careers enter into an association with professions that make significant contributions to the welfare of people of all ages. The curriculum of professional preparation includes the areas of study necessary to all teachers, and is specifically designed to develop competencies for teaching and leadership.

Career opportunities include: personal satisfactions in a work of service to others; a variety of positions available to qualified teachers and leaders; adequate salary; and the security necessary to effective work. A study of these professions indicates that the advantages far outweigh the disadvantages.

SUGGESTED PROBLEMS

1. Refer to your previous statement in answer to Problem 1 in the first chapter. Would you change your reasons for selecting a career on the basis of information you have gained from reading Chapter 2? In what ways?
2. List the problems or questions you have regarding the advantages and disadvantages of physical education, health education, or recreation (questions that have not been answered in either Chapter 1 or Chapter 2). Read a number of the references listed at the end of Chapter 2 and attempt to reach a solution to the problem.
3. Discuss with several teachers the advantages and disadvantages of teaching in general. List and compare the advantages and disadvantages. State whether you believe that the advantages outweigh the disadvantages and why.
4. Discuss the health aspects of education with one or more elementary school teachers. What problems seem of most importance to these teachers? Why?
5. Analyze state certification requirements for physical education and school health.
6. Study the differences between the preparation necessary for a school health educator and that necessary for a public health educator. In what ways do they differ?
7. Study job requirements for recreation positions in large city systems. List the positions for which you would like to qualify.
8. Discuss with recreation leaders the problems and work in recreation programs. Make a brief report of your interviews and indicate what influence, if any, the information you have gained has had on your plans for a career.

REFERENCES

American Association for Health, Physical Education and Recreation, *Health Education as a Profession,* Vocational Guidance Series No. 1, 1946.
————, *Physical Education—A Profession for Women,* Vocational Guidance Series No. 2, 1946.

American Association for Health, Physical Education and Recreation, *Physical Education—A Profession for Men,* Vocational Guidance Series No. 3, 1946.

————, *Recreation as a Profession,* Vocational Guidance Series No. 4, 1946.

Career as an Athletic Coach. Chicago: Institute for Research, 1949.

Coniff, James G., "I'm a Teacher Who's Getting Rich," *Saturday Evening Post,* 233:30, January 20, 1951.

DeGroot, Dudley, "Are We Ignoring Coaching as a Profession," *Journal of the American Association for Health, Physical Education and Recreation,* 21:30, December 1950.

Hicks, Dora, "Preparing Teachers for the Secondary Health Education Program," *Journal of the American Association for Health, Physical Education and Recreation,* 22:7, October 1951.

The Job of the Physical Education Teacher. Prepared for the War Department by the National Roster. Washington, D. C.: Government Printing Office, 1945.

Johnson, Ralph H., "Selection of Men Students for Professional Training," *Research Quarterly of the American Association for Health, Physical Education and Recreation,* 20:307, October 1949.

Lindsay, Edith M., "The College Health Educator," *Journal of the American Association for Health, Physical Education and Recreation,* 21:28, November 1950.

Maul, Ray C., "Has Demand Overtaken Supply?," *Journal of the American Association for Health, Physical Education and Recreation,* 24:11, November 1952.

————, "Wanted: Physical Education Teachers," *Journal of the American Association for Health, Physical Education and Recreation,* 24:12, May 1953.

Metcalf, Harlan G., "Recreation Education," *Journal of the American Association for Health, Physical Education and Recreation,* 23:19, February 1952.

Nash, Jay B., *Opportunities in Physical Education, Health and Recreation,* rev. ed. New York: Vocational Guidance Manuals, Inc., 1953.

Nixon, Eugene W., and Frederick W. Cozens, *An Introduction to Physical Education,* 4th ed. Philadelphia: W. B. Saunders Co., 1952.

Ohio Association for Health, Physical Education and Recreation, *Physical Education as a Career.* Columbus: The Association, 1946.

Personnel Standards in Recreation Leadership. New York: National Recreation Association, 1951.

Physical Therapy as a Career. Chicago: Institute for Research, 1946.

Recreation Leadership as a Career. Chicago: Institute for Research, 1949.

Rogers, James E., "Our Profession in America's Future," *Journal of the American Association for Health, Physical Education and Recreation,* 22:30, June 1951.

Romney, G. Ott, "Too Many Too Soon," *Journal of the American Association for Health, Physical Education and Recreation,* 22:36, May 1951.

Sharman, Jackson R., *Introduction to Health Education.* New York: A. S. Barnes and Company, 1948.

Uhler, William P., Jr., "On Being a Teacher of Physical Education," *Journal of the American Association for Health, Physical Education and Recreation,* 21:200, March 1950.

Weatherford, A. E., "Why Not Recreation Education," *Journal of the American Association for Health, Physical Education and Recreation,* 23:22, January 1952.

Courtesy of Androscoggin Camps

CHAPTER THREE

Careers in related fields

The preceding chapter was concerned with a discussion of careers in physical education, health education, and recreation. Professional opportunities in areas closely related to these fields have increased sufficiently in recent years to deserve special attention.

This chapter presents a general survey of the many areas of specialization related closely to these vocational fields. One purpose in presenting material on related vocational areas is to indicate special course requirements that might be added to an undergraduate program in order to prepare for a particular type of position. A knowledge of special requirements as well as of the possibilities for on-the-job experiences during undergraduate years is necessary to adequate preparation within the four-year period. It must be recognized that many of the specialized positions will require additional preparation. In such cases the added requirements and preparation are indicated.

Those fields are presented in which job placement for majors in physical education, health education, and recreation have been relatively frequent. Although specific employment possibilities are indicated for many of the special areas, job specifications, requirements, salaries, and working conditions change frequently. The basic information on areas and opportunities, together with the source material at the end of this chapter, provide the essential data necessary for an understanding of career opportunities in related fields.

Personal qualifications are similar to those listed for leaders in physical education, health education, and recreation and for other persons in responsible positions that involve working with others. These requirements include good health, a sense of humor, patience, emotional stability, and a pleasant personality. Additional special requirements are indicated under each section. Qualification for positions associated with federal and state institutions and agencies customarily is dependent on civil service examinations.

A brief survey of each field is presented to indicate requirements, nature of the work, working conditions, and job opportunities. The fields covered are as follows:

1. Public and private health agencies   5. Youth-serving agencies
2. Therapeutics   6. Industrial recreation
3. Safety education   7. Commercial recreation
4. Camping and outdoor education   8. Professional athletics

PUBLIC AND PRIVATE HEALTH AGENCIES

The work of public and private health agencies is directed toward the prevention, control, and solution of major health problems. Advancements in public health are the result of unceasing efforts to provide and maintain a healthful environment through programs for the control of communicable diseases, prevention of transmission of disease through water and food sources, and education for healthful living. Public and private agencies share the responsibility for the development of a vast program of public health services.

Requirements and nature of the work

The professional employees in public or private health work have been largely drawn from the ranks of highly qualified doctors, nurses, sanitary engineers, and research scientists. Professional programs to prepare the public health specialist have been developed only within recent years. It is now possible to begin specialization early in the college program for the general field of health. Graduate education is then directed toward specialization in public health.

The undergraduate curriculum includes the basic sciences,

general education, and professional education courses similar to those listed in Chapter 2 in the curriculum for majors in physical education, health education, and recreation. The specialized program of undergraduate work includes such courses as the following:

PROFESSIONAL COURSES IN HEALTH

24 to 50 semester hours

Personal and Community Hygiene
Public Health and Sanitation
Physical and Health Inspection
Social Health Problems

Tests and Measurements
Principles of Health Education
Social Work
Administration of Health Education
Field Work in Public Health

The worker in public or private health agencies must be interested in service to large groups of people rather than to individuals. Health educators are required to teach classes, work with other health personnel in the community or area, plan long-range programs, deal with statistical records, make speeches, conduct a program of public relations, and conduct meetings. The work requires administrative ability, interest in research, and adeptness in interesting people in health problems on all levels—community, state, and national as well as personal.

Working conditions

Work in most of the public health fields provides good job security with civil service, regular salary increases, promotions, tenure, and retirement programs. Private agencies provide benefits similar to those of the federal and state health programs. Working conditions are generally good and the employment is steady. Most of the programs include paid vacations, group insurance plans, and a 40-hour week with extra pay for approved overtime. Salaries are adjusted for service in foreign countries through additional living allowances and other provisions for the employee.

Salaries are improving and have kept pace with those in comparable professional and semiprofessional jobs. The salary range is from $2400 for beginners to $12,000 to $15,000 for executive and administrative jobs. Workers whose salaries are not high derive satisfaction from doing interesting and challenging work in an area of important public service.

Positions in public and private health agencies require specialized preparation and in some cases the relationship of salary to educational requirements is not favorable. Most jobs require at least a college degree plus a year of specialization and very few persons are employed in specialized health work without these qualifications. Administrative or supervisory positions require additional education as well as experience. The employee must continue to study and specialize to secure promotion to top positions.

Job opportunities

Positions range from routine work involving testing, analysis, and collection of data to supervisory and administrative positions. Expansion of the services of state and federal health programs has increased the demand for personnel in this area. International health programs developed through the World Health Organization and the Mutual Security Agency have contributed to the demand for qualified health workers who are willing to travel and serve in other countries. A person with public health training may be employed as school health director to work with the total health program in the school or community or as a school health educator.

Positions of interest to majors or minors in health education include those of Vital Statistician, Health Educator, and Medical Social Worker, which are available in such agencies as:

1. State and federal health departments
2. County and city health departments
3. The Veterans Administration
4. The United States Children's Bureau
5. Office of Indian Affairs
6. Commercial firms and industries

The following national voluntary agencies are among those which employ health educators, editors and writers of health publications, field workers, and executives:

1. National Tuberculosis Association
2. National Heart Association
3. American Cancer Society
4. National Foundation for Infantile Paralysis
5. YMCA and YWCA
6. Boys' Clubs of America

Special opportunities are provided for continuing graduate work or special preparation through some of the governmental health departments and voluntary organizations. Graduate assistantships are available to qualified graduates of undergraduate health curriculums. State assistance is granted by some states to those who have had preliminary training and experience in teaching or community work and qualify for advanced preparation. An illustration of such opportunities is the case of a recent graduate with a major in school health education who is now doing graduate work in public health under a special grant provided by a midwestern State Public Health Department.

THERAPEUTICS

Therapeutic work requires highly qualified specialists with extensive education in the biological sciences. Some colleges and universities offer pre-therapy preparation; others provide a complete professional course certifying graduates for specialized work in therapeutics. Students interested in the possibility of specializing in some branch of therapeutics should include in their undergraduate studies advanced courses in anatomy, physiology, analysis of movement, and other courses required for the certification of therapists. The biological science requirements for physical education and health education majors are also basic courses required for therapy specialization.

Many physical education majors take additional work to qualify as therapists. The basic preparation in physical education and health education, the biological sciences, physiology of exercise, body mechanics, and corrective exercise furnishes the background needed for specialization in the therapy fields. Additional work in other sciences such as physics, chemistry, and psychology is particularly valuable.

The four major areas of therapy specialization include:

1. Physical therapy   3. Exercise therapy
2. Occupational therapy   4. Recreational therapy

In addition to therapy work, corrective physical education has developed as a specialized field closely related to therapeutics. Undergraduate study in physical education provides the basic preparation for work in this area. Additional work in anatomy and physiology, together with clinical practice, is necessary to prepare for positions in corrective physical education.

Snow [1] has summarized the relationship of the several agencies working with handicapped individuals. His statements in regard to the physical educator's place and function are particularly pertinent.

1. A definite ethical appreciation of the exact relationship between the physical education worker and the medical profession is needed.

2. Many physical education workers in the therapeutic field are accepting responsibilities both in their teaching and in corrective work, with which responsibilities they should not be burdened.

3. Physical education students look to the medical profession for advice in corrective work, realizing the latent dangers, both psychologically and physically, which may be present in a therapeutic routine in the presence of certain pathologies.

PHYSICAL THERAPY

Physical therapy is carried on in connection with leading medical schools, and classes are taught by qualified medical personnel. Qualifications for preparation were established by the American Medical Association during World War II. The therapist works within the standards set up by the American Registry of Physical Therapy Technicians and the American Physical Therapy Association. Practical work during preparation is carried on under the supervision of expert orthopedists and other specialists.

Requirements and nature of the work

A college degree in physical education or nursing education is basic preparation for specialization in physical therapy. An additional year of study is required for certification as a physical therapist. Further specialization may be secured in any one of several fields following the completion of preparation in physical therapy.

The personal requirements include the physical strength and endurance to work with patients who may require lifting and carrying. Massage, passive movements, and active resistive exercise require muscular strength and stamina. The therapist works with the ill or the handicapped and must have many of the same qualities which make a doctor successful.

PROFESSIONAL COURSES IN PHYSICAL THERAPY

Anatomy	Orthopedics	Surgery
Physiology	Pathology	Therapy Exercise
Clinical Practice	Neurology	Principles of Medicine
Electrotherapy	Bandaging	Psychology
Hydrotherapy	First Aid	Occupational Therapy
Massage	Hygiene	Administration
		Social Service Work

The nature of the work requires the therapist to work under the direction of doctors and to carry out the prescribed program of treatment for each patient. The therapist uses physical measures such as exercise, manipulation, and massage. He must be skilled in handling various applications of heat, light, water, and electricity. He may work with cases of fracture, paralysis, and injury resulting from war damages, athletics, and automobile accidents. Crippled children, veterans, and handicapped adults are among those with whom the therapist works.

The main uses of therapy are to relieve symptoms and to speed recovery. In chronic conditions therapy relieves pain, increases circulation, stimulates organic functions, and brings about chemical changes in the body. The psychological values of therapy are often of definite benefit to the patient.

Working conditions

The field of therapy is one of service; it offers the personal satisfaction of assisting physically sick and handicapped persons. The treatment often brings immediate relief, and in many cases it is possible to follow the progress of the patient closely. Physical therapy has been accepted as a legitimate part of medical care and as a supplement to medical and surgical treatment.

Since the work of the therapist is carried on as a highly specialized service, therapy positions offer both security and permanent employment. The salary level has increased rapidly in recent years and now compares favorably with that in other professions requiring similar preparation. On the other hand the therapist faces certain occupational hazards, which include hard physical work and the possible exposure to communicable diseases. The work may be associated with the treatment and care of patients in mental and penal institutions.

The graduate of approved physical therapy schools has a choice of positions in many types of hospitals, schools, and clinics, including:

Veterans' hospitals	Schools for crippled children
Army and navy hospitals	Public health clinics
General hospitals	Industrial programs
Special clinics	

Several thousand physical therapists are now employed in the United States. There is a great need for more well-qualified people, and in particular, for more men therapists, since the majority now employed are women. The increase of war-injured patients in military and veterans' hospitals has emphasized the need for men with the physical strength and endurance necessary to care for adult male patients.

Scholarships sponsored by the National Foundation for Infantile Paralysis and other groups are available for physical therapy training. On completing the course the student must take a national examination before being listed as a registered physical therapist.

OCCUPATIONAL THERAPY

The program of occupational therapy is directed toward restoring handicapped minds and bodies through specialized programs to teach new work habits. The occupational therapist follows the recommended program prescribed by the physician but is responsible for selecting the types of activities that will bring about desired results.

Requirements and nature of the work

A specialized four-year college course in occupational therapy is required for work in this area, and a fifth year is frequently added. Such courses lead to certification as registered occupational therapists.

The occupational therapist assists patients in many vocational areas. All types of craft work, dramatics, music, shorthand, typing, radio repairs, and other practical fields of employment are emphasized. The sports and recreational phases of occupational therapy are receiving more and more attention. The therapist needs personal skill in arts and crafts as well as in the other therapeutic activities. He must be able to create an interest on the part of the patient and direct this interest toward active participation in craft or hand work. These activities are selected by the therapist for their remedial value, and may include actual vocational training as well as activities designed to relieve strain and develop recreational or social interests.

PROFESSIONAL COURSES IN OCCUPATIONAL THERAPY

Anatomy
Art (drawing, design)
Arts and Crafts (leather work, weaving, bookbinding)
Dramatics

Home Economics
Horticulture
Recreational Music
Psychology

The student also devotes time to advanced courses in theories of occupational therapy, medical and psychiatric social work, and group work, as well as to clinical work in hospitals.

Working conditions

Although occupational therapy is a new profession, starting salaries are quite adequate and there are usually provisions for increases on a regular basis. Working conditions are good and the future is relatively secure. The possibilities for specialization in research or supervisory activities are increasing. Extensive training is required for employment and salaries may not be commensurate with time spent in training. Work is with the handicapped and almost entirely in hospitals. Results may be slow and difficult to measure.

Job opportunities

There are job opportunities in such organizations as the following:

Orthopedic hospitals
Children's hospitals
Tuberculosis sanitariums
Veterans Administration facilities

Mental hospitals
Curative workshops
Special schools for the handicapped
Vocational rehabilitation centers

EXERCISE THERAPY

Exercise therapy is an area of treatment recently recognized by the Veterans Administration and is gaining status as a specialized phase of therapy. The exercise therapist cooperates with the physician, the physical therapist, and the occupational therapist.

Requirements and nature of the work

Requirements for exercise therapists include four years of college with specialization in physical education. The specialization should include courses in anatomy, remedial or corrective physical education, first aid, and hygiene. Applicants must also have completed a clinical practice course in exercise therapy or must have six months of clinical experience in the field. A civil service examination is required. Applicants must

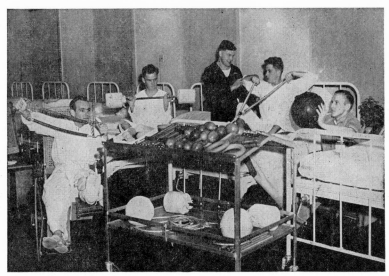

Courtesy of U. S. Navy

be citizens of the United States and must pass a physical examination. There is no written examination but applicants are rated on experience and qualifications.[2]

The work in exercise therapy in the Veterans Administration is directed toward giving physical exercise as prescribed by the attending physician. The purposes of the exercise program are to increase strength and assist in the restoration of bodily functions after illness or injury. The therapist assists the patient in

[2] Details of requirements are provided in *United States Civil Service Announcement No. 299* (Washington, D. C.: Government Printing Office, 1951).

ambulation and teaches him activities that will aid him to return to active life.

Working conditions

Therapists are employed under civil service programs, and a regular 40-hour week with overtime pay for additional time is common. Pay increases and provisions for advancement are customary. The employee works closely with the medical personnel and has opportunities for study and research. The therapist has an important place in the program of treatment and can derive great satisfaction from his contribution to the patient's recovery. A choice of location is possible in Veterans Administration facilities throughout the country.

Job opportunities

The number of job opportunities is not large but the demand has been greater than the supply. Employment is available for exercise therapists in Veterans Administration regional offices, centers, and hospitals throughout the United States. It has been estimated that the peak load of patients in veterans' hospitals will not be reached until 1980. Physical education graduates with the required qualifications have been employed immediately in this work since 1950.

Advancement may be slow but opportunities have increased recently. Salary increases are regular and the trend is toward a coordination of therapy services in the Veterans Administration. Capable persons may be called upon to assume supervisory or administrative responsibilities for the physical, occupational, and exercise therapy programs.

RECREATIONAL THERAPY

Recreational therapy plays an important role in the treatment of children as well as adults who are handicapped physically or mentally. A variety of recreational activities are offered in order to find those with greatest appeal to various people and activities having particular value. It is necessary to get the person into group activities that will contribute to his social adjustment and at the same time to control amount and intensity of activity. There are many types of games and activities of a recreational nature that make both physical and social contributions to the handicapped person.

Requirements and nature of the work

Preparation for work in recreational therapy includes experience in recreational activities of all types. Emphasis is necessary on music, art, and dramatic activities, as well as on individual and group sports. Advanced courses in psychology and group work are valuable to the recreation therapist. A major in recreation in a regular four-year college program prepares the student for work in recreational therapy.

The program includes special exercises and activities to aid in personal adjustment. The patient is encouraged to understand his limitations and appreciate the values of recreational and exercise activities. The program is planned both for immediate benefits and for long-range outcomes. An effort is made to develop correct attitudes on the part of the patient and he is encouraged to become independent in his own activity program. Normal aspects of development and enjoyment in activity are stressed.

Working conditions

The recreational therapist works in hospitals or clinics in close cooperation with other therapists and with physicians. Recreation personnel are receiving increased opportunities to develop programs in many types of institutions as the values of recreational therapy gain recognition. Salaries and general working conditions are similar to those for other therapists.

Job opportunities

There are opportunities for employment in recreational therapy in public hospitals, the Veterans Administration, schools, and rehabilitation centers. Particular emphasis is being placed on recreational therapy in mental institutions of all types. Requests for personnel exceed the supply available.

CORRECTIVE PHYSICAL EDUCATION

Corrective physical education has become increasingly important owing to discoveries and treatments that were tested in military hospitals during World War II. Greater emphasis is being placed on reconditioning and rehabilitation of all individuals with physical handicaps. "With twenty-three million handicapped individuals in the United States today, the problem of the handicapped is the concern of all of us." [3]

As a consequence of national emphasis, school and community efforts to meet the needs of people within the school program have been increased. New opportunities are being provided for handicapped persons to make the most of their capabilities.

Requirements and nature of the work

Students preparing to work with the corrective physical education program must have a knowledge of the pathology of the handicapping conditions, of the psychological and sociological problems of the handicapped, and must understand and apply modern educational principles. Special courses in remedial and corrective physical education and adapted sports, and increased attention to preparation in kinesiology and physiology of exercise are desirable.

After World War I a few programs of corrective physical education developed in schools, but personnel were not available in many cases and the handicapped child was frequently excused from physical education.

It is increasingly apparent that the physical educator has a definite responsibility for contributing to the health and welfare of all handicapped students who are attending his school. The contribution that physical education can make to the child

[3] George Stafford, *Preventive and Corrective Physical Education* (New York, A. S. Barnes and Co., 1950), p. iv. (Reprinted by permission.)

who is crippled, or whose physical condition otherwise hampers his efforts to make a satisfactory adjustment, is great. The physical education teacher must understand the limits within which he can work and must know the relationships which should prevail among the health specialists such as the school physician, the orthopedic specialist, the school nurse, the public health nurse, the physical therapist, and the teacher of physical education, and between this group and public health agencies.

The findings of health examinations indicate pupils who are unable to participate in the regular program. Individual attention for such pupils is essential. Even though many handicaps cannot be corrected, a program of corrective and remedial physical education can make real contributions. Particular efforts can be directed toward the improvement of body mechanics, the development of sufficient physical fitness, and the attainment of good habits and attitudes toward activity.

Preventive physical education for the elementary school child is most important and offers a field of vocational possibility. The introduction of health and physical welfare activities so that the child does not develop handicapping physical deviations is important. Minor difficulties may be corrected if they are given attention early in the child's life. These same minor physical deviations may become permanent if they are allowed to progress. The physical educator who is qualified to develop programs of prevention and correction can render great service in the elementary grades.

Working conditions

Corrective physical education in the schools is a unique field of service. Teaching physical activities to the handicapped person is a challenging and rewarding job. In order to do an effective job the physical educator must be continuously aware of the person's condition as determined by the doctor.

One of the major problems of educational administration is the adaptation of the program to the interests, capacities, and needs of the individual child. The physical educator should devise a program of activities that is flexible enough to provide for these variations among children. Individual corrective activities thus become a significant part of the program of physical education. Physical deficiencies and needs must be given attention but it is equally important to improve the social traits of handicapped children.

Job opportunities

There are opportunities for service in corrective physical education in any school program as a part of the total work of teaching physical education. Special opportunities are possible in schools for crippled children and in certain other public institutions.

SAFETY EDUCATION

The program of safety education includes teaching safety in classes, supervising safety instruction and programs, teaching classroom and behind-the-wheel driving, and carrying out other school safety activities. Work with organizations and groups outside the schools includes public relations and publicity, writing and publication of safety materials, field service, and the organization of programs of safety education.

Requirements and nature of the work

Safety education has developed on a national basis and involves many organizations and agencies. The schools, industries, communities, unions, insurance companies, and many others are interested in programs of safety education. The school programs involve separate courses as well as coordinated safety programs in other courses such as civics, home economics, science, shop, and physical education. Research and analysis programs are being developed in an effort to solve major safety problems.

The educational requirements for work in this area vary greatly. A few special programs are provided to qualify teachers of general safety and a considerable number of programs offer preparation for driver education instructors. Approximately 6000 high schools now offer special courses in driver education. There is a trend toward establishing state requirements for certification to teach safety and driver education in the schools. State courses of study provide programs for safety education in the elementary and secondary schools.

Preparation in safety education is frequently combined with preparation in health education and physical education, and with industrial arts. Special programs sponsored by automobile associations, the Red Cross, and other agencies are also directed toward safety education, and short courses and workshops in safety education are offered by many colleges.

Working conditions

The addition of specialized courses in safety education to the teacher education curriculum makes it possible to qualify as a teacher of safety and driver education. The teaching of safety provides an additional teaching field for health and physical education majors. Salaries are good, especially for the technical and supervisory positions.

Job opportunities

There are job opportunities as safety supervisors in elementary schools, safety education teachers in secondary schools, and teachers of driver education in junior and senior high schools. Among agencies employing specialists are the American Red Cross, the National Safety Council, highway departments, automobile associations, insurance companies, industries, youth groups, and municipal agencies. An example of special job opportunities in the field of safety is the work of the American Automobile Association in the promotion of safety and driver education. This organization now employs a number of field supervisors to work with public schools in the promotion of driver education and to prepare driver education instructors.

Safety education courses are offered in many colleges preparing teachers. Several states require all teacher education majors to take a course in general safety covering home, school, traffic, and vocational materials. Other courses offered are intended for administrators, safety coordinators, and teachers at various levels.

CAMPING AND OUTDOOR EDUCATION

The camp movement in the United States represents an important educational and recreational development, and one that is growing constantly. Current estimates indicate that between 10,000 and 12,000 camps serve between 3,000,000 and 4,000,000 campers annually.[4] Voluntary organizations and municipal agencies sponsor camps for underprivileged children on a nonprofit basis. Private camps are operated as profitable business undertakings while furnishing children excellent opportunities to gain the advantages of well-planned, well-conducted camp programs. Schools have developed camping programs ranging in extent from summer day camping to year-round programs of camping and outdoor education as a part of the school program.

A variety of camps exist for both children and adults. State and federal governments provide camping opportunities for individuals, families, and organized groups in state and national parks. Camp programs operated by private groups and individuals, and by various youth agencies, provide camping experiences emphasizing such activities as campcraft, woodcraft, nature study, music, social activities, group living, and personal development. Special camps offer programs of specialized work for handicapped persons in aquatics, sports, sailing, music, art, and education.

Organized camp programs are provided by such agencies as the YMCA, YWCA, Camp Fire Girls, Girl Scouts, and Boy Scouts. Churches and fraternal groups maintain camps for

[4] Margaret B. Hodges, ed., *Social Work Yearbook* (New York: American Association of Social Workers, 1951), p. 69; and Robert McBride, *Camping at the Mid-Century* (Chicago: Continental Casualty Co., 1953), p. 11.

children, for teen-agers, and, in some cases, for adults. Some large industrial firms operate vacation camps for their employees as a part of their program of planned recreation service. Schools have included camping in the program of education as a rather recent development, although the first camp in the United States was actually a school camp. A recent report by the American Camping Association [5] indicates a considerable interest in school camping and recognition of the values of camp experiences. School camps stress activities contributing to general education, group experiences, and recreation. Several states provide school funds for camping and a number of communities provide school camp activities for all children. In Michigan alone 75 school systems participate in school camping, and a total of 175 school systems have included camping as a regular part of the curriculum. Many more schools include day camping and outdoor education activities in their programs.

The newly developed field of outdoor education presents many opportunities for extending the school program. Well-organized programs of camping and outdoor education have been established in several states. The success of established programs of school camping and outdoor education in Michigan, California, and other states illustrates the desirability of developing similar programs throughout the country.

Requirements and nature of the work

Personal requirements for camp work include a desire and willingness to work with children closely in all of their daily activities. Camping, with the exception of day camping, is a 24-hour-a-day job. The camp counselor must like activity of all kinds and outdoor living in particular. He must possess personal skills in some areas of camp activity and must be able to assist with many activities in addition to his specialty. Good health, physical vigor, character, and maturity are essential.

[5] Robert McBride, *Camping at the Mid-Century*, p. 4.

Camp administration requires the ability to plan and organize programs, capability in handling details of business operation and management, and skill in group relationships. The camp director is responsible for the health, safety, and welfare of the campers. He also selects counselors and assigns them to camp duties. Since the success of the camp depends largely upon the capabilities and leadership of the counselors, the responsibility for their selection is great.

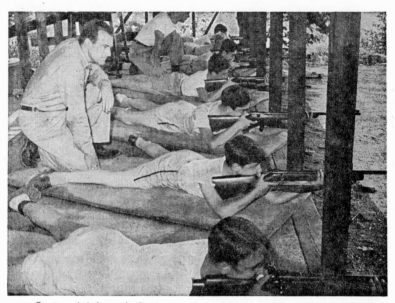

Courtesy of Androscoggin Camps

Majors in physical education and recreation are usually in demand as camp counselors. The health education major may also elect courses in recreation and camping to qualify for counseling work. Courses in camp counseling are particularly valuable to those who are interested in positions during summer vacations as camp counselors. Additional courses in arts and crafts, nature study, and woodcraft increase the versatility of the counselor and his value in the camp program.

Those who are interested in leadership in school camping

and outdoor education programs should be well-informed in a variety of fields. Nature study, which brings together all phases of biological science in practical field study situations, is receiving particular attention in the outdoor education program. The work approximates that of the naturalist, the national park ranger, and the camp nature specialist. Courses that provide a background for such work are important to the person who plans to participate as a leader in outdoor education.

The outdoor educator has to know his stuff in biology or be a vulnerable target. He must also be a competent fieldman. . . . Furthermore, he needs to be a humanist, writer, conversationist, psychologist, recreationist, camper, and expert in handling both adults and children in the field.[6]

Working conditions

Camping and outdoor education offer vocational opportunities in work that is usually out of doors and in a pleasant and stimulating atmosphere. Camp counseling requires long hours and great patience, but this disadvantage is largely offset by good living accommodations and the enjoyable nature of the work. Camp work is seasonal in most cases and offers full-time employment to a relatively limited number of persons. Salaries vary widely according to the type of camp and the experience of the counselor. Camp directors often command excellent salaries during the summer camping season. Salaries for full-time administrative positions compare favorably with many other administrative positions in education.

Job opportunities

The demand for camp counselors and camp specialists is increasing greatly. Camp directors visit college campuses early in the school year to employ staff members for the following season. Camp work provides good paying summer jobs for many physical education and recreation majors, and for some it may develop into a year-round vocation.

6 William G. Vinal, "Outdoor Education as a Profession," *Education,* 73:427, March 1953. (Reprinted by permission.)

Current interest in camping and the growth of the whole camping movement indicates the potential job opportunities. At present 10 to 15 per cent of all children have some kind of camp experience, and this percentage is increasing annually. Public funds are being provided in increasing amounts for camping and outdoor education, and many public and private agencies are giving attention to camp programs. The American Camping Association states:

> Organized camping out-of-doors, under good leadership in a functional democracy, should be the rightful heritage of all children. Inability to pay, cultural background, geographic location of the home, and physical or emotional handicaps should not prevent children from having a camp experience. The time is not too far off when a camping experience will be considered a normal part of the educational and recreational experience of every American child.[7]

Job opportunities for nature specialists are available in scouting, hosteling, camping, national parks, settlement houses, Veterans Administration projects, recreational therapy, public schools, teachers colleges, and professional programs for training recreation leaders. Reports indicate that there are more positions available than there are qualified people to fill them.[8]

It is estimated that there should be at least one counselor for every 6 to 8 campers. If this ratio is maintained, many thousands of camp workers will be needed.

YOUTH-SERVING AGENCIES

There are many private and semiprivate organizations sponsoring programs of health, physical education, and recreation. Among the better known of these are the Young Men's and Young Women's Christian Associations, The Catholic Youth Organization, the Young Men's and Young Women's Hebrew Associations, and the scouting groups. These agencies

[7] McBride, *op cit.*, p. 24. (Reprinted by permission.)
[8] *Social Work Yearbook, op cit.*, p. 72.

perform an important educational service in most American communities. Such groups generally try to supplement the programs of the school, home, and church with a wide variety of activities. Sports and recreation customarily play an important part in the services provided.

Professional opportunities in these agencies are numerous for persons with undergraduate preparation in physical education and recreation. The requirements and nature of the work are similar among the various organizations. A Bachelor's degree from an accredited institution, an undergraduate major in physical education or recreation, and some degree of specialization in social work and group leadership are customary requirements for positions in youth agency work.

Personal qualifications emphasize the characteristics that are essential in youth leadership in any field. Successful leadership experience is often required for appointment to a position in youth-serving agencies. Experience as a camp counselor, a playground leader, or a leader in campus clubs is of value in meeting the requirements for successful leadership activities.

Working conditions in well-established youth organizations include provisions for a 40-hour work week, retirement programs, paid vacations and sick leaves, and opportunities for advancement through graduate study and promotion to administrative positions. Working hours necessarily include night and weekend schedule assignments. Workers in these agencies carry on their programs outside school hours, and during school vacation. Many agencies provide placement services to employees to aid them in securing positions within the organization. In-service training through workshops, clinics, and schools and advisory or consultant services are provided for workers. A number of agencies conduct programs in foreign countries under the direction of staff groups from this country.

Salaries compare favorably with those in the teaching profession, although salary levels tend to be slightly lower for experienced leaders in agency work than for experienced professional persons in other fields. Administrative positions in large cities and in the national offices of youth organizations command very good salaries. The salary for a position of any nature is determined to some extent by the ability of the local community organization to finance the program and its leadership.

Career opportunities are varied and numerous in youth-serving agencies. A brief survey of the work and employment possibilities of several well-established organizations is presented in the following pages.

YOUNG MEN'S CHRISTIAN ASSOCIATION

The work in the YMCA is directed toward developing health and physical fitness, social and personal skills, and leadership qualities. Attention is given to educational and vocational guidance and to cooperative work with other community agencies. It is a Christian organization concerned with helping young people to know and understand the Christian way of life.[9]

Requirements and nature of the work

The general requirements for YMCA employment include graduation from college and special work in several professional areas. The professional preparation required includes 30 semester hours in prescribed fields. These fields are religious leadership, guidance, group leadership, administration, community organization, and field work. Courses in education, physical education, and recreation are also recommended. In addition to minimum preparation in these areas, professional work is required in one of the fields of activity offered in the YMCA. Among these are boys' work, student work, physical education, and administration.

The beginning employee in the YMCA has a variety of work responsibilities, among which are:

[9] *Professional Opportunities in the YMCA* (New York: National Council of the YMCA, n.d.).

1. Counseling
2. Conducting group activities
3. Directing social programs
4. Directing physical education and recreation
5. Working with volunteers and committees
6. Assisting with fund-raising programs
7. Cooperating with community groups

Working conditions

A worker in the YMCA usually begins as a junior secretary. He is eligible for promotion to a full secretary after a minimum of two years. Each secretary has a special job, such as boys'

Courtesy of Chicago YMCA—Photo by T. Kaitila

work secretary or physical director. The salaries paid are established by the local association and compare favorably with those of other workers in comparable fields. Adjustments are made on the basis of living costs, duties, and the supply of qualified men. YMCA employees may be promoted to the status of secretary after two years of successful experience and the completion of 30 semester hours of specified professional study.

The YMCA sponsors retirement programs, to which both employee and association contribute. Retirement is at 60 years of age. Low-cost insurance programs, group insurance, and medical plans are also provided. Hours of work vary and the individual employee may work on irregular schedules, although the usual work week is maintained in most positions. Annual vacations, increasing with length of service, are provided. Hours of work may be long and the requirements of most jobs in the YMCA are varied and demanding. Participation in the program is voluntary. The YMCA employee must develop programs that stimulate interest and attract young people.

Job opportunities

The YMCA offers many opportunities for students interested in a future requiring social, religious, physical education, and recreational service. There are approximately 3,000,000 members of the YMCA and job opportunities in more than 1700 YMCA units. Special YMCA programs are provided in Army and Navy associations and student associations in colleges, and in various parts of the world. Outstanding men may find unusual opportunities in some of these special programs.

Job opportunities are available in connection with various program activities. Many of these programs are carried on in service buildings supported by the YMCA. Such activities as athletics, swimming, music, dramatics, hobbies, and handicrafts are included. In addition to programs in the service buildings, the YMCA carries on other programs in the community. It has been particularly active in the support of camping activities. The YMCA has been a pioneer in many recreational sports, in physical fitness activities, in education, in job training programs, in vocational counseling, and in citizenship activities. All of these areas provide professional opportunities.

YOUNG WOMEN'S CHRISTIAN ASSOCIATION

The influence of the Young Women's Christian Association extends into the majority of communities through its programs for children, youth, and adults, under the leadership of qualified YWCA personnel. The YWCA was one of the first organizations for women to be founded in this country. Since 1858, it has devoted constant effort toward promoting educational and recreational programs for girls and women. The program of the YWCA includes health and physical education, posture, nutrition, family living, sex education, and an extensive program of adult education courses ranging from vocational to recreational education. The physical education and health education programs are coordinated under the direction of the health education departments of local associations.

Requirements and nature of the work

The personal requirements for YWCA staff members are high. The professional worker must be interested in social relationships and economic affairs as they affect the daily lives of people, and must have the ability to grow and develop an understanding of individuals and their worth. A sincere belief in the spiritual values of Christian ideals is an essential quality.

The minimum educational requirement for YWCA work is a Bachelor's degree from an accredited college. A major in health and physical education with a broad background of general education, including courses in the social studies, religion, and philosophy, qualifies women for positions in the work of the health education departments. Experience as camp counselors, recreation leaders, and campus organization leaders may be required by a local association. Volunteer work with youth groups is of value to the prospective YWCA worker.

Working conditions

Employment by the YWCA is customarily for a 12-month period. Vacations on salary include a one-month summer vacation and a one-week vacation at mid-year. A two-week sick leave on pay is provided. Leaves of absence for study are arranged by many local associations, and employees are encouraged to secure additional education. The normal working schedule includes a certain amount of work in the evening during a 40-hour week. The organization and staff member contribute jointly to the retirement program. Salaries vary according to the position held, and the education and experience of the worker. While salaries are somewhat lower than in many teaching positions they have shown consistent improvement.

Work in health education departments is carried on under pleasant conditions. The facilities available for the program of health and physical education are similar to those in many schools and colleges. The cooperative, friendly, and democratic relationships that exist among staff personnel, committee members, and volunteer workers contribute to enjoyable working conditions. In-service programs for staff members and opportunities to grow on the job are part of the personnel program of the organization. A short period of orientation is provided for new staff members during the first weeks of their employment. A four-week school is held annually for new employees under the auspices of the National Board of the Association.

Job opportunities

A wide range of positions is available in this country and in foreign countries. Program directors and executives are responsible for administrative work, program planning, working with committees and groups, helping to develop volunteer leadership programs, and interpreting the program of the Association in the community. Administrators work closely with community groups and leaders, and cooperate in many community undertakings. Assistants carry out many similar duties but have less responsibility for administration. The various types of positions are as follows:

Program Director in Community Association
Teen-Age Program Director
Assistant Teen-Age Program Director
Young Adult Program Director
Assistant Young Adult Program Director
Health Education Program Director
Assistant Health Education Program Director
Executive Director in Community Association
Executive Director of a Student Association
Assistant Director of a Student Association

The new employee usually serves as assistant in one of the special areas listed. After a period of successful service, American professional workers may be assigned by the Foreign Division of the National Board for service in other countries as advisers on local and national YWCA staffs in those countries. Foreign field staff are assigned in the following countries:

Argentina	Syria	Greece
Brazil	Turkey	Italy
Chile	China	Korea
Uruguay	Japan	Egypt
Mexico	Philippines	Thailand
India	Belgium	Liberia
Lebanon		

BOY SCOUTS

Professional work in scouting is primarily administrative work. The program is educational and recreational and is based on working with volunteer leaders and with boys. The professional group is made up of only about 2500 men who work with a program involving more than 750,000 volunteer leaders and over 2,000,000 boys. The scouting program is built on a foundation of local councils located throughout the country. Each council has a small professional staff and many volunteer workers. Councils are divided into districts with local volunteers conducting the program. The Field Executive works with local volunteers under the supervision of the Scout Executive.

Actually, those employed professionally in scouting have an administrative job that involves working with men and through a rather sizable volunteer organization. They do not deal directly with boys, but are responsible rather for the training and guidance of those who do work with boys.[10]

Requirements and nature of the work

A man interested in Boy Scout work should have a college degree with specialization in social science, recreation, business, or education. Personnel work, public speaking, psychology, and other similar courses can contribute to the preliminary preparation. The work is broad and varied, and practical leadership experience in student activities is valuable.

The Boy Scouts maintain a program through which college students may prepare for a career in scouting. This plan provides a series of projects to be carried out during free evenings, weekends, and vacation periods during the last two years of college under the supervision of local professional leaders. Any interested student can begin to prepare himself while still an undergraduate. Study and work experience with the local council provides familiarity with council operation and the work of professional Scout leaders.

In order to apply for formal preparation as a professional Boy Scout leader, a senior in college or a man who has finished his college work must have an interview with local and regional council executives. If his application is approved he attends a National Training School for professional leaders. Students are organized into scout groups and participate in an intensive 45-day training period. After this training the individual receives a temporary position in a Boy Scout Council. After the completion of training and field work the man is placed as a Field Scout Executive where his duties consist of work with

10 Personal letter from Gunnar H. Berg, Director, Professional Training, Boy Scouts of America, December 10, 1952. (Used by permission.)

the Council Board members and the District Supervisor, and responsibility for camping and other activities. The work involves travel and work with many volunteer leaders.

Personal requirements are similar to those in other recreation fields with the additional requirement of exceptional ability to work with volunteer leaders. The Scout Executive must like people and must work with them. He must have leadership ability and be able to plan and carry out programs requiring detailed preparation. It is a sales job and requires the finest kind of personal and public relations. Experience in scouting both as a scout and as a leader is an important requirement and can be of great assistance to men considering a career in scouting.

Working conditions

Leadership in scouting provides satisfactory experiences in work with community leaders, boys' groups, and recreational activities. Salaries are comparable with those in other positions requiring similar training and experience. In 1952, salaries for local Scout Executives averaged $5,989, with the highest quarter of the professional service receiving an average salary of $7,974.[11]

Travel allowances are provided for expense while away from home. These allowances usually provide for automobile, travel needs, and hotel expenses. Regular vacations, a retirement plan, and group insurance are provided. The retirement plan provides for retirement at 65 and involves joint contributions of the employee and the local council. Group insurance is partly subsidized by the National Council, and Scout Executives also participate in the Social Security program.

Work as a Boy Scout Executive requires long hours and the ability to perform a variety of services. The Scout Executive must be able to meet people effectively and to give unusual effort to the development and maintenance of scouting programs. His job covers a considerable area and usually requires travel away from home.

[11] *A Career in the Boy Scouts of America* (New York: Boy Scouts of America, n.d.), p. 15.

Job opportunities

The Boy Scout program has developed rapidly since 1910, until there are now scouting programs in every part of the United States. "More than 2,900,000 boys and men were enrolled in 81,000 units at the end of 1951." [12] The program has been accepted and is supported by civic, religious, and patriotic groups, and thousands of men serve as volunteer leaders and contribute funds to scouting.

The Field Executive after preliminary training may advance with experience and success on the job to positions as Assistant Executive Service Director or Executive Service Director. The National Personnel Division assists in finding opportunities for advancement within the scouting program.

BOYS' CLUBS

Boys' Clubs provide activity programs in many of the larger cities throughout the country. Attention is given to physical activities, health education, social skills, and individual guidance. The work is well established and more than 3,000,000 boys are served by these clubs.

Requirements and nature of the work

In addition to the usual personal characteristics, preparation for work in Boys' Clubs should include educational preparation in social studies and psychology as well as in the activities used in such programs. Experience with boys in camps or recreation programs is particularly valuable.

Chart 3 [13] indicates the kinds of work carried on in Boys' Clubs.

Working conditions

Employees in Boys' Clubs usually work a 40-hour week but the hours are frequently irregular. Many of the club programs

[12] *A Career in the Boy Scouts of America*, p. 2.
[13] From *Leadership in Boys' Clubs*, 2d ed. (New York: Boys' Clubs of America, 1948), p. 24. (Reprinted by permission.)

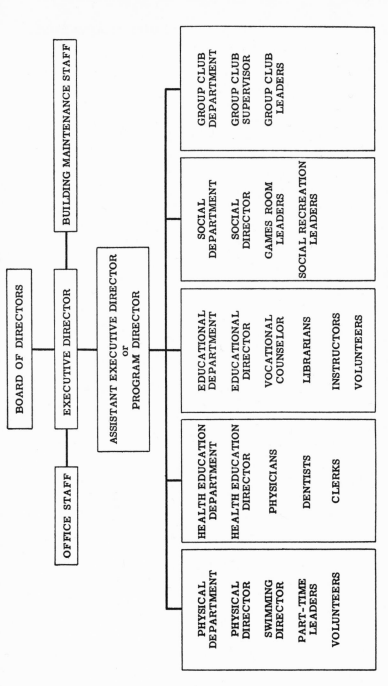

Chart 3. STAFF ORGANIZATION IN A SINGLE-UNIT BOYS' CLUB

are carried on in the evenings and on weekends. Salaries are comparable to those in other types of agency work.

Job opportunities

There are over 300 Boys' Clubs in the United States with more than 300,000 members. These Boys' Clubs employ several types of personnel. Among these are:

1. Executive Director—works with the Board of Directors, plans and supervises programs, administers the budget, and promotes membership programs.

2. Director—has many of the same duties as the Executive Director and works cooperatively with the Executive Director; his job is in charge of a unit in the organization.

3. Program Director—is directly concerned with the activities of the club; plans programs, works with program staff, and promotes activities.

4. Physical Director—duties include program planning, conducting activities, supervising the department, and maintaining equipment and supplies.

Other positions in Boys' Club work involve directing programs in health education, swimming, education, and social programs. Complete lists of duties and requirements are listed in the Leadership Bulletin of the Boys' Clubs of America.

GIRL SCOUTS

The Girl Scouts serve girls from 7 to 18 years of age through a nationwide program. The purpose of the Girl Scout program is to develop qualities and capabilities which contribute to wholesome interests, health, sound recreation, and skills in a variety of vocational and avocational areas. Self-reliance, resourcefulness, and initiative are emphasized as desirable outcomes of the program.

Requirements and nature of the work

The personal requirements for Girl Scout work are similar to those for other fields which require ability to work successfully with people. A Bachelor's degree from an accredited college and a minimum of 20 hours in the social sciences is required for employment. Other requirements for appointment to a Girl Scout position include two years of successful experience as a group leader and four weeks of experience as a staff member of an established camp.

The professional worker in Girl Scouting must be familiar with a variety of recreational activities; be adept in the program fields included in scouting; and have a thorough knowledge of the purposes and program of the organization. The Girl Scout staff member acts in an advisory capacity in many community programs, trains and supervises volunteer workers and group leaders, directs and assists at summer camp, works with other agencies in planning youth programs, and has many administrative responsibilities for the Girl Scout program.

Working conditions

Workers are employed on a year-round basis with provisions for one month of vacation and sick leaves. Irregular hours are balanced by arrangements for time off as compensation. Salaries vary according to preparation and experience and the responsibilities of the job, and are comparable to those in other youth organizations. The organization provides a retirement insurance plan and in-service training. Graduate study, for which fellowships are available, is encouraged. A follow-up program, coordinated with that of the local council, provides supervision and personnel work with new professional staff members to aid them to develop as competent professional persons.

Job opportunities

The employment opportunities in Girl Scouting are varied. World-wide affiliations create opportunities for association with the work in foreign countries. Some jobs involve travel and work with other professional staff members in various parts of the country. Administrative experience in a related field is required for the position of Executive Director in local communities. Positions are available in local and regional offices, and in the national headquarters for qualified persons. The Personnel Department of the Girl Scout National Headquarters selects candidates and recommends them for positions in local organizations.

CAMP FIRE GIRLS

The Camp Fire Girls, Incorporated is organized on a nationwide scale, and has as its purpose the perpetuation of the highest ideals of the home and the provision of leadership to guide the development of wholesome recreational interests and to promote health. The organization serves girls from 7 to 18 years of age through programs of recreation, camping, education, and youth leadership.

Requirements and nature of the work

The requirements for the professional leader in the Camp Fire program are similar to those in other youth agencies devoted to social service. The program of the Camp Fire Girls is organized through the National Headquarters and carried out through local sponsorship. The work of the professional staff members involves close cooperation with community leaders, the conduct of training programs for volunteer workers, leadership of Camp Fire groups and their activities, camp administration and counseling, and supervisory or executive work in local, district, or national offices.

Working conditions

The working conditions and salaries in Camp Fire positions are similar to those in other youth agencies. Working hours are often irregular, but are subject to adjustment according to the immediate demands of the work to be done, and approximate the normal 40-hour week. Personnel policies are favorable in regard to personal relationships, democratic representation, and provisions for security.

Job opportunities

Employment in Camp Fire work offers a wide selection of positions. Many jobs require experience with the organization and provide opportunities for advancement. On the local level, professional staff workers are needed as executives and assistants. District field and supervisory positions and work in the extension program of the organization provide job opportunities for experienced leaders. Work in the national headquarters of the Camp Fire Girls involves administration, field supervision, records, programs, and publications.

INDUSTRIAL RECREATION

Industries in recent years have recognized the place of recreation in the operation of their programs. Labor and management are cooperating in recreation programs and there is general acceptance of the benefits of recreation activities. The actual programs may be financed and conducted by management, jointly by management and labor, or entirely by the employees. Industrial recreation programs include activities and events similar to those in community programs. An Industrial Recreation Association has been formed to sponsor and promote this type of program.

Requirements and nature of the work

Employment in industrial recreation is possible for graduates of professional programs in recreation or physical education. The student interested in this area should take additional work in counseling and personnel fields as well as the usual sports and recreational activities. Industrial relations courses and work in administration and management are also valuable.

The work in industrial recreation involves program development and conduct of activities for industrial personnel and their families. In addition to sports and competitive programs conducted for men and women in the plant, interplant and intercompany competitive teams are frequently sponsored. Other activities include arranging family picnics and outings and management of playgrounds and similar recreational facilities.

The industrial recreation leader is frequently associated with personnel programs, which require abilities in counseling, public work, teaching, supervision of personnel, and other similar activities.

Working conditions

The advancement of recreation personnel is facilitated through extensive in-service training programs. Workers can prepare to assume responsibilities in recreation as well as in personnel and other areas of industrial operation. Salaries compare favorably with those in other recreational fields and there are opportunities for administrative positions. Many industries employ recreation workers who are interested in general personnel work, and employees are frequently moved from one plant to another to gain experience in the total program and plant relationships.

Job opportunities

A survey [14] of positions in industrial recreation conducted in 1951 indicated that there were 2250 full-time persons employed. Of this number 675 were women and 1575 were men. It was estimated at this time also that there were 6000 part-time industrial recreation workers. There is a great demand for specialists in this field. Although many of those employed are not college graduates, an increasing number are graduates of recreation and physical education programs. The recreation programs have been closely related to personnel divisions in industry and a number of recreation directors have had training in personnel work.

COMMERCIAL RECREATION

Commercial recreation consists of all forms of recreational activity that are carried on primarily to make a profit. Such

[14] Charles Brightbill, "Professional Recreation Personnel." Unpublished study, 1951.

enterprises are usually owned by individuals or corporations and provide services and recreational opportunities for which there is a public demand. Commercial recreation ranges from bowling alleys to radio broadcasting as well as to professional sports of all types. Many activities, such as fishing and hunting,

Courtesy of Chicago Park District

which are normally self-directed or sponsored through public recreation programs, are also provided commercially. The availability of professional guides and other services have encouraged wide participation in outdoor recreation.

Requirements and nature of the work

There are no academic requirements established for work in commercial recreation areas. The student in a recreation or physical education curriculum interested in some phase of commercial recreation must determine future vocational plans and prepare accordingly. Among the possibilities are: operating resort centers, such as hunting or fishing lodges, bowling alleys, and dance studios, or doing the program work in recreation in such commercial establishments.

Working conditions

There are opportunities to establish a personal business or commercial venture, the income from which is determined by effectiveness in the operation of the business. There is a freedom of operation and an opportunity to be one's own boss which is not possible in most other recreation work. Commercial recreation in many cases requires an outlay of capital in the operation of the business.

Job opportunities

Estimates of possible opportunities for employment in this area are virtually impossible. However, an analysis of the millions who participate in commercial sports and recreation activities annually reveals some of the possibilities. For example, there are many commercial resort facilities for fishing, hunting, and camping; there are thousands of bowling alleys and hundreds of dance studios. Management and teaching personnel are needed for all of these as well as many others.

PROFESSIONAL ATHLETICS

The field of professional athletics has developed extensively in the United States in recent years. There are opportunities for outstanding performers in a variety of sports. Those sports in which professional competition is best established are baseball, basketball, football, golf, tennis, boxing, wrestling, and ice hockey. There are also some opportunities for professional play in other sports.

Requirements and nature of the work

The preparation for successful participation in professional sports is primarily the acquisition of personal skill of a high level. In football and basketball, almost all of the players have been outstanding on college teams. In baseball, the minor leagues or college teams provide the training ground for major league play. Thus *skill* is the primary requirement for the professional athlete. It is also necessary to find the opportunity to sell that skill in a sports field.

A college education is not necessary but play on college teams and good coaching in colleges most frequently provide the stepping stone to successful professional careers. The athlete also has his college education as a backlog after his competitive days are finished. If he has a second vocation, he is better prepared for the future.

Other requirements are total good health, strength, and endurance. The professional athlete must also have the drive and the desire to become and remain a top-flight performer. Excellence requires long hours of daily practice and drill—the professional golfer, for example, will spend hours every day hitting thousands of shots in order to perfect his game.

Working conditions

Professional athletes are paid high salaries for relatively short working periods. The player has opportunities to travel although the travel is usually limited in scope. The work is relatively easy and the hours are short. The athlete is a hero and receives public acclaim. He may also make contacts that will help him.

Major disadvantages are that the life of a professional is short and that good salaries are paid only to outstanding performers. Most professional athletes are young. Only in golf and tennis is professional life relatively long and even this may be a period of only 10 to 15 years. The hazards of the job are very considerable—one bad season and a career is finished. A serious injury will finish a young professional although teams carry insurance on the players.

Salaries for professional athletes may be illustrated by those of baseball players. Most major league players earn from $5,000 to $10,000 a year and minor league players can earn up to $6,000 per year. Top salaries may run as high as $75,000. Provisions are made for pension funds in professional baseball, but such arrangements are not common in other professional sports.

Job opportunities

Organized baseball, the National Football League, and professional hockey leagues are some of the sport organizations that are well established and stable. The number of jobs is not large: for example, the baseball major leagues employ only about 500 players. The professional athlete may advance after his active playing years to work as a coach, team manager, business manager, or scout, or he may turn to promotional work or radio. Sporting goods companies employ a limited number of men and women as professional consultants in various sports. Men and women who have been top-ranking amateur players and who are qualified to conduct clinics for schools and colleges, private and public clubs, or resorts have, in many cases, made a contribution to sports education through programs of consultant services.

SUMMARY

A statement of the requirements for preparation and employment, the nature of the work, the working conditions, and the job opportunities for a variety of positions closely related to physical education, health education, and recreation has been presented. No attempt was made to present an exhaustive or complete list of the many opportunities in areas related to these fields. The particular possibilities listed and discussed are those in which placement has been frequent and for which personnel are regularly sought. Job opportunities may be available in other specialized areas. Additional organizations in which graduates have been placed are:

1. Catholic Youth Organization
2. Young Men's and Young Women's Hebrew Associations
3. American Youth Hostels
4. American Red Cross
5. Church recreation groups
6. 4-H Clubs and other rural recreation groups

Other opportunities include work in sports writing and publicity, radio announcing in the sports field, and sales and promotion of sports equipment. Sports officiating as a sideline to many of the opportunities listed provides a possibility for additional income. Students who are interested in career possibilities in one or more of these areas should seek additional vocational information directly from the agency, association, or organization providing employment.

SUGGESTED PROBLEMS

1. Study and report on the job opportunities in two private health agencies.

2. Discuss the duties and responsibilities of a physical therapist with a qualified therapist.

3. Visit corrective physical education classes in a college or high school program and prepare a report on procedures and activities.

4. Visit a Veterans Administration hospital to observe the work of the physical therapist, occupational therapist, and recreational therapist. Prepare a report for class discussion.

5. Determine requirements for admission to one of the approved physical therapy schools. What additional courses should you plan to take to qualify for admission to preparation?

6. Write to the National Safety Council for information on its functions and programs. Prepare a report for the class.

7. List the duties and responsibilities of a camp director.

8. Write to the headquarters of one of the youth-serving agencies requesting most recent information on job opportunities and salaries. For what positions will you be qualified when you graduate?

9. Observe the program and activities of a youth agency meeting. What experiences do you need to be able to lead such a meeting?

10. Prepare a report on the recreation program in an industrial plant.

11. Study the player benefits and salary procedures in professional baseball and compare them with those in other professional work.

REFERENCES

PUBLIC HEALTH AND PRIVATE AGENCIES

Careers in Public Health (Health Bulletin for Teachers), vol. xxi, pp. 25-30. New York: Metropolitan Life Insurance Co., 1950.
Employment Opportunities in Public Health (Committee Report). New York: American Public Health Association, 1945.

Health Education as a Profession, Vocational Guidance Series, No. 1, Washington, D. C.: American Association for Health, Physical Education and Recreation, 1946.

Kilander, H. F., "Today's Needs in Health Education," *Journal of the American Association for Health, Physical Education and Recreation*, 22:24, January 1951.

————, *Report on Conference on the Undergraduate Professional Preparation of Students Majoring in Health Education*. Washington, D. C.: Office of Education, Federal Security Agency, 1949.

Public Health, A Career with a Future. New York: American Public Health Association, 1948.

THERAPEUTICS

Bernier, Leo, and Arthur Tauber, "Physical Education in Medical Practice," *Journal of the American Association for Health, Physical Education and Recreation*, 24:32, November 1953.

Careers in Service to the Handicapped, American Physical Therapy Association, American Occupational Therapy Association, American Speech and Hearing Association, International Council for Exceptional Children. Chicago: National Society for Crippled Children and Adults, Inc.

Ewerhardt, Frank H., "Therapeutic and Remedial Exercises," *Journal of the American Medical Association*, 128:202, May 19, 1945.

Haun, Paul, "Recreation in the Mental Hospital—A Philosophy," *Journal of the American Association for Health, Physical Education and Recreation*, 23:7, September 1952.

Health and Physical Education for Elementary Schools of the State of Illinois, Bulletin No. 17. State Department of Health and Physical Education, Springfield, Illinois: September 1944.

Kovacs, Richard, ed., *Yearbook of Physical Therapy, 1942*. Chicago: The Yearbook Publishers, Inc.

Krusen, Frank, *Physical Medicine*. Philadelphia: W. B. Saunders Company, 1944. Of particular interest: Introduction, pp. 1-9; Ch. I, History of Physical Therapy, pp. 9-45; Ch. XIV, Mechanotherapy Exercise, pp. 550-630; Ch. XXI, The Teaching of Physical Medicine, pp. 763-779; Ch. XXII, The Hospital Department of Physical Therapy, pp. 779-793.

Oberteuffer, D., "Some Contributions of Physical Education to An Educated Life," *Journal of Health and Physical Education*, 15:3, January 1945.

The Outlook for Women as Occupational Therapists. Medical Service, Bulletin No. 203-2, Rev., Women's Bureau, United States Department of Labor. Washington, D. C.: Government Printing Office, 1953.

Phillips, B. E., "Hospital Recreation is Unique," *Journal of the American Association for Health, Physical Education and Recreation*, 23:29, May 1952.

————, "Recreational Therapy," *Journal of the American Association for Health, Physical Education and Recreation*, 23:23, June 1952.

Rathbone, J. L., *Corrective Physical Education*, rev. ed. Philadelphia: W. B. Saunders Co., 1954.

Snow, W. B., "Relationship Between Medicine, Nursing, Physical Therapy, and Physical Education," *Journal of Health and Physical Education*, 13:285, September 1942.

Stafford, G. T., *Preventive and Corrective Physical Education*, rev. ed. New York: A. S. Barnes and Co., 1950.

Stone, E. B., and J. W. Deyton, *Corrective Therapy for the Handicapped Child*. New York: Prentice-Hall, Inc., 1951.

Wood, Harlan C., "New Horizons in Physical Rehabilitation," *Journal of the American Association for Health, Physical Education and Recreation*, 21:335, June 1950.

SAFETY EDUCATION

Safety Courses for Teachers, A Report of the Higher Education Committee. Chicago: National Safety Council, 1952.

Seaton, Don Cash, *Safety in Sports*. New York: Prentice-Hall, Inc., 1948.

Stack, H. J., E. B. Siebrecht, and H. D. Elkow, *Education for Safe Living*, 2d ed. New York: Prentice-Hall, Inc., 1949.

Stack, H. J., C. C. Hawkins, and W. A. Cutter, *Careers in Safety*. New York: Funk and Wagnalls Company, 1945.

CAMPING AND OUTDOOR EDUCATION

Bonder, Abe, "Camping," *Social Work Yearbook*. New York: American Association of Social Workers, 1951.

"Camping and Outdoor Education," *Journal of Educational Sociology*, May 1950.

"Camping and Outdoor Education," *Bulletin of National Association of Secondary School Principals*, May 1947.

MacMillan, Dorothy Lou, *Outdoor Education*. Laramie, Wyoming: Bureau of Educational Research and Service, 1952.

Masters, Hugh B., "Values of School Camping," *Journal of the American Association for Health, Physical Education and Recreation*, 22:14, January 1951.

McBride, Robert E., *Camping at the Mid-Century*. Chicago: Continental Casualty Company, 1953.

Mortensen, Martin, "Training Leaders in Camping and Outdoor Education," *Journal of the American Association for Health, Physical Education and Recreation*, 23:14, June 1952.

Vinal, Wm. G., "Outdoor Education is a Profession," *Education*, 73:427, March 1953.

YOUTH-SERVING AGENCIES

YOUNG MEN'S CHRISTIAN ASSOCIATION

Careers in the YMCA. New York: Personnel Services, National Council of the YMCA, n.d.

Professional Opportunities in the YMCA. New York: Personnel Services, National Council of the YMCA, n.d.

Qualifications and Training for the Secretaryship of the YMCA. New York: Association Press, 1946.

BOY SCOUTS OF AMERICA

A Career in the Boy Scouts of America. New York: Boy Scouts of America, n.d.

A Preview of a Professional Career in Scouting. New York: Boy Scouts of America, n.d.

BOYS' CLUBS OF AMERICA

Leadership in Boys' Clubs, 2d ed. New York: Boys' Clubs of America, 1948.

YOUNG WOMEN'S CHRISTIAN ASSOCIATION

Going My Way? New York: National Board of the Young Women's Christian Association, n.d.

GIRL SCOUTS OF AMERICA

Jobs With a Future. New York: Personnel Department, Girl Scouts of America, n.d.

Professional Opportunities in Girl Scouting. New York: Girl Scouts of America, n.d.

INDUSTRIAL RECREATION

Anderson, Jackson M., "A Survey of Recent Research Findings in Industrial Recreation," *Research Quarterly of the American Association for Health, Physical Education and Recreation,* 22:273, October 1951.

————, "Industrial Recreation," *Journal of the American Association for Health, Physical Education and Recreation,* 21:26, November 1950.

Brightbill, Charles, "Professional Recreation Personnel." Unpublished study, 1951.

Fitzgerald, Gerald B., "Recreation as Your Career," *Journal of the American Association for Health, Physical Education and Recreation,* 23:27, November 1952.

See also *Industrial Sports Journal,* all issues, and recreation magazines.

PROFESSIONAL SPORTS

Professional Athletics as a Career. Chicago: Institute for Research, 1947.

Courtesy of MacMurray College
and Bill Wade Studios, Jacksonville, Illinois

CHAPTER FOUR

The professional student and college life

Although planning for a career and making a wise choice of a vocation are important, such plans are only the first steps toward successful preparation for a profession. The next step is to realize all of the possibilities of college life and activities as they relate to personal and professional growth. Success in college has been found to be directly related to the amount of intelligent planning carried on by students. Higher scholarship, better application of college learning to professional fields, and wider participation in campus activities are some of the results of sound planning.[1]

Planning for a successful college life is one of the next steps to be taken in preparing for a career. The importance of successful adjustment to college cannot be overemphasized. A student who fails to adjust to college frequently experiences difficulty not only in meeting personal and educational requirements but also in adapting to his work after graduation. The relationship of satisfactory personal and professional growth during college years to success in a career will become increasingly apparent in the following chapters.

PLANNING A SUCCESSFUL COLLEGE LIFE

Attending a college means changing from accustomed surroundings of home, high school, and community to an entirely

[1] Fred McKinney, *Psychology of Personal Adjustment*, 2d ed. (New York: John Wiley and Sons, Inc., 1949), p. 6; and E. J. Sparling, *Do College Students Choose Vocations Wisely?* (New York: Bureau of Publications, Teachers College, Columbia University, 1933), pp. 5-6 and chs. ix, x.

different way of living. Many students are on their own for the first time. They find themselves responsible for budgeting their own expenses; arranging study time and recreation; deciding on habits of diet, rest, and sleep; keeping well groomed and selecting clothes; and making choices of social groups and new friends without benefit of parental suggestions or control.

Many college students possess personal habits and attitudes that they hope to overcome or improve. They realize that strengthening certain traits will mean greater happiness during college years and more success after college. An attractive personality, industriousness, ability to concentrate, perseverance, leadership, and cultural interests are qualities that most students want to achieve. Shyness, lack of social poise, procrastination, and tendencies to show anger, irritation, or jealousy are characteristics students want to eliminate. The advantages to be gained from a college education are directly related to the effort each person makes to benefit from the opportunities that are present in college surroundings and through college life and study.

ORIENTATION TO COLLEGE

Orientation is a process that has started with the first plans for a college education, the tentative or definite choice of a career, and the selection of a college. The process never ceases during undergraduate years. The degree of planning and the purpose back of it may determine whether or not a student becomes well adjusted to college, to college life and activities, and to the profession he has chosen.

Every effort is made to help new students become oriented to college. First, college catalogs and other descriptive materials are designed to familiarize students with the general organization and purpose of the institution. Rules, regulations, and requirements are explained in detail. Work opportunities, student activities, and college organizations are listed and described in printed bulletins. Second, a week is generally set aside before registration, or prior to the beginning of class work, to acquaint new students with the campus, the faculty, college traditions, and social life and activities. Third, older students, faculty members, guidance personnel, and departmental advisers assist the new freshmen with the many problems involved in selecting courses, completing registration, finding buildings and classrooms, and becoming acquainted with other students.

Finally, orientation courses and counseling services are available to students. Although it is apparent that a single course will not accomplish a complete introduction to college or the major field, such courses have value in assisting students to understand the curriculum and what is expected of them as students. Counseling experts are qualified to aid students in many ways, and should be consulted without hesitation. It is well to remember that the intelligent person seeks competent aid for vocational, social, and emotional problems in much the same way that he consults a physician about his physical health problems.

In addition to these aids it is the responsibility of each student to contribute to his own orientation. The following suggestions may be of assistance in planning, carrying out plans, and realizing the greatest possible benefit from a worth-while, enjoyable college life.

Get acquainted with the college

New students are frequently overwhelmed by the amount of information and materials that are given out during Freshman Week. Many students glance at the various booklets and discard them, only to find that they have been held responsible for the information that they contain. Catalogs and other informational material should be retained and used for reference.

Rules and Regulations. The rules and regulations governing registration, fees, deposits, and other expenses are usually described in the catalog. Procedures for changing schedules and dropping courses, and regulations governing class attendance, represent information with which every student should be familiar. Housing rules should be understood and complied with. Unintentional violation of a regulation may cause needless embarrassment and scholastic difficulty.

Living Accommodations. Young men and women who are away from home for the first time have many adjustments to make. They are particularly fortunate in colleges where dormitory living units provide pleasant and comfortable surroundings among students with the same interests. College supervision of living accommodations customarily provides for adequate standards in healthful surroundings, good food, and individual guidance by competent counselors. Off-campus living quarters should be under college regulations in order to insure satisfactory living standards. Students who are interested in joining fraternities or sororities should talk with friends and teachers about the expenses, advantages, and disadvantages of fraternity life.

Services Available to Students. Colleges and universities assume many responsibilities for the health and general welfare of students. Services provided usually include medical care, psychological counseling, reading and speech clinics, and financial assistance. Students should inform themselves of the extent of services available and should not hesitate to take advantage of them.

Working Opportunities. The provisions made by many colleges for working on the campus are a great advantage to students who must earn some part of college expenses. Work opportunities are usually diverse and include such jobs as assisting with laboratory work; typing in campus offices; library duties; helping to repair, issue, and care for equipment in and around the gymnasium; and field work on the athletic fields and tennis courts. Opportunities for work in the college community are largely dependent on the nature of business and industry in the locality.

Scholarships and Loan Funds. Worthy students are customarily assisted with the expenses of their education by various scholarships. Certain scholarships are outright awards; others provide for tuition for a stipulated number of years. Scholarship loans are self-perpetuating; the recipient has the privilege of using available money during his college years and then repays the loan after he graduates. Loan funds operate on the same general principle or as short-time emergency loans.

No student who needs financial assistance and who qualifies for it should hesitate to take advantage of scholarships and loans in order to attend college or to help meet expenses while in college. It is usually considered an honor to merit financial assistance of this nature. Qualification for scholarships and loans is based not only upon scholastic accomplishment but also upon evidence of need. It is customary to require personal recommendations and to investigate a student's qualifications before granting scholarships or loans.

Buildings and Classrooms. Handbooks and catalogs customarily include a map of the campus and a directory of the buildings. Learn the location of the buildings and the classrooms in which classes and meetings are scheduled. Determine the approximate time it takes to get from one building to another, and keep a record of the time and place of scheduled classes. Students who take the time to find classrooms before the first meeting of each class seldom miss the first class or the important meetings they are supposed to attend.

The Library. The library is one of the most important buildings on a campus. Reference rooms, reading rooms, the reserve book room, and the circulation department are all designed to assist students with their assigned and independent reading. Recreational reading rooms are usually available. Learn the library hours, the time for checking books in and out, and the regulations for the use of the books. Cooperate with the library staff and other students by being prompt in returning books and by meeting the regulations. Form the habit of consulting the members of the library staff when assistance in locating a book is needed.

Recreational Facilities and Programs. Student unions, club rooms, and athletic facilities provide centers for many student activities. Each campus includes provision for many recreational interests. Class and school parties and social events occur throughout the school year. Weekly activity calendars are usually posted on various bulletin boards on the campus. Student handbooks and other publications provide information about coming events and activities that are available to all students. Such materials can be secured from the offices of Dean of Men or Women, Student Personnel Bureau, and other sources. Many new students will be interested in participating in various recreational programs. Ask others for information; invite friends to attend or plan to join a group. Learn ahead of time where and when events are scheduled and take advantage of the many opportunities that will be made available for participating in activities, making new friends, and forming worth-while interests.

Student Activities and Cultural Opportunities. Student handbooks provide information about the many recreational activities, organizations, and campus social events. Concerts, dramatics, and other events of a cultural nature are customarily provided as part of the college program. Student activity tickets usually include the privilege of attending college-sponsored entertainment. Special student rates are frequently offered for community programs.

Get acquainted with the faculty

The reputation of an institution is largely dependent upon the kind of people who are selected to make up the faculty group. Many outstanding leaders in education may be included on the faculty. Students who fail to take advantage of the opportunity for studying under well-known people, or of making contacts with them through student activities, frequently miss valuable experiences.

Students should take the initiative in speaking to their instructors on the campus or elsewhere, since if classes are large a faculty member may have difficulty in recalling all the names and faces in his classes. When faculty members are present at social gatherings or other student affairs, students should introduce themselves, take time for a short conversation, and express appreciation for the faculty members' presence.

Ranks and Titles. The variety of ranks, titles, and offices of the average college faculty presents a bewildering problem to many entering students. The rank held by a faculty member may be determined by the number of years he has served the institution, by the degrees he holds, by some outstanding research or writing he has done, or by other noteworthy achievements. The following are the basic ranks and the usual requirements for each rank:

1. *Instructor.* Successful teaching experience and the possession of a Master's degree.

2. *Assistant Professor.* Teaching experience of sufficient length and success to merit professorial rank, combined with either advanced study beyond the Master's degree or a Doctor's degree.

3. *Associate Professor.* A combination of experience, advanced study, and contributions to the professional field. A Doctor's degree is usually one of the requirements of this rank.

4. *Professor.* A full professorship is customarily granted only to those teachers who have achieved all of the qualifications for the preceding rank and, in addition, have given outstanding service to the institution, the profession, and the community through research, writing, and other contributions to education.

Other instructional ranks may include those given to full-time or part-time teachers who act in the capacity of research workers, teaching fellows, or graduate assistants. As a rule, these ranks are reserved for persons who are carrying out research or graduate study toward advanced degrees and who are qualified to teach college classes or conduct laboratory work.

A variety of titles are used in institutions. They are usually connected with administrative positions and are indicative of the type of responsibility carried out or the office or department represented. Titles may include:

1. Head, Chairman, or Director of a department or a division of the university.

2. Dean of a division, school, or college within a university, or of students or faculty.

3. President.

Form of Address. The correct form of address is determined largely by the custom followed in the institution or according to the preference of the teacher concerned. While it is proper to address a faculty member holding a Doctor's degree as *Doctor,* certain teachers may prefer *Miss* or *Mister* in the classroom. A teacher with a Doctor's degree who holds a professorial rank may be properly addressed as either *Doctor* or *Professor.* A dean is customarily addressed as *Dean,* and the president of an institution is correctly addressed as *President.*

It is a good practice to consult the college catalog for information concerning teachers and the courses they teach, and to be familiar with their publications. Other suggestions that may be helpful in becoming acquainted with faculty members, and in addressing them correctly, include:

1. Learn the names of the instructors of all courses attended.

2. Look up the correct title, rank, and duties of the various teachers and administrative officers.

3. Find out the preferred form of address for various members of the faculty from older students, or from the office secretaries of the department with which the person is associated.

4. Plan to make contact with the instructor of each class, each semester. Make an appointment for a stated time. Have a definite purpose for seeing the instructor, such as a problem to be discussed or a question to be asked. Be on time, be friendly and natural, and show real interest in the subject being discussed. Leave within the set time, or at the first indication that the conversation should be brought to a close.

Nonacademic Personnel. Many people who are important to the administration and operation of an institution do not hold academic rank. Administrative personnel usually have definite titles and are qualified for the work they do through preparation and experience. These officials direct the offices carrying on the business and services of the institution. Other personnel are essential to the supervision, operation, and maintenance of the buildings and grounds of the campus.

The importance of the custodial staff to the efficient operation of the physical plant will soon become apparent to major students.[2] The upkeep of gymnasiums, swimming pools, courts, and athletic fields is impossible without the cooperation of men and women who take a real pride in them and make a constant effort to maintain them in excellent condition. Students will find that a spirit of mutual respect, helpfulness, and friendliness customarily exists among faculty members, students, and custodians.

Plan a schedule of time

The change from high school to college places each student on his own responsibility for planning his time, attending classes, studying, and selecting the things he will do in his leisure time. Physical education, health education, and recreation majors spend a great deal of time in laboratory courses, intramurals, and other activities related to their major fields. Students who do not plan carefully often find that they neglect their social life and campus activities, or that they have difficulty in keeping up with class work. Planning should always be flexible and easily adjusted to time requirements as they change during the week. Consider the following suggestions in planning a schedule:

1. Sleep: Allow for eight hours of sleep each night.
2. Meals: Plan to spend approximately two hours daily at meals.
3. Classes: Allow from 18 to 20 hours a week for class attendance.
4. Study: Provide for approximately two hours a day of study time for each hour of lecture credit and one hour for each laboratory class credit.
5. Extra Study: Leave some time for extra study sessions and

2 *Note:* Whenever the term "major" is used, it applies to both major and minor students in the professional programs of physical education, health education, and recreation.

term papers or long assignments, or for review before examinations.

6. Recreation: Plan at least two hours a day for recreation, dating, and campus activities.

7. Personal Care and Grooming: Set aside sufficient time for grooming, dressing, and other personal care.

Work out a schedule that includes these suggestions. Adjust it to meet other time requirements.[3]

It will be found that from 6 to 12 hours of unplanned time remains to be used for other things. Students who work in addition to attending classes find that a carefully planned schedule allows for an unexpected amount of time for leisure, although adjustments are necessary to provide for additional working hours.

Plan course work and study

Plans for study should be based on the stated requirements of each course. Not all classes require the same amount of preparation or study. For example, certain courses require extensive library reading; others require written reports or term papers necessitating both reading and original writing; some classes are centered largely in laboratory work and require less outside study. An intelligent understanding of class work pays dividends in terms of scholastic success.

Attend Classes Regularly. Consistent attendance is necessary in order to benefit from instruction, class discussions, and question-and-answer sessions between the instructor and class members. Reports from other students or borrowed class notes are seldom a good substitute for the class that has been missed.

Be Alert. Attention must be cultivated as a habit. The many distractions in a classroom, daydreams, concentration on personal affairs, all may lead to the habit of using a class as an opportunity to catch up on campus gossip, write letters, or sleep. The alert student usually finds the subject matter in-

[3] Adapted from *Effective Study Procedures* (Urbana, Illinois: Student Counseling Bureau, University of Illinois, n.d.).

teresting and challenging, is ready to participate in class discussions, understands the purpose of the class, and turns in assignments on time.

Learn to Take Good Notes. Notes serve as a reference for lectures and reading and help with review for examinations.

1. Keep brief notes. Do not attempt to record the exact words of an instructor or copy from a text.
2. Organize both lecture and reading notes according to topic.
   a. List subtopics under main headings.
   b. Use a consistent system of outlining.
3. Study and revise notes soon after lectures.
4. Keep notes for each class separate and in order.

Develop Good Study Habits. Plan a time and place for study. Arrange working space and lighting to provide for the best situation possible.

1. Study where there are few distractions if possible.
2. Study at regular times.
3. Collect materials, clear a working space, and adjust lighting before starting to study.
4. Avoid studying when sleepy, fatigued, or ill.
   a. Secure sufficient sleep each night.
   b. Consult the health service if colds, headaches, or eyestrain are recurrent.

Prepare Carefully for Examinations. A student who has good notes, has been attentive in class, and has kept up with outside reading should be able to prepare for and take examinations with confidence.

1. Find out from the instructor what type of test will be given, and what material will be covered.
2. Review all notes and summarize them.
3. Think through possible questions.
   a. Organize material to answer questions.
   b. Check through notes for additional points.
4. Organize a study group of interested students.
   a. Divide topics and possible questions.
   b. Ask each other questions and compare answers.

5. Understand the differences between objective and essay-type examinations, and plan studying accordingly.

Take Examinations Intelligently. Mental attitude is of great importance in taking an examination. Fear or nervousness works against the person taking the examination. Try to overcome any feelings of inadequacy, and concentrate on the answers to the questions. Remember the materials studied and build up a feeling that the examination is a challenge to be met.

1. Objective examinations
   a. Read all directions carefully.
   b. Read statements and questions through carefully.
      1) Concentrate on the meaning.
      2) Note questions that give no alternative. (Such statements customarily include words such as *always* or *never.*)
   c. Answer questions that can be answered immediately—leave debatable questions until later.
   d. Check the answers carefully before turning in the examination. Carelessness in omitting questions or misinterpreting statements may be found in a careful check.
2. Essay examinations
   a. Read all questions before starting to write.
   b. Estimate the amount of time that can be given to each question. Decide which ones can be answered easily and quickly, and those which will be most difficult.
   c. Concentrate on one question at a time.
      1) Think through the answer.
      2) Write out the answer briefly, being careful to give the information requested.
         a) Summarize the points to be covered.
         b) Explain the points briefly. Be concise.
   d. Check all answers carefully before turning in the paper.

PERSONAL AND SOCIAL DEVELOPMENT

The professional student should make every attempt to develop the qualities that will increase the possibilities for success in his future work. College life offers opportunities for personal growth. Social development is largely dependent on experiences a person has had at home, in school, and with his friends, combined with his personal traits and attitudes. Desirable personal characteristics are attained and maintained through conscious efforts.

Maintain a pleasing, well-groomed appearance

Attractiveness is more than good features, a nice figure, or expensive clothes. Attractive people take advantage of their best qualities. Cleanliness, erect carriage, well-pressed and appropriate clothes, and a pleasant expression mark the person who uses good judgment in personal appearance.

Girls should capitalize on their best features. Attractive hair styling; careful choice of colors; conservative, well-designed clothes; and good taste in make-up can all be accomplished with a minimum of expenditure. The practice of good posture while sitting, walking, and dancing results in ease and gracefulness and contributes to a sense of relaxation and self-confidence in social situations. Women majors should make definite efforts to appear feminine in dress and action.

Men may find that the informality of campus clothes becomes slovenly rather than casual if they fail to maintain habits of good grooming. A good haircut, regular care of the nails, a clean shave, and clean clothes contribute immeasurably to the impression they make. Good habits in standing, sitting, walking, and dancing are as essential for men as for women students.

Sport clothes and outfits for active participation should always be immaculate. The major student as well as the teacher is responsible for maintaining a professional appearance at all times.

Learn to speak well and to use good English

The use of the voice is an important social asset if a person has learned to speak in a well-modulated tone, enunciate without shouting, and express himself without recourse to slang. A high, squeaky, or harsh voice may become a social liability and a distinct disadvantage to a teacher. Learn to speak in a pleasant voice. The quality of one's voice frequently reflects personality to others.

Physical education and recreation majors will find that voice-consciousness is important in their work and in their social lives. The volume developed for use in a gymnasium or on an athletic field is unpleasant in a social group and may become embarrassing in public places. Speech courses and clinics are usually available as one of the services of a college or university. Students should take advantage of such services and find out whether they need special work in speech.

Cultivate good manners and practice them

Etiquette is nothing more than a combination of good taste, common sense, and consideration for others. A person who causes embarrassment to others through lack of self-restraint, conspicuous behavior, or unwillingness to conform to social standards of conduct is considered crude and unmannerly. An act that shows thoughtfulness, kindliness, or consideration is rewarding to the person who has displayed it and raises that person in the opinion of others. Good manners should be cultivated until they become spontaneous attributes. Good manners are basic to good sportsmanship.

Improve personal habits that affect others favorably

The ability to get along with others and to display characteristics that create a free, easy, pleasant feeling of friendliness are considered qualities of social intelligence.[4] Social behavior consists of the response made to other people, the degree of

4 McKinney, *op. cit.*, p. 394.

cooperation shown, sensitivity to others, and sympathy with their problems. Personal habits of sociability, friendliness, and happiness characterize the well-adjusted person.[5] Recognition of social responsibility leads to the development of abilities that will contribute to the ease of other people in social situations. Frequently a person who feels self-conscious finds that he is able to forget himself when he helps other people to relax and enjoy themselves. The ability to contribute to the social ease of others is a requisite for teachers and leaders, and is usually developed through constant practice.

Increase Social Resourcefulness. Practice doing the things that will help to develop resourcefulness in social situations.

1. Encourage others to talk about their interests, hobbies, friends, and experiences. Be attentive and indicate interest.

2. Take responsibility for helping with social affairs. See what needs to be done, offer to help, and show enjoyment in doing it.

3. Find out about people in a group. Learn their names and something about them.

4. Study procedures for organizing parties, games, and other social activities, and try them.

5. Recognize the good points in others' work and comment on them favorably.

6. Show consideration for the opinions of others, and be able to express an opinion without becoming argumentative.

7. Be democratic when in charge of an event or a group activity. Consult others and accept their suggestions if they are worth while. Remember that responsibility is an honor; do a good job without becoming overconfident. A degree of humility has always been the mark of great men and women.

8. Concentrate on being a good member of a group. Give leaders the cooperation that is merited and that would be appreciated if positions were reversed. Good leaders are good followers.

[5] Arthur I. Gates, *et al., Educational Psychology,* 3d ed. (New York: The Macmillan Co., 1950), p. 617.

Make friends and acquaintances

Friendliness is a personal attribute that demands constant improvement. Some people seem to be naturally friendly, able to talk easily with strangers or casual acquaintances and to create a feeling of warmth and sincerity in all their contacts. Others, of a more retiring nature, find it difficult to enter into the social contacts that produce sound friendships or encourage a wide range of pleasant acquaintances. The ability to be friendly, tolerant, and understanding, combined with a sense of discrimination in the selection of close associates, is an important characteristic for teachers to develop.

The quality of friendliness, the ability to make acquaintances, and the development of friendships deserve special consideration. Human relationships affect daily living, happiness, attudes toward work and recreation, and the conduct of individuals and social groups. There are, naturally, people who do not have common interests or whose personalities are not mutually attractive.

A pleasant acquaintance is often possible between people whose personalities do not attract each other to the point of great friendship. The mature person learns to accept the difference between friends and acquaintances. In regard to acquaintances, McKinney states:

> Acquaintances are individuals who are met and known superficially. Friends on the other hand are those for whom we have a *deeper* affection.[6]

He distinguishes between friends and acquaintances in terms of the "depth of relationship," as follows:

> No doubt there are some people who, in the more profound meaning of the term, have no friends. They know many people well enough to call them by their first names, but there is not an

[6] Reprinted with permission from Fred McKinney, *Psychology of Personal Adjustment,* 2d ed. (New York: John Wiley and Sons, Inc., 1949), p. 402.

intimate relationship or an affection which entails sacrifice and permanent ties. There are many persons, in contrast, who insist that they have many very good, staunch friends.... The friends are persons in whom they would confide, to whom they would turn for help and find genuine understanding and to whom they would, in certain circumstances, give their most cherished possessions.[7]

The ability to acquire acquaintances and make friends, in the truest sense of the word, represents an accomplishment in maturity. High-school boys and girls have the habit of forming groups or cliques that tend to be exclusive of those not in their particular group. Many times they fail to recognize that some of their choices of friends are unwise and limit friendships of a more desirable nature. The development of wholesome boy-girl relationships during high school, increasingly intelligent choices of associates, and normal, healthy friendships with young men and women during college years are a result of accumulated experiences in friendship.[8]

Participate in college activities, clubs, and social groups

Student activities are of importance to the physical education major who expects to qualify himself fully for his profession. The habit of wide participation in college activities contributes to a range of interests and an increase in self-assurance that should extend the ability of each person in school and community relationships.

The influence of student activities on personal development is recognized as an important factor in a well-rounded college education.[9] The modern viewpoint of education considers student life and activities as contributing to, and supplementing, the formal curriculum rather than being isolated from it.

---

[7] *Ibid.*, pp. 401-402. (Reprinted with permission.)

[8] Luella Cole, *Psychology of Adolescence* (New York: Rinehart and Co., Inc., 1942), pp. 217-247.

[9] Esther Lloyd-Jones and Margaret Smith, *A Student Personnel Program for Higher Education* (New York: McGraw-Hill Book Co., Inc., 1938), pp. 165-168.

Courtesy of University of Illinois

Colleges and universities carry out this philosophy by encouraging student activities, helping to finance them, and assigning faculty members or other specialists to help students conduct them. The term "extracurricular," while still in general use, implies the same meaning today as "cocurricular," a more accurate term now used to describe college-sponsored activities that take place outside of the classroom.[10]

Students of physical education, health education, and recreation should apportion a share of participation to areas other than athletics and physical recreation. The benefits to be derived from broad interests contribute directly to the background of a person who will be expected to participate widely in many recreational affairs. In addition, experience in many student activities provides an opportunity to develop leadership qualities and social skill with various groups of people, and expands social and avocational interests.

The extent of participation in cocurricular activities should be determined by each individual to secure a balance between study, work, and recreation. Some students need to engage in a wider area of activity; others overparticipate to their own disadvantage. Participation in a well-selected number of activities has definite advantages in getting a job. The results of a number of studies show that students who participate actively in a number of cocurricular activities tend to have a higher level of scholastic achievement, and are better adjusted socially, than those who participate to a limited degree or not at all.[11] It is possible, of course, that less participation would result in even higher scholastic achievement, although the reports gave no definite evidence of that effect. Overparticipation is a problem that each person must regulate for himself. The

10 A. Blair Knapp, "Student Organization and Student Activities," *Current Trends in Higher Education: 1949* (Washington, D. C.: National Education Association, 1949), p. 55; Phil B. Nardmore, "Student Activities," *Current Trends in Higher Education: 1949,* p. 26; *Report of the President's Commission on Higher Education* (New York: Harper and Bros., 1948), vol. i, p. 32.

11 Stuart Chapin, "Extra-curricular Activities of College Students: A Study of College Leadership," *School and Society,* 23:212-216, Feb. 1926.

Stuart Chapin and O. Myking Mehus, *Extra-curricular Activities at the University of Minnesota* (Minneapolis: The University of Minnesota Press, 1929).

Albert B. Crawford, "Extra-curriculum Activities and Academic Work," *Personnel Journal,* 7:121-129, July 1928.

James E. Knox and Robert A. Davis, "The Scholarship of University Students Participating in Extra-curricular Activities," *Educational Administration,* 15:481-493, October 1921.

amount of outside work, the requirements of professional preparation and study, and the time spent in participation should be carefully planned for and adjusted to fit into a planned time schedule.

Athletics. The values of athletics in social adjustment have been widely accepted. It has been found that participation in athletics increases sociability, creates better adjustment, improves the participant's social status through his recognition as a worth-while member of a group, and aids in developing a wholesome personality.[12] In addition it has been found that the scholastic standing of participants in intramural and intercollegiate athletics is as high as, or higher than, that of nonparticipants.[13] These studies have been made of men participants for the most part. A reasonable viewpoint has been advanced by Leavitt and Price to the effect that:

> Since it is a matter of observation that men participate more freely in sport activities than do women, and in colleges men are usually allowed more freedom as to activities in evening hours than are women students, it may be assumed that women's sport participation would interfere even less with their studies.[14]

[12] McKinney, *op. cit.,* pp. 413-15; Fred McKinney, "Personality Adjustment of College Students as Related to Factors in Personal History," *Journal of Applied Psychology,* 23:660-668, December 1939; Lawrence Rarick, "A Survey of Athletic Participation and Scholastic Achievement," *Journal of Educational Research,* 37:174-180, November 1943.

[13] C. W. Hackensmith and L. Miller, "A Comparison of the Academic Grades and Intelligence Scores of Participants and Non-Participants in Intramural Athletics at the University of Kentucky," *Research Quarterly of the American Association for Health and Physical Education,* 9:94-99, March 1938.

Paul Washke, "A Study of Intramural Sports Participation and Scholastic Attainment," *Research Quarterly of the American Association for Health and Physical Education,* 11:22-27, May 1940.

Paul Washke, "Some Objectives of Intramurals," *Journal of Health and Physical Education,* 10:87, 124, February 1939.

Norma M. Leavitt and Hartley D. Price, *Intramural and Recreational Sports for Men and Women* (New York: A. S. Barnes and Co., Inc., 1949), p. 104.

Madeline R. Somers, "A Comparative Study of Participation in Extra-curricular Sports and Academic Grades," *Research Quarterly of the American Association for Health, Physical Education and Recreation,* 22:84-91, March 1951.

[14] Leavitt and Price, *Intramural and Recreational Sports for Men and Women,* p. 104. (Reprinted by permission.)

These conclusions are important to the major student both in relation to his own participation and as the basis for helping other students realize that time spent in recreational programs of athletics need not create an adverse effect on their scholastic standing.

Dance. The various forms of dance that are a part of the program of physical education are usually included in the list of campus activities as social recreation. Active participation in many social events is dependent on ability to dance. Social dancing is a definite asset to any student and increases his ability to enter into enjoyable social relationships. Square dancing offers a vigorous type of activity and increases opportunities for corecreational contacts in club groups and informal gatherings as well as at large all-campus dances. Men and women majors learn skills in social and square dancing that will be of value to them in teaching and in social situations. They should take advantage of opportunities to participate in dance activities.

Modern dance is strenuous and requires a good sense of rhythm and excellent coordination. Modern dance clubs, open to both men and women students, provide experience with movement, the use of various forms of accompaniment, and an opportunity for creative work. Dance recitals produced by such clubs involve experience in staging, lighting, costuming, make-up, and original choreographic planning. Students interested in dramatics and music will find many possibilities for extending their abilities through participation in a dance group.

Music. Anyone who plays an instrument, sings, or is interested in listening to music will find many congenial companions. Colleges and universities usually provide for music through courses, concerts, and various musical organizations. Listening hours during the week and on Saturdays and Sundays are customarily a part of the program of a student union; orchestras, choruses, glee clubs, marching bands, and student-organized dance orchestras offer opportunities for students to participate in the music program. Professional students who are interested in music and have talents for music benefit from continued participation.

Dramatics. Dramatic activities present the possibility for a lifelong interest in a fascinating medium for avocational enjoyment, self-expression, and personal development in poise and self-confidence. College dramatic productions are an ideal workshop for students who are interested in drama, stagecraft, design, or other aspects involved in producing a play. The ability to assist or take part in community dramatics is of advantage to a teacher or leader.

Debate. Students who have developed ability in debate will find opportunities for debating activities in college. Since teachers and leaders are expected to be capable of speaking easily before large groups of people, experience in public speaking is of definite value to them.

Journalism. Students with ability and interest in writing, or with experience in high-school news writing, may enjoy and profit from working on college publications. Feature articles on sports, regular columns devoted to intramural and interscholastic athletics, and reports on club and professional events are usually included in campus daily or weekly papers. The annual, or yearbook, of a college customarily includes write-ups and pictures of athletics, dance activities and other recreational events in the cocurricular program. Major students who work on publications find that the experience affords valuable contacts with other students, and provides a background for handling publicity after they enter the professional field.

Student Organizations. Social, service, and religious organizations and clubs touch on nearly every interest represented in a student body. Most groups are coeducational, but certain organizations are strictly for men or women. Student-elected officers usually conduct the functions of student clubs with the advisory assistance of a faculty sponsor, who is frequently selected by the membership on the basis of his interest in the purpose of the group and the respect in which he is held by students. The various organizations include those based on church affiliations, departmental clubs, and honor societies which require stated standards of scholarship and achievement in special fields. Every major should be an active member of the professional organization in his department, regardless of other affiliations.

Student Government. Student government associations involve leadership positions, committee work, and numerous student-directed undertakings that require the cooperation of many students for successful results. The student who is willing to work with others in carrying out the functions of student government has many opportunities for social and leadership experiences through active participation in some phase of student association work.

Membership in Social and Fraternal Groups. The question of membership in social clubs, fraternities, and sororities is one that merits careful consideration. There is no doubt that such organizations contribute materially to the social life of students, encourage scholastic accomplishment, stimulate leadership in campus activities, and promote loyalties within their groups. On the other hand, it is quite possible that under certain circumstances they may contribute to emotional disturbances, create practices of discrimination, and bring unwarranted pressures to bear on their individual members.

False values placed on the advantages of a given fraternity or sorority have caused some students to withdraw from college when they failed to receive bids from the groups of their choice. The only conclusion that can be made from such over-emphasis on membership in a social organization is that these students have failed to reach the level of maturity necessary for determining standards and values, and are unable to face real life situations and disappointments. The ability to make mature judgments and to meet and overcome adversity is essential to the achievement of a college education and the development of personal competency for a profession.

It is suggested that factual information be secured concerning both the advantages and disadvantages of Greek-letter organizations. Every person interested in membership in a fraternity should read information of the type compiled by Mc-Kinney [15] and Freeark,[16] and should discuss the matter with nonmembers, active members, and alumni representatives of these organizations.

SUMMARY

The planning that has resulted in the selection of physical education, health education, or recreation, as a career, the choice of a college where the best possible preparation may be obtained, and admission to a college or university represent steps toward achieving an education for a profession. Successful orientation to college life; the development of ability to work out a well-balanced program of study, recreation, and rest; and the direction of efforts to improve personal and social development are further steps in planning. College life and activities outside the classroom are closely associated with the curriculum. Intelligent participation in student activities contributes not only to personal growth but to future competency.

SUGGESTED PROBLEMS

1. What do you need to know about your college to become better acquainted with it?
    a. Make a list of the things you should find out.
    b. Study the catalog, student handbooks, and other materials that are available to students. Ask questions of other students and of faculty members. Locate buildings and other facilities.
    c. Check off items on your list as you find out about them, and add new items as they occur to you.
2. What do you know about your instructors, other faculty members, and administrative officers?
    a. Consult the catalog for information.

15 McKinney, *Personality Adjustment,* pp. 419-423.
16 C. H. Freeark, *Neophyte: Whence and Whither, Fraternity Management* (Lincoln, Nebraska: 1938).

b. Find out what your instructors have done professionally in graduate study, writing, and committee work with professional organizations, and through their teaching.

3. Plan a schedule of time. Refer to the suggestions given in the preceding pages, and develop a schedule that seems to meet your particular needs. Follow it, revise it as needed, and estimate whether it has been helpful in planning wise use of your time.

4. List the organizations and activities in which you are a participant. Ask yourself some pertinent questions about your reasons for belonging to clubs and student groups, and for participation in activities.

a. Are you a "joiner," or do you select the groups of which you are a member on the basis of definite interests?

b. Do you plan to contribute time and effort to each organization of which you are a member?

c. Why do you participate in some activities and not in others?

d. Have you made a wise selection of activities? Are there others in which you would gain more in the way of personal development?

REFERENCES

Chandler, J. R., *et al.*, *Successful Adjustment in College.* New York: Prentice-Hall, Inc., 1951.

Cole, Luella and Jessie Mary Ferguson, *Student's Guide to Efficient Study,* 3d ed. New York: Rinehart, Inc., 1946.

Hamrick, R. B., *How to Make Good in College.* New York: Association Press, 1940.

Hook, H. N., *How to Write Better Examinations.* Champaign, Illinois: Stipes Publishing Co., 1940.

McKinney, Fred, *Psychology of Personal Adjustment.* 2d ed. New York: John Wiley and Sons, Inc., 1949.

The Psychology of Getting Grades, Columbia, Missouri: Lucas Brothers, 1935.

Robinson, F. P., *Effective Study.* New York: Harper & Brothers, 1946.

Wrenn, C. Gilbert and Robert P. Larsen, *Studying Effectively.* Palo Alto, California: Stanford University Press, 1949.

Courtesy of University of Illinois

CHAPTER FIVE

Leadership development

Students have a definite responsibility for helping to plan their own educational experiences. It is true that in some colleges and universities students have little influence on the curriculum and seldom have an opportunity for participation in the planning of course work. In other schools students participate democratically in planning programs and classroom procedures. In such situations, students and faculty plan jointly to determine institutional policies that affect student life and activity. Student opinion is a powerful factor if it is well directed and intelligently expressed. The development of leadership ability is essential if students are to merit the privilege of planning cooperatively with faculty members.

Educators who believe that students should have a share in planning of this nature have made the following statement regarding student participation in planning.

> Democratic procedures should be employed in colleges preparing teachers to the extent that students will be urged to share with the administration and faculty in the cooperative planning of activities.
>
> (1) Students have a responsibility in helping to improve the content and instructional technics of the college by: (a) seeking opportunity of sharing in the cooperative planning of courses; (b) assuming responsibility, in cooperation with instructors, of inviting successful teachers and community leaders to participate in class discussions; (c) participating in evaluation of instruction and administration thru machinery jointly agreed upon by students, faculty, and administration.
>
> (2) Students should feel a responsibility for community service and utilize their growing abilities to work with people. This can

be best accomplished by actual community participation in a planned, well organized program of activities.

(3) Students should study carefully the significance and value of free public education, to the end that its importance in the survival of our democracy is fully realized and appreciated.

(4) *Students should affiliate with professional organizations, such as Future Teachers of America,* thereby making their own education assume greater significance and, also, laying the foundation for later membership and active participation in local, state, national, and international teacher organizations.[1]

Each student should recognize his obligation to assume self-direction for his own development, to learn to participate in democratic group action, and to seek opportunities for experiences that will contribute to his capabilities, and to seek ways to develop as a professional person. Student membership in the American Association for Health, Physical Education, and Recreation represents an important affiliation with an active professional group. Membership provides opportunities for participation in worth-while activities as a member of a national organization.

The development of leadership ability is one aspect of professional preparation that requires active and continuous effort on the part of each student. There is no substitute for practical experience in leadership. Work done in a leadership capacity in college programs, with community groups, and as leaders in welfare, camp, and recreation positions contributes materially to professional competency.

A wide range of experience in campus and community programs and professional groups is an important step in developing abilities on a professional level. An understanding of what leadership means and the opportunities it offers to develop and practice habits of professional conduct is an important factor in growth as a professional person.

[1] The Bowling Green Conference, *The Education of Teachers.* As quoted in: *Future Teachers of America Ninth Yearbook* (Washington, D. C.: National Education Association, 1949), pp. 189-190. (Reprinted by permission.)

LEADERSHIP

Leadership is customarily described as "good" or "bad" on the basis of the actions or accomplishments of the group led. Actually, similar qualities of leadership in different leaders may result in group activities that are constructive and socially desirable, or may bring about activities that are destructive and condemned by society. There are many types of leadership and leaders. Some persons seem to be naturally endowed with qualities which encourage others to follow them; other persons achieve leadership through persistent effort and intelligent practice.

A good leader is well informed and well prepared to lead the group by whom he has been chosen. He has confidence in his ability to carry out the responsibilities he has assumed. He believes that a group should be allowed to cooperate with him in planning the experiences in which it will participate. He is interested in developing confidence, helping others to realize their abilities, and providing opportunities for all members of the group to work together intelligently.[2]

A good leader recognizes his responsibility for constructive and worth-while activity by the group and democratic participation by all members, rather than dominance by a person or small group. Good leadership requires acknowledgement of majority opinion, recognition of minority expression, and sincerity in efforts to reach intelligent solutions through cooperative actions.[3] A good leader has qualities which encourage others to respect him, to trust and support him, and to enjoy working with him. In brief a good leader:

1. Is responsible for the obligations he assumes.
2. Shows originality and displays initiative.

[2] *Developing Democratic Human Relations Through Health Education, Physical Education and Recreation, First Yearbook* (Washington, D. C.: American Association for Health, Physical Education and Recreation, 1951), pp. 106-114.

[3] *Practices of Promise in the Understanding and Use of the Democratic Process,* National Association for Physical Education for College Women, Supplement to Annual Proceedings, April 1949.

3. Possesses a thorough knowledge of, and a sincere interest in, the work to be done.

4. Has common interests with the members of the group, and respects them as individuals.

5. Works well with other people, and is capable of delegating responsibilities to others and of helping them meet their obligations.

6. Provides every person in the group with an opportunity to belong and take an active part in the work undertaken.

7. Respects the rights and opinions of others.

8. Gives others opportunities to express ideas and carry out plans.

9. Is fair, honest, capable, and a good follower.

10. Understands and practices democracy.

Physical education, health education, and recreation offer wide opportunities for the development of leadership ability. Sound programs are possible only through the active cooperation of the boys and girls with whom the teacher and leader work. Cooperative planning and conduct of activities by the leader, his associates, and the participants contribute to ability in leadership.

LEADERSHIP OPPORTUNITIES

Undergraduate professional students have excellent opportunities for leadership experience in cocurricular programs of physical education, health education, and recreation, and in other student activities. The professionally-minded student takes an active part in conducting the intramural and extramural sports program in the college as well as engaging in active participation as a team member. Additional experience may be gained by assisting with youth groups in hospitals, working on summer playgrounds, and counseling in summer camps. Community programs for children and young people and industrial recreation programs offer further possibilities for securing experience in leadership.

Students should secure information concerning employment on a paid or volunteer basis in the college community, in their local communities during summer vacations, and in summer camps located throughout the country. Organizations and individuals frequently inform a member of a department of physical education, health education, and recreation of openings for qualified and interested students. Some departments maintain a file of information on positions available to students and assist with placement in volunteer and part-time work during the school year and in full-time summer positions.

Previous experience as a member or leader of youth organizations offers opportunities to learn more about the requirements of good leadership, use new materials and skills acquired in college courses, and re-evaluate personal abilities. Special interests and hobbies, abilities in music, dramatics, arts and crafts, and other talents should be maintained and developed.

The skills learned in professional classes also form a background for leadership opportunities. Students should start working as leaders with boys and girls early in professional course work and continue to strengthen their abilities as future physical and health educators and recreation workers. Actual, firsthand knowledge of children can be gained only through observing them, playing and working with them, dealing with their problems, recognizing their needs, and helping plan activities through which they may develop their intellectual, social, physical, and emotional capacities. "To know children one must work and play with them." [4]

The possibilities for leadership in the average college or university and the surrounding community are discussed in the following pages. Other areas should be investigated for further opportunities.

[4] Camilla M. Low, *The Child and the Community*, rev. ed. (Madison, Wisconsin: Department of Education, University of Wisconsin, 1953), p. 10. (Reprinted by permission.)

College programs of recreation and competition

Many leadership opportunities are to be found in college programs of recreation. Competitive athletics offer further possibilities for leadership development.

Intramural Sports. The program of intramurals requires extensive organization and entails many details of administration. Major students are able to contribute materially to the success of the program. Their leadership may make it possible to carry on a wider range of activities than could be provided without their assistance. Leavitt and Price, in the following statement, stress the point that experience in intramural administration contributes to the professional competency of teachers:

> Physical education teachers on the job will have opportunities to organize and conduct intramural programs. Excellent preparation can be offered them through participation in the conduct of the college intramural program. Any teacher education institution should provide students with both the opportunity to participate in a broad, well-organized program of intramural sports and of holding positions as leaders so they will be better qualified to aid in such functions when they are in the field.[5]

Women students find wide opportunity for leadership in promoting the intramural program, helping to determine policies, and assisting with the administration and conduct of intramurals through the coordination of effort between the Women's Recreation Association [6] and the Physical Education Department. Many similar possibilities are available to men students in conjunction with the intramural managerial system, which is customarily used as a basis for the operation of the men's intramural program.

[5] Norma M. Leavitt and Hartley D. Price, *Intramural and Recreational Sports for Men and Women* (New York: A. S. Barnes and Co., Inc., 1949), p. 50. (Reprinted by permission.)

[6] *Note:* The terms "athletic association" and "recreation association" are used interchangeably. The trend at present is to use the term "Women's Recreation Association," owing to the extent of the program customarily sponsored for women students.

Some of the usual opportunities associated with the organization of intramurals, and available to capable students under the leadership of faculty advisers, include:

1. Administrative responsibilities in student organizations
   a. Policy making or cooperative policy planning
   b. Planning and carrying out promotion and public relations
   c. Finance and budget making
   d. Formulation of student rules and regulations for intramurals
   e. Planning of special events and club programs
   f. Program planning
2. Managerial work
   a. Organization of competition and tournaments
   b. Conduct of tournaments
   c. Scheduling of games and playing areas
   d. Checking of eligibility
   e. Issue and supervision of equipment
   f. Provision of officials
3. Coaching
   a. Organizing coaching practice
   b. Teaching and coaching players
   c. Planning team and individual play
   d. Assisting with team organization
   e. Helping analyze team play in games
4. Officiating
   a. Carrying out duties of officials in pregame situations
   b. Conducting games

Extramural Athletics. Extramural athletics include the various events carried on between colleges. Conference and nonconference games; swimming and track and field meets; golf, tennis, and wrestling matches; sportdays; and telegraphic contests make up the extramural program.

Men students benefit from serving as manager of intercollegiate teams. Knowing how to organize practice sessions and drills and how to arrange for individual coaching is valuable in later work. Since care and maintenance of equipment and uniforms is an important factor in sports, the opportunity to observe and assist with maintenance is of value to undergraduate students. Well-skilled and capable students may be asked to assist with aspects of coaching. Many organizational problems similar to those for intramurals arise in extramural sports administration on a more extensive scale. Among arrangements major students may have responsibilities for are:

1. Scheduling of games
   a. League rules governing schedules
   b. Functions of the athletic director and coaches in scheduling
   c. Regulations applying to conference and nonconference games
   d. Eligibility
2. Pregame arrangements
   a. Promotion and public relations
   b. Public address system operation and management
   c. Radio broadcasting and televising contracts
   d. Ticket sales
   e. Traffic control
   f. Regulation of spectator traffic, seating, and conduct
   g. Safety regulations, fire control, police protection
   h. Entertainment and special programs
   i. Preparation of playing area and equipment
   j. Officiating
3. Game procedures
   a. Home team courtesies to visiting team
   b. Order of appearance of teams for practice and the game
   c. Introduction of officials and captains
   d. Starting the game
   e. Game intermissions
   f. Ending the game
4. Postgame evaluation
   a. Relations between teams, officials, coaches

b. Publicity releases
c. Financial reports
d. Evaluation of traffic and spectator provisions
e. Review of efficiency of game arrangements and procedures
f. Coaching evaluation

Women students find leadership opportunities in programs of extramural competition in various sports, and through the organization and planning of sports days and invitation tournaments. Students customarily take an active part in such events and should participate in the preliminary arrangements as well as in the actual conduct of the final program. Among the details usually associated with the sports program for women's extramural competition are:

1. Preliminary arrangements
   a. Investigation of available dates
   b. Estimation of number of teams possible to accommodate
   c. Selection of interested college groups
   d. Contacts with colleges for promotional purposes
   e. Specific invitations including details of arrangements
      1) Housing
      2) Meal provisions
      3) Schedule of games
      4) Rules and regulations for tournaments or contests
2. Organization plans
3. Schedule of games
   a. Accommodations for visiting players
   b. Campus publicity and promotion
   c. Hostess provisions and courtesies to visiting players
   d. Entertainment and social activities
   e. Provisions for visiting faculty through student-faculty planning
   f. Preparation of areas and equipment
   g. Officiating
4. Evaluation of planning and conduct of events

Club Activities. Many sports and recreational activities are developed on a club basis. Club programs involve student leadership in promoting and carrying out their functions. Individual and dual sports are frequently on a corecreational basis and provide opportunity for men and women to work and play cooperatively. Planning regular meetings, practices, tournaments, or demonstrations within the clubs or with other clubs forms the basis for experience in leadership. Dance clubs, which have been described previously, offer further opportunities for professional experience.

Recreation Programs. Programs sponsored for the student body, whether for men or women alone or for corecreational groups, offer numerous leadership situations. Men and women students must work cooperatively to develop corecreation programs if they are to attract a large proportion of the student body. Provisions may be made for informal play, tournaments, social and square dancing groups, and a variety of social games. Leadership in recreational programs is a good background for active participation in the organization and conduct of community programs.

Lectures, Clinics, and Demonstrations. It is customary for major departments to secure the services of outstanding leaders of physical education, health education, and recreation to lecture, conduct clinics, or give demonstrations. Professional students frequently assist with many of the details involved in arranging the schedule, planning publicity, promoting interest, handling ticket sales if financial support is not provided otherwise, and assuming responsibility for social activities honoring the guests.

College-sponsored programs for high-school students

Colleges and universities sponsor a variety of events for high-school students. Those with which professional students come in close contact include local, county, and state tournaments and meets for boys, play days and sport and dance clinics for girls. Such events offer experience in working with large groups, conducting large-scale meets, and making contacts with high-school boys and girls.

Community programs

The community in which a college or university is located usually provides programs of recreation, youth leadership, and welfare that offer possibilities to professional students for voluntary leadership experiences. Schools, hospitals, churches, public and private agencies, and community organizations sponsor activities of various kinds for children, youth, and adults requiring leadership ability. Although qualified persons are usually employed to direct programs, assistance is generally welcomed and students of physical education, health education, and recreation are customarily in demand.

Community leadership increases knowledge of community life, develops skills in personal relationships, and increases ability as an active leader. Such experiences also coordinate with college classes concerned with civic enterprise, community cooperation, school and community relationships, and the value of public and private agencies.

Among the agencies sponsoring youth activities in the average community are the school, the recreation and welfare departments, youth organizations, churches, and fraternal organizations. In many cases these groups provide qualified leaders who are willing to allow students to assist with the programs of activities. Other organizations carry on programs with the assistance of volunteers who are eager to secure help in planning programs, conducting games, organizing groups, and carrying out various club activities.

It is necessary to determine the available community resources for leadership and to find out the qualifications that are necessary for leaders in the programs sponsored by the different agencies. It may be possible to assume limited responsibilities with certain groups and develop the abilities needed for greater participation in the programs.

Municipal Recreation. Community recreation conducted by a municipal department of recreation on a year-round basis usually includes indoor and outdoor sports, games, swimming, dancing, and social activities. Students who can teach games, conduct tournaments, officiate, teach and guard at swimming pools and beaches, supervise play activities of small children, or coach sports will find many opportunities for volunteer or part-time work in recreation programs during the school year. Municipal recreation departments often employ qualified students as camp counselors in municipal camps. Summer employment usually is dependent upon meeting definite requirements for appointment. Civil service examinations, oral and practical examinations by a recreation board, and residence in the community may be among the stipulations to be met by applicants for summer playground appointments.

Youth-Serving Agencies. In the average community, some of the following organizations provide possibilities for leadership with children, teen-age groups, and young adults:

Young Men's Christian Association	Future Farmers of America
	Boy Scouts of America
Young Men's Hebrew Association	Boys' Clubs of America
	Girl Scouts of America
Young Women's Christian Association	Camp Fire Girls
	4-H Clubs
Young Women's Hebrew Association	Future Homemakers of America
Catholic Youth Organization	Church youth groups and clubs

All the above agencies sponsor programs of recreation for various groups. Sports, games, dancing, social recreation, and outdoor activities including camping are offered in their programs.

Other agencies for youth and social welfare that may offer opportunities for experience in professional leadership include:

Child welfare agencies	Orthopedic hospital recreation groups
Nursery schools	
Private kindergartens	Social welfare agencies
Settlement houses	Municipal recreation departments
Youth councils	

Students should take the initiative in securing information concerning an organization or group before they assume the responsibilities of leadership in that organization. The following suggestions are listed as a guide to the information that a student should secure before assuming leadership obligations.

Courtesy of Androscoggin Camps

1. Name of agency, organization, or sponsor
2. Location and telephone number
3. Person to be contacted when applying for a position, or reporting for assigned work
4. Available transportation and amount of time to allow for travel
5. Purpose of the organization
6. Groups served through the program
7. Age range of the participants
8. Type of program
9. Hours expected on duty
10. Duties and responsibilities to be assumed
11. Type of employment (volunteer, part-time, or full-time)

12. Remuneration

13. Facilities and equipment available for the program

The health education specialist can seek opportunities to be of service in social agencies. Students working with various health agencies may assist in making up reports, handling press releases, and conducting meetings and conferences. Opportunities to develop speaking ability and skill in the use of visual aids should be particularly useful to the student.

Schools. School programs of recreation in which professional students may find opportunities include before-school, noon-hour, and after-school activities. In schools where children arrive some time before the beginning of the school day the problem of organizing some form of active play arises. Unless some leadership is provided the results may be destructive, or unwholesome, and detrimental to both the school and the children. The playground and the gymnasium are normal places to congregate prior to school, and the activities require supervision, leadership, and cooperation between children and teachers. Many possibilities are present for assisting classroom teachers with the planning and conduct of programs for pre-school hours, and for special-interest groups during school hours.

Noon-hour programs usually include both active and quiet games, social recreation, and club activities. Students who are willing to assume responsibilities in relation to noon-hour programs will benefit from the experience they obtain. After-school recreation may include not only the regular intramural activities, but also hiking, cooking out, picnics, and other group activities of a similar nature. Opportunities to assist with coaching and officiating may be available to capable students. Special-interest or club groups meeting during activity periods or school hours offer possibilities for leadership by students with talents in the areas of interest represented by such activities as cheerleading, marching, band, dramatics, and music.

Arrangements for volunteer leadership in club activities should be discussed with teachers who are responsible for school clubs. Permission to assist with school programs involves responsibility for promptness, dependability, familiarity with and maintenance of school regulations, and full cooperation with the teachers in charge of the program in return for the opportunity to improve professional abilities.

COOPERATION IN LEADERSHIP

One of the problems professional students face is the necessity for adjusting to the fact that good leadership includes encouraging leadership development in others. Certain aspects of intramural and extramural athletics and campus, school, and community recreation may be carried out capably by persons other than those with a major or minor in physical education. It is of great importance that every person who possesses ability to contribute to recreational programs should have an opportunity to do so. Students majoring in physical education, health education, and recreation should assume the obligation of encouraging non-majors to participate on committees, help with planning and conducting activities.

The degree to which majors contribute to democracy in leadership influences the attitude of the campus at large toward the professional group. It is well to remember that one of the most extensive recreational interests of many persons lies in the area of physical activities. It is upon this interest that a large part of the cocurricular program is developed in schools and colleges, and that municipal recreation and social agencies operate their programs effectively.

SUMMARY

While curricular and cocurricular experiences provide many opportunities to become familiar with the requirements of leadership, the development of capable leadership is a responsibility to be accepted by professional students. The professionally-minded student recognizes a personal obligation to contribute to his own professional growth. He must, on his own initiative, acquire experiences which extend beyond the curriculum and better qualify him for membership in his profession.

The opportunities for voluntary leadership are many and diverse. Leadership experiences contribute to ability to assume professional responsibilities. In turn, the leader adds to the extent and effectiveness of the program in which he works, and the development of leadership opportunities for others with whom he is associated, or for whom the program is offered.

SUGGESTED PROBLEMS

1. List the youth organizations to which you have belonged.
   a. What leadership responsibilities have you held as a member?
   b. With what organizations are you familiar enough to become a volunteer leader?
   c. What can you contribute as a leader to a youth organization?
2. How much time can you allow for recreation work with nonschool or school groups?
   a. Do you have time to prepare to teach games, dancing, and social activities?
   b. Are you willing to assume responsibility for duties with intramural, extramural, club, or community programs?
   c. Why is it necessary to limit volunteer leadership according to the time that can be planned consistently for such work?
3. Write a letter of application for a position as a playground director or camp counselor. Indicate your qualifications and your experience in playground or camp situations and with youth organizations.
4. List the qualifications that you consider essential to a good leader.
   a. How well do you meet these qualifications?
   b. What are your weak points?
   c. How can you improve and strengthen your abilities?
   d. Why is it important to do so?
5. Write to one or more of the organizations listed on page 365 for materials describing qualifications for leaders and for information available concerning the purpose of the organization.

REFERENCES

Ainsworth, Dorothy, "Contributions of Physical Education to the Social Service Agency," *Journal of the American Association for Health, Physical Education and Recreation,* 21:325, June 1950.

Allen, Catherine L., "Training Student Leaders in Group Recreation," *Journal of Health and Physical Education*, 20:315, May 1939.

Anderson, Jackson M., "The College Goes into the Community," *Journal of the American Association for Health, Physical Education and Recreation*, 21:238, April 1950.

————, "Industrial Recreation," *Journal of the American Association for Health, Physical Education and Recreation*, 21:26, November 1950.

Chambers, Merritt M., *The Community and Its Young People*. Washington, D. C.: American Council on Education, 1940.

de Huszar, George B., *Practical Applications of Democracy*. New York: Harper and Brothers, 1945.

Hodgkins, Jean, "Making Use of Student Leaders," *Journal of the American Association for Health, Physical Education and Recreation*, 21:222, April 1950.

Hunsaker, H. B. and Rachel B. Yokum, "Coeducational Camping and Hiking," *Journal of Health and Physical Education*, 16:245, May 1945.

Kretchmar, Robert T., "Corecreation for Major Students," *Journal of the American Association for Health, Physical Education and Recreation*, 21:174, March 1950.

Larson, Mel, "Student Paper Cooperation in Promoting an Intramural Program," *Athletic Journal*, 20:20, March 1940.

Midwest Association of College Teachers of Physical Education for Women, "Policies for Sports Days and Intramural Athletics for College Women," *Journal of Health and Physical Education*, 13:295, May 1942.

Miller, Ben, "Hostelling—New Roads to Youth," *Journal of the American Association for Health, Physical Education and Recreation*, 22:20, January 1951.

National Recreation Association, *Some Leadership "Do's."* New York: The Association, n.d.

National Section for Girls' and Women's Sports, *Desirable Practices in Athletics for Girls and Women*, rev. ed. Washington, D. C.: American Association for Health, Physical Education and Recreation, 1953.

Nordly, Carl, "Training Student Officials," *Journal of Health and Physical Education*, 17:16, January 1946.

Norwat, Anna M., "An Experiment with Bulletin Boards," *Journal of Health and Physical Education*, 13:152, March 1942.

Overstreet, H. A., *Professional Leadership in the Field of Public Recreation*, New York: National Recreation Association, n.d.

Partridge, Ernest, and Catherine Mooney, *Time Out for Living*. New York: American Book Co., 1941.

Perry, Dorothy, and Irene Gilbert, "Student Coaches' and Officials' Clubs," *Journal of Health and Physical Education*, 17:492, October 1946.

"Prescription for Your Bulletin Board," *Journal of the National Education Association*, 39:680, December 1950.

Romney, G. Ott, *Off-the-Job Living: A Modern Concept of Recreation in the Postwar World*, New York: A. S. Barnes and Company, 1945.

Shainwald, Dickie, "The Development of a Co-Recreation Committee," *Journal of Health and Physical Education,* 19:50, January 1948.

Swenson, Jean, "A Coeducational Sports Day," *Journal of Health and Physical Education,* 18:266, April 1947.

Tead, Ordway, *The Art of Leadership.* New York: McGraw-Hill Book Company, Inc., 1935.

Tunis, John, *Democracy in Sports.* New York: A. S. Barnes and Company, 1941.

Courtesy of Androscoggin Camps

CHAPTER SIX

Undergraduate teaching and field work experiences

Effective leaders of children and youth must be versatile, experienced, and mature; they must know and understand young people and be capable of skillful teaching and wise guidance. Chapter 5 discussed the importance of leadership development, and the opportunities for voluntary participation in leadership responsibilities. This chapter is concerned with the experiences in teaching and leadership that are included in the program of professional preparation.

The professional curriculum provides a variety of practical experiences which contribute to skill in teaching and leadership. Some professional courses include practical assignments of work in schools, recreation centers, youth-serving organizations, and community agencies. These laboratory experiences may begin as early as the first year of preparation. In contrast to voluntary leadership, these assignments are carried out as a part of course work under the direct supervision of experienced teachers and leaders and are designated as professional laboratory experiences. Certain of these assignments are required for teaching certification or for employment as recreation leaders.

PURPOSE OF PROFESSIONAL LABORATORY EXPERIENCES

The purpose of professional laboratory experiences is to help qualify prospective teachers and leaders for their careers. Practical work in school and community programs makes it possible to observe children at work and at play, to participate in their activities, to teach and lead them, and to assist professional workers in the conduct of their program. These experiences offer the advantage of early association with leadership responsibilities of a professional nature, and expert guidance by experienced leaders. In addition, such experiences provide opportunities for participation in community affairs and programs. Professional laboratory experiences give the student:

1. Familiarity with school and community agencies, such as a recreation center, a youth-serving organization, or a private or public health agency.

2. Understanding of the work of the school or agency, the people it serves, and its problems.

3. Acquaintance with the whole job of the teacher or leader, and how it is carried out.

4. Experience in working with a staff of professional leaders.

5. Ability to accept and carry out responsibilities.

6. Practice in leadership, including guiding and counseling.

7. Experience in assisting a teacher or leader with all of his duties.

8. Skill in self-evaluation, and the ability to accept and benefit from suggestions and evaluations made by others.

9. Understanding of the ways in which theory learned in courses is applied in practice.

In summary, the purpose of professional laboratory experiences for prospective teachers is to provide opportunity to observe and experience the work of the teacher both in and out of the classroom, to participate in the major areas of the teacher's work, to study the school as a whole, and to understand the responsibilities of the teacher and the school to share in community activities.[1] Similarly, laboratory experiences make it possible for prospective recreation leaders to develop essential skills, to secure practical experience under supervision,

[1] Camilla Low, *The Child and the Community,* rev. ed. (Madison, Wisconsin: Department of Education, University of Wisconsin, 1953), p. 3.

and to qualify for positions of responsibility that require experience in the work of a recreation leader.[2]

IMPORTANCE OF PROFESSIONAL
LABORATORY EXPERIENCES

The importance of the program of professional laboratory
experiences is twofold. First, such experiences furnish practical
on-the-job information about the child, the home, and the
community. Second, these experiences provide opportunities to
develop ability to work cooperatively with others, to show
initiative in practical assignments, and to contribute to programs in schools, recreation centers, youth organizations, and
community agencies.

The work of leaders in physical education, health education,
and recreation requires that they be capable of contributing to
the total program of education. They must be expert in their
own areas and competent to maintain cooperative working relationships with other leaders. They must know about the various
programs for children and youth in the community, and the
needs of the community for leadership. They must understand
the nature of education and the relationship of their work to
the education of young people.

The nature of education

Education is concerned with all experiences which contribute
to the learning, the development, and the behavior of children
and youth. This concept of education recognizes that all influences of everyday living contribute to the total process of
education. The school, the home, and the community provide
a broad program of education for wholesome living and responsible citizenship. The quality of leadership in all aspects
of education is of such vital importance that it is essential that
only those persons who are highly qualified should be responsible for leadership of children and youth.

2 Participants in National Recreation Workshop, *Recreation for Community
Living: Guiding Principles* (Chicago: The Athletic Institute, 1952), p. 136.

It is only through working with children that one becomes familiar with the diversity of interests, abilities, attitudes, and problems that is found in any group of boys and girls. The influences of the home, the school, and the community affect a child's behavior, his social relationships and activities, his mental and physical health, and his growth and development. The problems of each child are the problems of the teacher and leader and they must be met with wisdom and understanding. Laboratory experiences offer opportunities to observe such problems and to become familiar with the methods used by experienced professional leaders in solving them.

Social inequalities and economic limitations may create emotional disturbances and behavior disorders among children. Children of racial minority groups often come from home environments that differ from those of boys and girls with whom they are closely associated. Such differences may be the causes of poor adjustment to school groups and playmates. Some children have the advantages of a closely knit, affectionate family and the security it offers; others have been denied sound family relationships and are starved for affection and recognition. Some have had wholesome play opportunities; others come from areas where healthy, happy play is impossible. The behavior, attitudes, and characteristics of boys and girls are the results of such influences. Their differences challenge the understanding and initiative of the professional leader. It is through knowledge of the influences that affect children, the attainment of skill in guiding them so that each child may grow as an individual personality, and the ability to help each child achieve his potentialities that the leader becomes competent to guide and teach.

The purpose of education can be realized only through intelligent, competent, and skillful leadership. Professional laboratory experiences serve to increase the ability of prospective teachers and leaders to contribute to the education of children and youth, and to understand the responsibilities that are the obligation of all professional persons associated with any aspect of education. The following statement indicates these obligations clearly:

> Education in our democracy is concerned with all of the children of all of the people. Broadly conceived, its prime objective is to discover the abilities and needs of each of these children, to guide each in the development of his potentialities, to help each to acquire the attitudes and the appreciations, the modes of behavior, and the knowledges and skills which he needs to adjust adequately to his environment, and to contribute purposefully to its betterment.[3]

The nature of education indicates the great importance of teachers and leaders who are familiar with children and their homes and who understand the relationship between the community and the total program of education. Professional laboratory experiences serve to develop the right kind of teachers and leaders.

The child

The study of the child—his growth, development, characteristics, interests, and needs—and of the ways in which the home, the school, and the community contribute to the education of young people is an important area of professional education. Professional courses in physical education, health education, and recreation make specific reference to these areas and their contribution to child growth and development. The practical nature of laboratory assignments offers unique opportunities to become more fully acquainted with children through close association with them. The following suggestions are offered as guides to follow while learning to work with children:

1. Observe the activities of children, with and without adult leadership.

2. Participate with children in their activities.

3. Compare the development and behavior of boys and girls with the characteristics typical of their age groups.

3 Low, *The Child and the Community*, p. 5. (Reprinted by permission.)

4. Find out about the interests, abilities, and needs of individual children.

5. Observe the social conduct of groups and the degree of acceptance of individual children by the groups to which they belong.

6. Note the way in which leadership develops, and determine whether leadership is granted for ability, personality, or dominance.

7. Help children with their problems. Observe leaders as they assist children, and note the methods that are particularly successful.

8. Learn to know individual boys and girls as people.

9. Take advantage of opportunities to teach and guide children, and learn to evaluate the results objectively.

10. Remember that few teachers and leaders follow identical methods, and that familiarity with a variety of methods provides a wide choice for future use.

The school

The school represents a common denominator in the experience of children. Although all schools are operated for the same general purpose, schools differ according to the philosophy of the school staff, the policies of the school, the facilities, and the environmental surroundings. There are numerous practical ways of becoming familiar with schools.

1. Visit schools and become familiar with different kinds of school buildings, outdoor and indoor play areas, classrooms and laboratories, and various types of school equipment.

2. Become acquainted with teachers in the school, and their classroom work.

3. Assist with the supervision of the cafeteria, the library, and noon-hour recreation.

4. Observe teacher-pupil relationships in classroom and co-curricular activities.

5. Attend faculty meetings and discussion groups concerned with:

   a. Teacher-pupil planning and evaluation
   b. Selection of instructional materials
   c. Evaluation of pupil growth and development
   d. Curriculum planning
6. Observe and assist with the school program:
   a. Instruction and evaluation
   b. Cocurricular activities
   c. Health examinations and follow-up
   d. Personal records and guidance programs
7. Learn and participate in the many duties of the teacher.

The home

The key to understanding the child may be found in his home. The understanding, sympathy, and wise guidance of parents is considered part of a child's heritage. The American way of life emphasizes the right of a child to healthful surroundings, adequate food and shelter, an education, medical and dental care, and a happy childhood. The majority of homes supply the essential needs; some homes provide many extra advantages; others provide inadequately for their children. Every person who works with children should be familiar with their home surroundings and relationships. Laboratory experiences make it possible to learn how to understand the quality of a home. Several methods may be used to become familiar with homes and parents.

1. Visit several homes and meet parents.
2. Study records of the home backgrounds of individual children. Check records for evidence of provisions for the welfare of the child, such as correction of defects in vision, hearing, teeth, and general health. Note other indications of parental interest in the child's progress.
3. Participate in conferences between the child, the parent, and the teacher.
4. Attend meetings of parents and teachers.
5. Become familiar with the general economic level of the

children in the school, the nature of their parents' employment, and the types of housing in the school community.

6. Be alert to evidences of cooperation between parents and teachers and other school officials.

The community

The nature of the community is an important factor in education, recreation, and health. Improved housing conditions, adequate provisions for health, welfare, cultural and recreational opportunities, and good schools are dependent upon the attitudes and efforts of the members of the community. Community organizations and public and private agencies promote programs of health and recreation for children, youth, and adults, and furnish qualified leaders to conduct those programs. Industrial firms often develop recreation areas and make them available for the use of people in the locality. Joint use of athletic fields, swimming pools, parks, and auditoriums by schools and community groups frequently makes possible more extensive programs of recreation than could otherwise be provided. An understanding of a community requires a knowledge of the resources available, the kind of people who make up the community, and the general nature of community activities.

1. Secure information about natural resources, such as lakes, rivers, parks, picnic areas, and opportunities for camping, hunting, fishing, and other outdoor activities.

2. Investigate the types of industry, occupational groups, racial groups, and the general economic level of the population.

3. Become familiar with provisions for public health and welfare, recreation, and experienced leadership.

4. Participate in community activities and programs:
   a. Church activities for school-age boys and girls, and for young adults
   b. Hospital programs of recreational, occupational, and rehabilitation therapy
   c. Institutional programs for exceptional children (deaf, blind, mentally retarded, emotionally disturbed)

d. Community drives, civic improvement programs, youth forums
e. Community-sponsored activities for young people
f. Open forums on youth problems, recreational needs, and school-community planning

THE PROGRAM OF PROFESSIONAL
LABORATORY EXPERIENCES

All colleges and universities require student teaching of prospective teachers, but provisions for other professional laboratory experiences prior to student teaching are not always included in the curriculum. Field work assignments, comparable to student teaching, are usually included in the professional program in preparation for leadership in recreation and in youth and social service agencies. In colleges where student teaching or field work experiences are the only laboratory assignments, voluntary leadership work in school and community programs should supplement these assignments.

The possibility of working with some part of the public school or community recreation program should be discussed with college teachers. Their support can be enlisted and they can help to arrange for participation in these activities. Experience in such school activities as noon-hour or after-school recreation, social affairs, sport or play days, and intramural tournaments is possible, and volunteer services are needed by youth-serving organizations and municipal recreation programs. Volunteer or part-time work in civic welfare and health departments offers further possibilities for practical experience.

Laboratory experiences customarily begin with the observation of the activities of children in and out of school, opportunities to become familiar with the work of the teacher, and a general introduction to the organization and functions of the school as a whole. Youth agencies, community recreation departments, and public health agencies follow the same general plan. The period of orientation is followed by participation in leadership which involves helping with individual or group projects. Gradually the participant takes more responsibility until finally some of the work of the teacher or leader is assumed. These experiences provide a sound background for effective leadership and the development of skill in teaching. The three functions—observing, participating, and leading—are closely related.

Observation

Observation is the method most frequently used to understand the behavior of children. Observation offers opportunity to study a child in a variety of situations, to learn how he reacts to other children, to determine whether he is accepted or rejected by his own group, and to estimate how well he learns.[4] The operation of leadership and the relationships between the teacher or leader and those with whom he works can also be studied. The role of the teacher or leader becomes more apparent through observation than through written descriptions.

Visiting a classroom, watching children play, or attending a club meeting may be interesting to the observer, and still fail to increase his knowledge of boys and girls or his understanding of significant occurrences unless he makes his observation with a definite purpose in mind. Observation should provide greater familiarity with young people, an understanding of the work of the teacher or leader, and an awareness of educational principles as they are applied in practice. Observation furnishes excellent opportunities to:

1. See the child as he really is, rather than as adults think he should be.

2. Observe the variations, as well as the normal characteristics in growth, development, and skills, among children of similar ages.

3. Recognize the interrelationships between mental, emotional, physical, and social growth and their influences on behavior.

[4] Gertrude Driscoll, *How to Study the Behavior of Children* (New York: Bureau of Publications, Teachers College, Columbia University, 1941), p. 27.

4. Understand the ways in which environment affects children by becoming familiar with school records of individual children and then observing them in their school and play activities.

5. Study the work of the teacher and leader as he carries out his duties.

6. Realize the practical importance of the study of child growth and development, psychology of learning, and principles of teaching and leading children.

7. Understand the relationship between professional course work and professional leadership by detecting the methods used to put theory into functional use.

How practical is observation? The reports made by students following observation experiences [5] illustrate some of the values they found in observation.

Student A: I also learned a great deal about what types of things boys and girls of various age groups are interested in, how to stimulate their interest in these activities, how children play together, and how they respond to the personality and teaching of their instructors. The children at the Center usually came from large families. They seemed unconscious of their morbid surroundings and the things that were holding them back. The things they were learning were what they learned on the streets. When they talked to each other, they always talked about what had happened in the streets—seldom in school. They were aggressive and sensitive. They acted as if they expected punishments. . . . Other handicaps hold them back, too. I saw several cases where glasses or medical care were needed. Most of them were thin and small for their ages. They wore ragged shoes and hand-me-down clothes. Their school work could not have been very good, but I am positive it could have been much better.

Student B: I have learned about children in many ways, but the way that seems most important to me has been through observation. By watching the expressions, I have learned to detect approval or disapproval, ill-health, and other conditions of the individual. It is most beneficial to just sit back and listen—a group of girls seven to

[5] *Some of the Things Students Have Learned from Their Experiences.* Taken from a report on experiences students have gained through the course in Field Service Projects in Education, College of Education, The Ohio State University (mimeographed). (Used by permission.)

eleven can tell you many things that are of interest to school teachers and just people in general. I was extremely fortunate in having a mixed racial group and a mixed religious group. At first, there was a noticeable intolerance on the part of some girls. By some suggestion and much guidance, we came to understand the problem and when I left I felt sincerely that the problem was solved in one instance, and religious tolerance would be evidenced for a long time in those girls no matter what beliefs to the contrary. We examined the beliefs that the girls had held and even though they *were* only children, they learned, and I did too.

Participation

Participation experiences include assisting with activities, helping plan and conduct programs, and practicing the art of teaching and leadership. Participation, combined with periods of observation, emphasizes the need for expertness in teaching and leadership. Experiences of this nature illustrate the concept: *a good teacher is a leader; a good leader is also a teacher.*

Voluntary participation as a student leader in campus activities, in school and community programs, and in the work of youth agencies has been discussed in the preceding chapter. Laboratory experiences are equally useful in helping students to develop the qualities essential to professional leaders and teachers. The purposes of participation experiences are indicated in the following statement, which is applicable to all leaders as well as to teachers.

> All are directed to developing a teacher who will be effective in her relationships with pupils, with staff members and with citizens of the community; a teacher who will know how to cooperate with individuals and groups, how to contribute to child welfare, how to make intelligent utilization of school and community resources to provide the most favorable setting for pupil development.[6]

The opportunities for varied participation experiences in school and community programs of physical education, health

[6] Camilla Low, *The Child and the Community*, p. 12. (Reprinted by permission.)

education, and recreation are numerous. Participants may help to select and use audio-visual materials, prepare bulletin board displays, assist with promotional campaigns for health and safety, keep records, and conduct discussion groups. Certain activities are specifically related to the major field and the area of instruction and leadership associated with it.

Physical Education. Participation in school programs of physical education, in community recreation programs, and in youth agency work make it possible to assist with activities and responsibilities such as those included in the following list.

SCHOOL PROGRAMS OF PHYSICAL EDUCATION

1. Physical examination
2. Motor skill tests
3. Preparation of equipment and playing areas
4. Supervision of shower and dressing rooms
5. Instruction of groups and classes
6. Programs for the physically handicapped
7. Coaching and officiating
8. Intramural tournaments
9. Preparation and administration of tests and evaluation of progress
10. Special programs such as play days, meets, school parties
11. Supervision of recreational play
12. School camp activities

COMMUNITY RECREATION PROGRAMS

1. Classification of participants
2. Supervision of play of small children
3. Organization of teams and tournament play
4. Instruction
5. Club activities for teen-age boys and girls
6. Coaching and officiating
7. Day camp programs
8. Playground, community center, and teen-age center programs
9. Swimming instruction and lifeguard duties
10. Camp counseling

YOUTH AGENCY PROGRAMS

1. Leadership programs for youth groups
2. Sport, game, and dance activities and programs
3. Coaching and officiating
4. Social programs
5. Club programs
6. Camp programs

Health Education. Professional students of health education participate in school and community health programs as part of their participation experiences. Many of the activities in the various public and private health programs that provide opportunities for student participation appear in the accompanying list.[7]

SCHOOL HEALTH PROGRAMS

1. Medical and physical examinations: weighing, measuring, testing
2. Screening and follow-up programs
3. Annual health examinations and clinic work
4. Visitations with school nurses
5. Health instruction
6. School lunch programs
7. School and camp sanitation and safety inspection programs
8. Health drives and special programs

COMMUNITY PUBLIC HEALTH PROGRAMS

1. Adult education health programs
2. Public health conferences on child health and welfare
3. Health surveys and drives
4. Public health dental clinic work
5. Orthopedic and mental hospital therapy
6. Mass tuberculosis X-ray and screening programs and round-ups
7. Visitations and work in community and county health departments

[7] H. F. Kilander, ed., *Report on the Undergraduate Professional Preparation of Students Majoring in Health Education* (Washington, D. C.: United States Office of Education, 1949), pp. 44-45.

Courtesy of University of Illinois

VOLUNTARY HEALTH AGENCY PROGRAMS

1. Red Cross Blood Bank programs
2. Drives—tuberculosis, heart, cancer, poliomyelitis, and others
3. Agency program work

Recreation. A wide range of experiences in school and community programs for children, teen-agers and young adults is available to students preparing for recreation leadership.

SCHOOL PROGRAMS OF RECREATION

1. Recreational play before school, during noon hour, and after school
2. Intramural tournaments
3. Special programs—all-school parties, picnics, carnivals
4. Social recreation
5. Programs and projects in recreation education
   a. Nature study
   b. Arts and crafts, shop work
   c. Music
   d. Dramatics
6. Recreation for atypical children
7. School camp recreation
8. Club programs
9. Promotional programs for school recreation
10. School-community programs for young people and adults

COMMUNITY RECREATION PROGRAMS [8]

1. Playground leadership
2. Camp counseling
3. Teen-age center programs
4. Community center activities
5. Program leadership
   a. Activities for small children
   b. Activities for school-age children and youth
   c. Special club and hobby groups—photography, model building, and others
6. Scheduling, planning, and supervision of facilities and programs
7. Promotional campaigns for community recreation

VOLUNTARY AGENCY PROGRAMS

1. Program leadership
2. Group and club leadership in youth organizations such as Boy Scouts, Girl Scouts, YMCA, and YWCA
3. Camp counseling
4. Membership drives and campaigns

[8] Refer to page 183 for additional recreation leadership opportunities.

HOSPITAL RECREATION

1. Recreation for children
2. Recreational therapy
3. Occupational therapy

INDUSTRIAL RECREATION

1. Recreation for children and teen-age youth
2. Recreation for young adults
3. Social recreation for families

The reactions of students who have participated in professional laboratory assignments show that they have profited from their experiences, as indicated in the following statements [9] about participation assignments.

Student A: Working with a group of children such as found at this agency is a valuable experience for anyone, for it certainly gives one insight into the behavior of children, their problems, and how they are dealt with by an experienced and skilled staff. . . . I feel that it is important for every person interested in civic affairs to have some knowledge of the activities which are carried on in some of the state-supported institutions.

Student B: In working at the agency I have had the opportunity to test my hypothesis on children who "don't like school and school teachers," as one said. I approached a learning situation from all angles I could think of and with all types of children. With one exception, I found that I was able to teach more if I spent more time in attempting to establish good relations with the child. If they liked me, teaching was a pleasure; if they didn't, I got nowhere until I stopped, removed the block of dislike, and rebuilt the path with likes.

A group of women physical education majors who had participated in elementary- and secondary-school programs during the junior year were asked to evaluate their experiences. Experiences were then listed according to those considered of greatest value, those in which more opportunities were desired, and those having little value or definitely unsatisfactory. The results are as follows:

---

[9] *Some of the Things Students Have Learned from Their Experiences, loc. cit.*

MOST VALUABLE EXPERIENCES

1. Teaching all or parts of lessons
2. Lesson planning
3. Planning with pupil leaders for pupil responsibilities
   a. Attendance records kept by squad leaders
   b. Shower checks
   c. Issue and care of equipment
4. Administering skill tests
5. Scoring and marking tests and scaling scores
6. Officiating
7. Self-evaluation conferences with instructors

ADDITIONAL EXPERIENCES DESIRED

1. More opportunity to work with boys and girls in the school program
2. More experience in teaching complete lessons
3. More opportunities to teach before the junior year
4. Increased experience in determining marks for classwork
5. More experience in organizing groups for instruction
6. More opportunity to help select tests to be given

A number of the participants commented on the need for greater criticism of their teaching and planning of lessons. Group conferences with instructors at the beginning of the assignments and individual conferences held at regular intervals with their cooperating teachers were listed as being of particular value. One student comment is typical of this reaction:

> One of the most helpful things was the conference with the instructor in charge of the class. At the beginning of the participation period with each class the instructors met with us and discussed the work that we would do. Some of the instructors met with all of the students who were to work with them; others met with us individually at all times. In this way, we knew what we were to do, the kind of classes we would help with, and the way the classwork would be organized. We also found out what would be expected of us. The individual conferences following teaching periods were particularly helpful. In my case, I felt sometimes that the instructors I worked with were not critical enough when I didn't do a very good job of teaching a class, but perhaps they were afraid that it would make me unsure of myself the next time

if they told me all the things that were wrong. The individual conferences gave me a good chance to evaluate myself and the way I
worked with children, or with the college students.

One participating student suggested that all participants
should list their objectives before starting an assignment and
that they should be rated by cooperating instructors at the end
of their work on the degree to which objectives had been accomplished. She concluded: "It is important that the student
take responsibility for meeting objectives that are unique to her
alone." A second student made the following statement:

> I believe something should be done so that we can begin to
> work with boys and girls earlier than the junior year by helping
> teach their classes. You don't understand the application of the
> theories your instructors teach in college classes until you have
> some experience trying to use these theories yourself.

Contributions of this kind are helpful to everyone concerned
with the program of professional laboratory experiences. College teachers who help plan experiences, and the cooperating
teachers and leaders with whom participants work, need such
suggestions in order to improve the opportunities made available to students. In addition, when both participating students
and professional workers plan cooperatively, it is possible to
determine experiences which best prepare individuals to assume the professional responsibilities of student teaching and
field work.

Student teaching and field work

Student teaching and field work experiences are more extensive than those of participation. At the beginning of these
assignments time is spent observing the program, becoming
familiar with the duties, and participating in the work of the
regular staff member. As soon as possible, additional responsibility is assumed under the supervision of the cooperating
teacher or leader. Supervisory guidance and assistance is provided as needed. Staff members and supervisors act as con-

sultants on proposed plans for work and in evaluating work accomplished.

Student teaching assignments make it possible to work with the same group of pupils over a period of time, to take an active part in teaching them, and to develop teaching plans with the help of an experienced teacher. Field work is a comparable assignment for work in the programs of public and private agencies such as recreation departments, community centers, and youth-serving agencies. A period of work experience with the daily responsibilities of regular staff members is the best and most practical way to learn what is expected of a professional worker, the way he carries out his duties, and the relationships between staff members in a coordinated program. Students should make every effort to profit from the wide range of opportunities provided in student teaching or field work assignments.

Student teachers are customarily assigned to teach in elementary and secondary schools; field workers are usually placed in agency programs providing experiences in activities related to the major field. A recreation major may be assigned to work with leaders responsible for the conduct of a program in a community center or in a youth organization, or in a recreation program in a children's hospital. A major in public health may be given an opportunity to work in a public health department. Majors in physical education and health education usually do their student teaching in a school program.

Student teaching and field work assignments vary widely, both in the nature of the experiences and in the amount of time allowed for them in the curriculum. The amount of time spent in a school varies from an hour with the same class several times a week to block-of-time off-campus teaching, which requires spending full time in the school for a period of weeks. Block-of-time assignments usually require actual residence in the school-community during the teaching period. Similarly, field work assignments may be on an hourly basis, for a school term or longer, or involve part-time or full-time work in an agency program.

Internship

An intern program, similar to that of internships in medicine, is usually carried out during a fifth year of study. An intern is generally appointed to a regular position on a part-time basis, and may receive a nominal salary. The work of the intern is supervised by college supervisors and regular staff members of the school or agency in which he works.

OPPORTUNITIES FOR PRACTICAL EXPERIENCE

Practical experience in the areas of physical education, health education, and recreation may be included in the curriculum as a part of laboratory assignments, or may be made available by volunteer participation or full or part-time leadership work. Youth-serving agencies and programs of school camping and outdoor education offer many possibilities for securing experience related to the major field. The increasing number of hospitals offering some form of recreational or occupational therapy for patients require many volunteer workers who are qualified to assist specialists with their work.

Leadership experiences with these programs should contribute to a better understanding of boys and girls, to an awareness of the educational purposes and contributions of these programs, and to greater familiarity with the requirements of leadership. In addition, each experience strengthens a person's abilities and increases his qualifications for part-time and summer employment during school years, as well as for the work of his future career.

Youth-serving agencies

The work of youth-serving agencies in a community constitutes a powerful force for the welfare of young people. The combined efforts of private and public agencies represent a comprehensive program which, despite its extent, fails to reach and serve many of the youth of the country. The importance of recreation for all people is so great that governmental units not only provide extensive areas and expert leadership, but spend many millions of dollars annually to develop and increase recreational opportunities. Such organizations as the YMCA, the YWCA, Boy Scouts, Girl Scouts, Camp Fire Girls, the Jewish Welfare Board, the Catholic Youth Organization, and boys' and girls' clubs promote extensive programs of youth service. The school has a definite role in recreation, and is the logical center for many community activities. The Educational Policies Commission has recommended that boards of education promote recreation as a part of their educational responsibility, and that public-school properties should be opened for public use outside of school hours.[10]

Experience in the work of youth-serving agencies serves as a background for understanding the importance of cooperative efforts among all agencies providing for out-of-school education for children and youth. Such experiences also emphasize the need for more and better programs and extended services to meet the needs of boys and girls who are not included in any type of program. As a part of work in a youth-serving agency, it is advisable to:

1. Find out what voluntary youth-serving agencies provide programs and leadership in the community.

2. Become familiar with the nature of the program offered, and the approximate number of children participating in the activities of the programs conducted by the various organizations.

3. Determine the extent of one or more agency programs.

a. What activities are offered?

b. Does the program include a wide range of activities for various age groups?

c. Is camping a part of the summer program?

4. Become familiar with the work of the leaders who are in charge of programs.

[10] Educational Policies Commission and the American Association for Health, Physical Education and Recreation, *Educational Policies for Community Recreation* (Washington, D. C.: The Commission, 1940), pp. 26-28.

a. Take part in leadership activities.

b. Learn the purposes of the agency, study the over-all program, and become acquainted with office work, program planning, and methods of organizing and conducting activities.

5. Learn the interests, characteristics, and capabilities of the boys and girls who participate in the program.

a. Attempt to determine the needs of individual boys and girls.

b. Find out what their homes are like, and what other community groups they belong to.

6. Evaluate the ways in which the program contributes to the needs of the young people it reaches.

Camping and outdoor education

A significant educational development in recent years is that of school camping and outdoor education. The tremendous growth of organized camping in the United States has developed largely outside the field of education. Although some state, county, and municipal recreation departments have sponsored camps, youth organizations, churches and private groups or individuals have been largely responsible for the widespread growth of the camping program.

School camping and outdoor education, as a part of the school program, show one way in which the educational undertakings of the school have extended beyond the traditional subject matter of learning. Michigan, California, Ohio, Indiana, Florida, Oregon, Washington, New Jersey, and Pennsylvania have pioneered successfully in the organization of school camping.

The development of school camping has made it possible to take an entire class of school children into a camp setting for a period of a week or longer during the school year. Teachers, college students, and members of the camp staff act as counselors. Children live and work together, carry on the daily work of the camp, and learn about animal and bird life, soil, woods, and plants. They study the relation of conservation of land and water to health and economy. The child becomes an active member of a cooperative, democratic social group and learns by doing the things that contribute to the daily living and relationships of that group.

Courtesy of Androscoggin Camps

Work with school children during a period of school camping offers unique opportunities to learn to understand children. If the professional curriculum does not include provisions for laboratory assignments in connection with camping and outdoor education, voluntary work as a camp counselor should serve as an equally worth-while experience during summer vacations. School camping and outdoor education are rapidly being accepted as a part of the school program, and the need for qualified persons to conduct school camps and to act as counselors is increasing. Professional students of physical education, health education, and recreation should seek opportunities to work as counselors in this phase of the school program and should:

1. Study the program of camping and outdoor education and become familiar with the activities of daily camp life.

2. Become acquainted with the resources available in the surrounding country that lend themselves to a practical study of nature, conservation, woodcraft, and outdoor recreation in a natural setting.

3. Participate in planning the program of activities, projects in community living, and administrative provisions for health supervision and service, food selection and preparation, safety, and sanitation.

4. Participate in as many of the duties of the camp staff as possible.

5. Become familiar with the problems, interests, and abilities of individual children.

6. Observe the relationships between children in their work and play, and between the counselors and children.

7. Evaluate the results of the camp experience with teachers, camp staff, and children.

Hospital recreation

The therapeutic value of recreation during illness and convalescence is of such importance that leading hospitals have established extensive programs of recreation adapted to the abilities and limitations of patients. The Veterans Administration hospital program includes comprehensive recreational activities under the direction of specialists. Hospitals for the physically and mentally defective provide specialized services in recreational therapy. The recreation program for children in institutional and orthopedic hospitals requires numerous volunteer and part-time workers, in addition to the regular staff. All of these programs offer practical experience to professional students of physical education, health education, and recreation and experience in these areas develops useful skills. Work in hospital recreation makes it possible to:

1. Become acquainted with individual patients, their limitations, prescribed activities, and interests.

2. Learn the methods used by specialists to encourage participation.

3. Study and become familiar with the scope of the program, the various activities included, and the types of equipment in use.

4. Develop an understanding of procedures followed in hospital routines, the various persons assigned to positions of responsibility, and the work they carry out.

5. Help specialists evaluate the accomplishments of individual patients, estimate their needs, and develop programs designed to meet their requirements.

Other opportunities

The discussion of youth agency programs, school camping and outdoor education, and hospital recreation has served to illustrate the general nature of experiences available, and suggests self-directed investigations beyond the activities of a program. Numerous agencies other than those specifically mentioned offer possibilities for laboratory experiences. Regardless of the type of experience, the opportunity for practical leadership should be of primary concern.

Each experience offers opportunities to learn more about boys and girls, to become more adept in leadership, to become familiar with the responsibilities of professional workers, and to develop professional skills. Work with experienced professional leaders is a valuable addition to professional preparation. The guidance and assistance of such leaders helps to correct weaknesses and improve abilities. Such experiences may be among the most valuable aspects of undergraduate professional preparation.

SUMMARY

Undergraduate teaching and field work experiences offer practical on-the-job contacts with children and young people for the prospective teacher or leader. Such experiences improve understandings of the purpose and scope of the educational program and better qualify prospective teachers and leaders to meet the requirements of their future professions. The observation of children at work and at play, participation in their activities and in the work of the teacher or leader, and responsibilities for the conduct of programs in laboratory situations provide an essential background for effective professional leadership.

Association with the work of the schools and other community agencies creates an understanding of the services provided for children and youth, and of the importance of cooperation among these agencies. Work as a member of a professional staff is an excellent source of practical experience and develops an appreciation of leadership responsibilities.

SUGGESTED PROBLEMS

1. Consider your experiences as a member of a youth organization or a school group. How does the guidance of an adult leader or teacher affect:

a. The relationships within the group?

b. Democratic participation of members of the group in planning activities or events?

c. Opportunities for each individual to increase his abilities and skills, or to contribute to the group?

2. Make a list of the experiences you have had with children that have given you a better understanding of individual boys and girls.

a. What have you learned about children that will help you as a teacher or leader?

b. In what ways have these experiences increased your ability to work with children?

c. What particular examples of leadership among children have you found to be outstanding?

3. What have you learned about child growth and development from your relationships with boys and girls?

a. What questions about growth and development have been raised by the experiences you have had?

b. How do variations in growth and development affect children in their relationships with each other?

c. How do variations in growth and development affect teen-agers in their own groups?

4. What can you do to create opportunities for undergraduate teaching and leadership experiences if the curriculum of your college does not provide these experiences?

a. How would you go about making arrangements to participate in a school program?

b. How would you secure work as a volunteer or part-time leader in an agency program or a community health department?

5. Discuss laboratory experiences with students who have participated in laboratory assignments. Note the comments they make, the situations they have found most interesting and challenging, and those in which they have had problems.

a. How can you profit from such discussions?

b. What can you do to find out why problems arise in working with children and how they may be solved?

6. Observe a group of boys and girls at play without leadership and write a report of your observation.

a. What evidence did you notice of leadership among the members of the group?

b. Was the behavior of individual children conducive to enjoyment in the activity?

c. Was there agreement about the way in which the activity was carried on?

d. In case of disagreement, how was it settled?

7. Observe a group of boys and girls playing under adult leadership and compare the behavior of the two groups.

REFERENCES

American Council on Education, Commission on Teacher Education, *Helping Teachers Understand Children*. Washington, D. C.: The Council, 1948.

Baruch, Dorothy M., *Understanding Young Children*. New York: Bureau of Publications, Teachers College, Columbia University, 1949.

Berquist, Ivan W., *Teaching Unruly Boys to Excel*. Boston: House of Edinboro, 1952.

Cassidy, Rosalind, and Hilda C. Kozman, *Counseling Girls in a Changing Society*. New York: McGraw-Hill Book Co., Inc., 1947.

Chambers, M. M., and Elaine Exton, *Youth—Key to America's Future*. Washington, D. C.: American Council on Education, 1949.

"Child Growth and Development, Characteristics and Needs," *Journal of the American Association for Health, Physical Education and Recreation*, 20:233, April 1949.

Cole, Luella, *Psychology of Adolescence*, rev. ed. New York: Rinehart and Co., Inc., 1947.

Cunningham, Ruth, and associates, *Understanding Group Behavior of Boys and Girls*. New York: Bureau of Publications, Teachers College, Columbia University, 1951.

Davis, Elwood C., and John C. Lawther, *Successful Teaching in Physical Education*, pp. 281-386. New York: Prentice-Hall, Inc., 1948.

Gates, Arthur I., Arthur T. Jersild, T. R. McConnell, and Robert C. Chall-
man, *Educational Psychology*, chs. i, ii, pp. 560-581, 740-753. New
York: The Macmillan Co., 1950.
Hartley, Ruth E., Lawrence K. Frank, and Robert M. Goldenson, *Under-
standing Children's Play*. New York: Columbia University Press, 1952.
"Health and Physical Fitness for All American Children and Youth,"
Journal of Health and Physical Education, 18:3, January 1946.
Horace Mann-Lincoln Institute of School Experimentation, *How to Con-
struct a Sociogram*. New York: Bureau of Publications, Teachers Col-
lege, Columbia University, 1947.
Jersild, Arthur T., *Child Psychology*, rev. ed. New York: Prentice-Hall, Inc.
1947.
Johnson, William H., "Preparing the Adolescent for a Well-Integrated
Life," *Mental Hygiene*, 23:587, October 1939.
Kirkendall, Lester A., *Helping Children Understand Sex*. Chicago: Science
Research Associates, 1952.
Kozman, Hilda C., Rosalind Cassidy, and C. O. Jackson, *Methods in
Physical Education*, rev. ed., chs. ii, iii, iv, vii, viii, xix. Philadelphia:
W. B. Saunders Co., 1952.
LaSalle, Dorothy, *Guidance of Children Through Physical Education*, chs.
iii, iv, vi, vii. New York: A. S. Barnes and Co., 1946.
Lehman, H. C., and P. A. Witty, *The Psychology of Play Activities*. New
York: A. S. Barnes and Co., 1927.
Liebers, Arthur, *How to Organize and Run a Club*. New York: Oceana
Publications, 1953.
Manley, Helen, and M. F. Drury, *Education Through School Camping*.
St. Louis: C. V. Mosby Co., 1952.
McNeeley, Simon A., and Elsa Schneider, *Physical Education in the School
Child's Day*, Bulletin 1950, No. 14. Washington, D. C.: Federal Se-
curity Agency, Office of Education, 1950.
Miller, Leo, "Competition as a Factor in Learning," *Journal of Health
and Physical Education*, 16:504, November 1945.
National Society for the Study of Education, *Forty-Third Yearbook, Part
I: Adolescence*, chs. i-vii. Bloomington, Illinois: Public School Pub-
lishing Co., 1944.
Purbeck, Marian, and William Uhler, "Pupil Leadership in the High
School," *Journal of Health and Physical Education*, 15:10, January
1944.
Redl, Fritz, *Understanding Children's Behavior*. New York: Bureau of Pub-
lications, Teachers College, Columbia University, 1949.
Sehon, Elizabeth, Marian Anderson, Winifred Hodgkins, and Gladys Van
Fossen, *Physical Education Methods for Elementary Schools*, rev. ed.
Philadelphia: W. B. Saunders Co., 1953.
Solomon, Ben, *Leadership of Youth*. Putnam Valley, New York: Youth
Service, Inc., 1950.

Spotlight the Children in Physical Education. Detroit: Department of Health and Physical Education, Detroit Public Schools, Detroit Board of Education, 1951.

Strang, Ruth, *Reporting to Parents.* New York: Bureau of Publications, Teachers College, Columbia University, 1947.

Strauss, Bert, and Frances Strauss, *New Ways to Better Meetings.* New York: The Viking Press, 1951.

Your Child from 6 to 12, Children's Bureau Publication No. 324. Washington, D. C.: Government Printing Office, 1949.

Courtesy of University of Illinois

CHAPTER SEVEN

Professional responsibilities
and relationships

Participants in professional laboratory experiences have certain personal and professional responsibilities toward their assignments in addition to meeting the requirements of the actual work involved. They are expected to have the personal qualities required of professional leaders, a sound professional attitude, acceptable personal and professional conduct, responsibility toward work assignments, and cooperative and mature relationships with co-workers, parents, and young people.

It is always helpful to know something about the various people who may be associated with an assignment, and their relationship to a school or agency program. School, college, and agency administrators, supervisors, classroom teachers, and professional leaders cooperate in the conduct of a program of professional laboratory experiences. It is to be expected that the various people who have helped plan this program will, at some time, visit and observe school and community programs where laboratory assignments are being carried out. It is natural for them to be interested in both the success of the program and the work of students assigned to it. Every student should look forward to opportunities to meet and talk with persons who have helped develop laboratory experience as a part of the professional program.

A general survey of the various professional leaders, their official responsibilities, and their relationships to the program of practical laboratory work in schools and community agencies is included in this chapter. Since the ability to work harmoniously and cooperatively with others is one of the requisites of good teaching and leadership, emphasis is placed upon general suggestions for establishing and maintaining satisfactory relationships with professional leaders.

PERSONAL RESPONSIBILITIES

One of the first things that should be done before starting on an assignment in professional laboratory work is to reappraise personal qualities, attitudes, and philosophy toward professional work. Intelligent consideration of the factors that affect success and the determination to benefit from all professional experiences have a direct bearing on successful performance. In making an appraisal of this nature it is important to maintain an objective viewpoint. The acknowledgment of personal assets with frankness, and without undue pride, is necessary. Similarly, a person who recognizes weaknesses should try to correct them.

Personal qualities

Personal appearance is often a deciding factor in first and subsequent impressions made on others. A pleasant contact made at an initial meeting helps to pave the way for agreeable and profitable relations on following occasions. Good grooming, courteous consideration of others, a pleasant voice, poise, and a genuine spirit of friendliness and enthusiasm contribute immeasurably to relationships with children and adults alike. Material in Chapter 4 and the self-appraisal chart in Chapter 1 should be reviewed in preparation for assignments in laboratory experiences.

Professional attitude

A professional attitude is a composite of many things, and is expressed through personal and professional standards of conduct. A sincere belief in the worth of a profession is fundamental to the development of a sound professional attitude. Ethical conduct as a member of a profession implies loyalty and courtesy to colleagues, intellectual and emotional maturity, and dignity and poise in carrying out work. The determination to succeed, to benefit from all opportunities for growth, and to contribute in some way to programs of professional work is fundamental to a satisfactory professional attitude.

The possession of a good professional attitude is evidenced in many ways. Professional interest is shown by continued efforts to improve understandings, to strengthen weaknesses, and to meet the personal requirements of good leaders. Belief in the worth of a profession is shown by devoting sufficient time to work to insure meeting obligations, by willingness to arrange additional time for conferences, and by participating in voluntary work beyond the actual requirements of an assignment.

Professional standards of conduct affect personal behavior in many respects. Conduct in public often reflects the degree of acceptance of social and professional standards. The following examples, which are actual cases, illustrate the ways in which professional attitudes toward standards of conduct are apparent to others.

Student A. When *A* started her major work in physical education she made a favorable impression. She was pleasant, friendly, and interested in her work. Although she was overweight, she made a neat, clean appearance on the campus. *A* was a capable performer in many activities. Gradually her appearance became sloppy; she began to appear in the college community wearing Army fatigues and boots. Her noisy, rude behavior caused much unfavorable comment and criticism of both *A* and her college department. *A*'s adviser discussed the problem with her and discovered that *A* believed that her personal conduct and appearance off campus had no relationship to her professional work or standing.

A careful appraisal of her characteristics and a comparison between them and requirements for physical education teachers resulted in *A*'s decision to attempt to overcome the impression that had been created. Fortunately, since her interest in physical education as a career was sincere, *A* was able to show real progress during the following year. Her scholastic record, class work, and general accomplishments improved sufficiently to warrant a recommendation that *A* should be encouraged to continue her major work. She showed greater thoughtfulness in relations with others, her grooming and personal conduct improved, and she gave evidence of qualities that would make her an acceptable teacher and member of a community.

Student B. B was an outstanding high-school athlete. He entered a state college on an athletic scholarship and decided to prepare for a coaching position. His plans included a period of years spent in professional athletics following graduation from college, then a good coaching position secured through his athletic prowess. *B* continued to make records as a college athlete. He was popular and well-adjusted socially, and had many ardent fans. Since *B* had no interest in teaching, however, few professional courses held interest for him.

Representatives of several professional teams commented favorably on his athletic ability, and his future as a professional player seemed assured. *B* maintained an acceptable scholastic record with little effort, but failed to show any real interest in college work. He kept training rules faithfully during sport seasons, but gradually built a reputation for dissipating during off-seasons. Finally, he broke training during the football season in his senior year, was arrested on a disorderly charge, and was dropped from the team. He completed his last semester of college on probation for conduct as well as for low grades during the previous semester. He had failed to complete the requirements for a teaching certificate, but had sufficient credits for graduation from the college.

B signed a contract for professional football and played brilliantly for one season; he was injured the following fall and his contract was not renewed. He then returned to college, completed requirements for a teaching certificate, and attempted to secure recommendations from his college professors to help him gain employment in a teaching position. It is understandable that his recommendations were not outstanding, and that he had difficulty in finding a position.

Professional growth

The determination to profit from all experiences, to overcome weaknesses, and to benefit from situations demanding initiative, originality, and independent thinking is fundamental to professional growth. The ability to improve, to act upon suggestions, and to conduct self-directed study and planning is a mark of growth. The suggestions of supervising teachers and leaders are based on their interest in helping professional students become more skillful in their work and in their relations with others. Their criticisms and interest in improvement are professional in nature and should be welcomed and accepted in an equally professional manner. An acceptance of the role of the teacher or leader is another aspect of maturity.

Adjustment to professional work

Laboratory experiences, even when they involve only observation, are professional in nature. Each experience represents a way of learning more about programs, teachers and leaders, boys and girls, and the different ways of carrying out professional work in teaching and recreation leadership. It is important to adopt the attitude that each situation represents an opportunity to learn more about the work of competent leaders. No one method is perfect; no one method will work in all situations; a method that is successful for one person may not be practical or useful for someone else. The attitude with which a person accepts standards of conduct approved by the community and procedures followed by the school or agency may determine how well he is accepted as a working member of a staff. Willingness to meet the requirements demanded of other teachers and leaders is essential to winning the full approval of those persons. It is well to remember that even experienced workers recognize the wisdom of becoming fully familiar with a new position before making adverse criticisms or suggestions for improvement.

A student should become acquainted with the work of an entire agency or school as soon as possible after he is assigned to assist with any part of the program. There is a tendency to become so absorbed with the job at hand that the rest of the program seems unimportant. This tendency is particularly true of physical education in the schools, since so much of the work is conducted in areas not directly connected with other classrooms, or is entirely outside the school building. Many of the routine problems of physical education, such as the supervision of dressing rooms and showers and the issue and care of sports equipment, do not occur in relation to other classes. It is possible to become so involved with details that the concerns of the rest of the school seem completely unrelated to the physical education program. It is important to understand the high degree of coordination essential to the smooth functioning of any school or agency.

Acceptance of responsibilities

The responsibility for professional obligations begins when a person reports to a school or agency on an assignment for a professional laboratory experience. The same degree of punctuality and dependability will be expected of a student teacher or field worker as of a professional worker. Professional courtesy and consideration for supervising teachers and leaders require that notification be given at the earliest possible time should an emergency of any kind prevent meeting an assigned responsibility or attending a meeting. It is helpful to keep a small notebook and make notes on specific procedures to be followed, since it is often difficult to remember details without reference to a written notation. Points in question should be referred to the regular staff member for clarification.

Responsibilities for Observation and Participation. The opportunity to watch a skilled professional person and to get acquainted with boys and girls before starting to work with them is a responsibility as well as a privilege. It is possible to become so impatient to take over the work that the benefits of observation are lost. Participation, as a result, is less effective than it would have been had methods been observed more carefully.

Alertness during observation increases familiarity with the procedures to be followed and better qualifies a person to assist successfully. Similarly a student teacher or field worker who is well acquainted with the way a professional person works is better prepared to assume responsibilities after observing and participating in the group that will be put in his charge later.

Planning. Planning is one of the most important aspects of a successful program. Every activity requires extensive planning. A written plan, whether it is for a lesson or for a club meeting, should make provisions for desired outcomes and for meeting the needs of boys and girls. A good plan combines the experiences of previous work with the plan of proposed work. Planning is a responsibility that provides opportunities for creative work. Physical education classes, recreation groups, and campers require instruction that is carefully planned at all times. The leader's familiarity with activities does not eliminate the necessity for written plans. It has been said that "No teaching is any better than the carefulness of the planning which has preceded the teaching." [1]

Preparation. Preparation is effective only when it is directed toward a definite plan of action. It includes complete familiarity with the plans to be carried out, anticipation of situations that may arise and provisions for them, exact information to be given, and arrangements for equipment and other instructional materials. A sufficient amount of time should be allowed to check information; obtain needed supplies; prepare materials and equipment and floor or field markings; and inspect the area to be used before starting work with a group. The results of planning and preparation are usually observable after the instruction has been presented.

Evaluation. Evaluation is an important process in determining the result of work. Various methods are used to appraise the effectiveness of teaching and leadership, and to estimate the achievement of boys and girls. Participants, student teachers and

[1] Quoted by permission from Ruth Evans and Leo Gans, *Supervision of Physical Education* (New York: McGraw-Hill Book Company, Inc., 1950), p. 214.

field workers, supervising teachers and leaders, college supervisors, and children are all involved in any evaluation of teaching and leadership. The devices used in evaluation may include a combination of self-appraisal, individual and group conferences, rating charts, appraisal scales, and tests.

The attitude of a person toward his own evaluation determines how much benefit he gains from any method of evaluation and from opportunities to receive suggestions from experienced professional persons. The success of conferences and the effectiveness of other methods of evaluation are largely dependent upon the degree of cooperation shown by those concerned.

Cooperative planning

Planning of any kind demands some original and independent effort as well as an opportunity to combine independent and cooperative work. The suggestions and recommendations of supervisors and supervising teachers or leaders often form the basis for coordinated planning by several participants or among student teachers or field workers. Participants who are assigned to work with the same classes taught by a student teacher, or those who are participating in a youth agency where field workers are helping to conduct a program, find many opportunities through joint planning to improve their program responsibilities. Similarly, cooperative planning is carried on with children in schools and agency programs.

The importance of ability in cooperative group planning is becoming increasingly apparent in modern programs of physical education, health education, and recreation and in the programs of youth organizations. The terms *coeducation* and *co-physical education* refer to activities participated in by groups composed of both boys and girls. There is a definite trend toward incorporating coeducational instruction in individual and dual sports, swimming, diving, life saving, boating, and dance for boys and girls in the upper grades and high school. Classes in health education customarily are composed of both boys and girls. Corecreational activities are sponsored as a part of school, community recreation, and youth agency programs.

The development of such programs has created the necessity for joint planning by men and women teachers of physical education and health education, and among leaders in community recreation and youth organizations. Provisions for participation by boys and girls in cooperative planning for corecreational and coeducational activities tend to insure their interest, support, and leadership in making such programs successful. Experiences in group planning increase skill in working with others and in helping children and young people develop qualities of cooperation and leadership.

PROFESSIONAL RELATIONSHIPS

Professional laboratory experiences involve many contacts with professional people, children, and parents. The impressions made during meetings and casual encounters are very important. The experience gained through opportunities to meet and confer with administrators, teachers and leaders, children, parents, and other members of the community contributes to a better understanding of the programs of schools and agencies. It is important to know something about the positions held by the various school and agency officials, and the responsibilities each person carries out in his position.

Administrators

Some administrative offices involve the responsibility and supervision of the over-all operation of a school system or agency; other positions entail responsibilities for divisions or departments within a system. For example, the majority of school systems are headed by a superintendent of schools who works in cooperation with the school board, assistants, supervisors, school principals, department heads, and teachers to organize educational opportunities for children, teen-agers, and adults in the community. Each person has certain administrative responsibilities to perform in connection with his own work. Similarly, in a local YMCA or YWCA, the entire organization is under the direction of an executive who works cooperatively with board members, secretaries or program directors, assistants, volunteers, and the custodial staff to administer the program, public relations, finance, facilities, and other aspects of the organization's work.

The functions of administrators are most easily understood in relation to an entire school. The principal is responsible for the over-all administration of the school, the school budget, school policies, and public relations. He must coordinate the efforts of teachers and other school personnel so that the school will be a healthful, happy place for children. He must maintain close contact with teachers and pupils, and must devote constant effort toward creating a democratic and cooperative atmosphere in the school. The school has become the center of community activities. Parents and other members of the community are drawn into the activities of the school, and the community is being used as a practical laboratory for the school. An important part of an administrator's work is to make these relationships profitable for both school and community.

Administrative duties performed by teachers include securing materials and supplies, estimating budget needs, scheduling class and extra-class activities, and making provisions for equipment. In addition, the physical education teacher is responsible for the supervision and maintenance of gymnasiums, pools, locker and shower rooms, and playing fields. Many of these responsibilities become familiar to a prospective teacher during his participation in professional laboratory experiences. Comparable duties are carried out by leaders in youth-serving agencies.

It is customary in some schools for the principal to hold a short conference with students who are assigned to assist with any part of the school program. Some agency administrators follow the same practice with participants and field workers. An administrator may visit briefly while a student is teaching a class or leading a group in some activity, or may observe occasionally during the entire time work is in progress. It is to be expected that the administrator will then confer with the teacher or leader concerning his impression of the work he has observed.

The procedure to follow when a principal or other administrator visits may be indicated by the supervising teacher or leader before the occasion arises, or may be left to the discretion of the student. The visitor may be interested in seeing the written plan prepared as a guide for the work, or may prefer to observe the group without reference to a plan. A smile and nod are usually sufficient indication that his presence is welcomed. Under no circumstance should the presence of any visitor be allowed to distract the teacher's attention from the group or the activities.

Supervisors

Supervisors and teachers or leaders form a coordinated working unit to create conditions favorable to the growth and learning of children. The supervisor acts as a consultant and helps to discover more effective ways of organizing learning situations, presenting activities, and providing challenging and meaningful experiences. Supervision has been described as "an expert technical service primarily concerned with studying and improving conditions that surround learning and pupil growth." [2]

A supervisor, whether from the college, from the public school office of education, or representing an agency, visits and observes in order to obtain information that may be of help to the teacher or leader. It is only through seeing activities, studying the behavior of boys and girls, and analyzing the problems that may be interfering with good results that a supervisor is able to help create more favorable conditions.

The question of what to do when a supervisor arrives is determined by courtesy and the wishes of the supervisor. The following practices are usually acceptable:

[2] A. S. Barr, William H. Burton, and Leo J. Brueckner, *Supervision*, 2d ed. (New York: Appleton-Century-Crofts, Inc., 1947), p. 11.

1. Acknowledge the supervisor's arrival with a smile or nod and continue with the activities of the group.

2. Offer the written plan for reference and indicate the instructional aids that are being used if an opportunity arises to do so.

3. Introduce the supervisor to the group when it is brought together for discussion, or at a point when there will be no interference with the activity. A simple, brief introduction is sufficient. It should include the supervisor's name and his capacity as a visitor. No further explanation is needed.

4. Visitors offer an opportunity for children to practice courtesy and develop social poise. Children should be taught to greet visitors quietly and make them feel welcome. A supervisor appreciates the thoughtfulness of both the child and his teacher or leader when a child assigned to act as a host or hostess leaves activity briefly to provide a chair or make him feel welcome.

5. Arrange a joint conference with the supervisor and the supervising teacher or leader following a supervisory visit. Suggestions made during the conference should prove helpful, and should be accepted and incorporated in following work plans. If a conference cannot be arranged immediately, make an appointment for an early discussion of the work observed by the supervisor.

6. Plan an evaluation of the work observed by the supervisor so that it will be possible to contribute to the conference. Cooperative planning and evaluation require contributions from all the persons involved in it.

Supervising teachers or leaders [3]

A close and mutually beneficial relationship exists between supervising teachers and leaders and students assigned to carry out professional laboratory experiences under their direction. These experienced persons contribute a valuable service to the

[3] The terms *critic teacher* and *cooperating teacher* have the same meaning as *supervising teacher*. Leaders in agencies who act in the same capacity as classroom teachers in relation to students assigned to professional laboratory experiences are designated as *supervising leaders*.

college and the students with whom they work. Every effort should be made to insure their continued cooperation by making the experience profitable for them also.

The majority of supervising teachers and leaders are democratic in their relations with boys and girls, co-workers, and student assistants, although pressures of professional duties or personal life may occasionally result in attitudes and practices that appear autocratic. Tact and self-restraint in passing judgments that may be unfair are expected of a person whose supervisor is irritable, temporarily unreasonable, or apparently under tension. An attempt should be made to avoid creating additional problems.

The following suggestions are made to emphasize the importance of meeting responsibilities in ways that contribute to sound professional relationships.

1. Arrive promptly for the first meeting. Determine the time, place, and date and be there in time to locate the correct office or room without delaying the conference.

2. Prepare a neat schedule of class and working hours to facilitate arranging a work program and special conference time.

3. Determine the exact nature of the duties to be carried out. If lesson plans or other forms are to be prepared before conducting activities, learn what is expected and when such plans are due. Plan carefully, follow the preferred forms, prepare them neatly, and keep a copy for reference. Be prompt in meeting requirements, and note suggestions for improvement.

4. Report for each teaching or working assignment in sufficient time to make necessary preparations for equipment and areas, and to assist with the supervision of dressing and locker rooms, or such other work as may be of assistance to the person in charge. If it is necessary to change into a gymnasium costume, make provisions for the time required to change.

5. Keep all personal equipment, supplies, and teaching costumes in a neat condition. Be sure that all articles of clothing are clean and well cared for. Leave the dressing room in order at all times.

6. Assume responsibility for all equipment checked out. Supervise the way in which it is used, and follow the established procedures for returning it to the proper storage space.

7. Assist with all routines followed by the teacher or leader. Leave all areas and equipment in good condition for the next class or group using it. Assist children with problems connected with lockers, showers, and dressing. Small children need help with shoe laces and buttons; older children frequently lose personal possessions and have difficulty with lockers.

8. Allow sufficient time, if possible, to listen to comments regarding teaching, problems in connection with individual children, and suggestions for future work.

9. Volunteer to assist with special preparations, cocurricular activities, and special programs.

10. Follow up opportunities to study children's records, make home visits, assist in reports, and engage in conferences with children and parents.

11. Remember that the supervising teacher or leader is responsible for the program, the children, the activities, and the maintenance of established policies and procedures. Even though a student teacher or field worker is given full responsibility for teaching and leadership, the regular professional staff member is obligated to see that boys and girls benefit from the work and experiences provided for them. When situations arise that require some variation from the customary procedure, it is wise to secure approval for the proposed change. It is both unprofessional and discourteous to challenge or disregard a decision made by a supervising teacher or leader.

Classroom teachers

The classroom teacher selects his pupil's activities, provides for their individual needs, and applies an intensive knowledge of the background of each child to the wise guidance of that child. All experiences that affect the child are the concern of the classroom teacher, including those in physical education, health education, and recreation. In many cases the classroom teacher is responsible for instruction in these areas, and the specialist acts only as a consultant to assist classroom teachers in their work.

Even though specialists possess a wide technical knowledge and a thorough understanding of the developmental needs and characteristics of children, the classroom teacher works much more closely with individual children and becomes better acquainted with them, particularly in the elementary school. Close cooperation between classroom teachers and those who are responsible for physical education, health education, and recreation provides opportunity for joint planning and more effective programs for boys and girls. The knowledge of each teacher supplements that of the others.

Youth leaders

Many youth leaders are concerned with activities not directly related to physical education, camping, and recreation. Welfare and service activities, homemaking, agriculture, conservation, and numerous other activities are included in the program of youth agencies. Professional leaders are aware of the value of every part of a program, and of cooperating with each other so that all activities will be successful. They exchange ideas and information, and coordinate their undertakings. Every person who works with an agency program should recognize his responsibility to help out with all parts of the program.

Parents

Parents are an important part of every school, recreation program, or youth agency, and their interest and participation in the formation of policies and the development of programs is valued and encouraged. They may be somewhat skeptical of the wisdom of allowing a student to help guide and teach their children, or uncertain about the capability of young people who are in charge of a group of boys or girls in a summer camp or on a playground. It is essential that contacts with parents result in the impression that the person in a capacity of leadership is friendly, poised, thoroughly acceptable, and a competent teacher and leader.

Occasions for meeting parents casually may occur from a chance meeting with the child and his parents on the street; but many children in such circumstances may point out their teachers and youth leaders to their parents without introducing them. Young teachers are usually amazed at the number of parents who know them by name, sight, and reputation. It is to be hoped that such descriptions are enthusiastic and that the impressions parents gain are favorable.

Parents who are able to visit a school or a youth agency usually expect to talk with the persons who know and work with their children. An opportunity to participate in a short conference with a parent, a child, and a supervising teacher or leader is an excellent experience. Teachers, leaders, and parents have a mutual interest in the success of a child in meeting problems, finding satisfactory outlets for his abilities, and improving in social and emotional adjustments. The significance of parent-teacher-child relationships becomes apparent through such contacts and provides the teacher with insight useful in his work.

RELATIONSHIPS WITH YOUNG PEOPLE

Boys and girls frequently model their standards and conduct on those of an older person they like and admire. The influence of teachers and leaders on young people is great, and the effect of teachers' personalities undoubtedly accounts for the varying degrees of success among teachers of comparable ability.[4] Fortunately, traits that affect others unpleasantly are remediable if a person discovers the qualities that are in need of correction and is willing to correct them. Desirable personal characteristics are as important in contacts with children as in social situations. The real test of a teacher's personality is often whether or not he can establish satisfactory relationships with the children in

[4] Raleigh Schorling, *Student Teaching* (New York: McGraw-Hill Book Co., Inc., 1940), p. 18.

his classes. The qualities that make teachers liked or disliked are also applicable to youth leaders.

Hart,[5] who compiled the characteristics of teachers who were liked and those of teachers who were disliked from his study of some 10,000 high-school seniors, emphasized the unusual ability

Courtesy of Chicago Park District

of the high-school senior to make mature judgments, and was impressed by the high purpose and idealism of high-school students. His study is worth consideration as a guide to personal efforts to improve traits of personality and habits that may affect children and young people adversely.

At the top of the listing of qualities of the best-liked teacher were helpfulness, friendliness, good disposition, interest in pupils, ability to make work interesting, skillful class control commanding the respect of pupils, and impartiality. The opposite

[5] Frank W. Hart, *Teachers and Teaching* (New York: The Macmillan Co., 1934), pp. 130-132, 250-251.

traits appear in similar order in the list describing the least-liked teacher. The frequency of references to partiality, favoritism, "pets," and "picking on" pupils indicates the importance of neither favoring nor showing personal disapproval or dislike for any boy or girl.

Small children usually respond naturally and with warmth to an older person who is friendly, sincerely interested in them and their activities, and who gives them a sense of security. A child who seems unresponsive, resentful, or uncooperative should be given evidence of the teacher's real interest in him. Difficulties in adjustment to his own group, feelings of insecurity at home, and many other factors may make a child seem to dislike teachers and leaders, other children, the school, and the community organizations with which he comes in contact.

The willingness of children and high school boys and girls to offer assistance to an older person they like and admire, and to spend time getting better acquainted or discussing their problems with such a person, may create attachments that require tact, understanding, and resourcefulness. Young teachers and leaders who are flattered by the attentions of personable children or young people of high school age, often encourage close personal relationships through their failure to realize that guidance is needed to redirect interest of pupils to companions of their own ages. Some persons who are socially or emotionally immature, or who are disturbed in their personal lives, may seek satisfaction through closer association with much younger people than is wise for either the younger person or the adult.

College students who are participants, student teachers, or field workers in high schools or youth organizations may find that they are strongly attracted to high-school-age boys and girls who are near their own ages. The temptation to date an attractive high-school student may be natural, but it is considered highly inadvisable and actually unethical. It is difficult to avoid familiarity and even disrespect on the part of other high-school students who are aware of the friendship. Young teachers occasionally ignore convention and make personal friends among students who attend the high schools where they teach. Such action causes criticism among other teachers, parents, students, and members of the community, and may result in the loss of a position and unhappiness to both individuals involved. A school board may be justified in the conviction that poor teacher-pupil relationships are evidence of unsatisfactory personal adjustment on the part of the teacher. Tead presents a similar viewpoint in the following statement:

> Equally fundamental is the avoidance of ... teachers who are allowing their behavior with students to be compensatory for a frustration deriving from some inadequacy in their personal life. Evidences of the milder forms of poor adjustment are found in the individual who is a show-off, who enjoys being severe or cruel, who insists on domination and meticulous obedience, who strives to gain popularity by being a soft teacher, or who at the other pole is bitterly sarcastic or caustic, or who is on the other hand too intimate and too personal in relations with students.[6]

The establishment of sound relationships with children and young people is a definite responsibility of everyone who works with them. Respect for the worth of the individual, participation in democratic living, and use of professional ethics contribute to these relationships.

SUMMARY

The development of a professional attitude, recognition of responsibilities, and an understanding of professional relationships are essential to successful professional laboratory experiences. Satisfactory personal relationships with boys and girls who participate in programs used for laboratory assignments are significant indications of good personal and professional adjustment, and of the sound mental health that is essential to the teacher and leader.

Willingness and ability to accept and benefit from suggestions and criticism, to appraise accomplishments in strengthening per-

---

[6] Ordway Tead, *College Teaching and College Learning* (New Haven: Yale University Press, 1949), pp. 9-10. (Reprinted by permission.)

sonal qualities, and to evaluate the results of teaching and leadership with intelligence are evidence of both personal and professional growth. Each person bears a share of the responsibility for these factors, which are signs of successful work in professional laboratory experiences.

SUGGESTED PROBLEMS

1. Write a statement describing what you hope to gain from assignments to professional laboratory experiences.

2. List a number of things that you plan to do to establish satisfactory relationships with:
   a. Boys and girls
   b. The college supervisor
   c. Supervising teachers and leaders
   d. Parents
   e. Classroom teachers or youth leaders, other than your supervising teachers and leaders.

3. List the qualities that you believe are desirable in teachers and youth leaders. Refer to your answers to Problems 3 and 4 of Chapter 1. How would you change your list?
   a. Do you believe that youth leaders should possess the same qualities as teachers? If so, state why you hold that opinion. If these qualities differ, why do you believe that these differences can exist without adversely affecting the work of the person?
   b. In what ways do your own qualities need to be improved? How do you plan to accomplish these changes?

4. Do you know of any actual case of a poor student-teacher relationship?
   a. Describe the case, and show how it has affected both the teacher and the pupil.
   b. What was the effect on other pupils?

5. What is your opinion of dating between a high-school teacher and a high-school student? Can you give any reasons, or cite any examples, to show that this practice is unwise?

REFERENCES

Boardman, Betty, "A Senior Looks at Student Teaching," *Journal of the American Association for Health, Physical Education and Recreation,* 19:168, March 1948.

Cunningham, Ruth, and associates, "Leadership and the Group," *Journal of the National Education Association,* 37:502, November 1948.

Davis, Calvin O., "The Rewards of Teaching," *School and Society,* 50:691, November 25, 1939.

Fenton, Norman, *Mental Hygiene in School Practice,* chs. xvi-xix. Palo Alto, California: Stanford University Press, 1943.

Graybeal, Elizabeth, "A Consideration of the Qualities Used by Administrators in Judging Effective Teachers of Physical Education in Minnesota," *Research Quarterly of the American Association for Health and Physical Education,* 12:741, December 1941.

Guiot, Germaine G., *Student Teaching in Physical Education.* New York: A. S. Barnes and Co., 1941.

Kebric, Burt M., "Problems of Beginning Teachers of Physical Education in the High Schools of California," *Research Quarterly of the American Association for Health and Physical Education,* 16:42, March 1945.

Lindsay, Margaret, "Ask Yourself Some Questions," *Journal of the National Education Association,* 40:173, March 1951.

Makechnie, George, "An Approach to the Problem of Practice Teaching," *Journal of the American Association for Health, Physical Education and Recreation,* 20:307, May 1949.

McCuskey, Dorothy, "What is Good Teaching—Our Changing Understanding," *Journal of the National Education Association,* 37:424, October 1948.

————, "Human Relationships in Teaching," *Journal of the National Education Association,* 37:504, November 1948.

Murray, Ruth, ed., *So You're Going to Teach?* Detroit: Wayne University, 1952.

Rautman, Arthur L., "The Physical Education Teacher as a Personal Model," *Journal of the American Association for Health, Physical Education and Recreation,* 21:70, January 1950.

Schorling, Raleigh, *Student Teaching.* New York: McGraw-Hill Book Co., Inc., 1940.

Solomon, Ben, "So You're Going to a Convention," *Journal of the American Association for Health, Physical Education and Recreation,* 19:179, March 1949. (Reprinted from *Youth Leader's Digest,* November 1947.)

Unruh, Adolph, "An Ingenuity Quotient," *Journal of the American Association for Health, Physical Education and Recreation,* 38:188, March 1949.

Courtesy of University of Illinois

CHAPTER EIGHT

Professional leadership in physical education health education and recreation

The meaning, purpose, and significance of a profession are the basis for the requirements of preparation and for the high standards expected of professional students. The undergraduate professional curriculum is designed to provide opportunities to develop personal skills and competencies, and to form certain concepts and understandings of professional work. The development of an appreciation for the basic purposes, interrelationships, and general content of the subject area is essential. The following brief presentation of historical background and statements of aims and objectives provides the background for an understanding of professional leadership in physical education, health education, and recreation.

HISTORICAL BACKGROUND

The meanings of physical education, health education, and recreation have been affected by educational beliefs throughout history. The concept of education in ancient Greece resulted in harmonious development of physical and mental abilities with outstanding results. Attitudes toward physical development and health changed during following eras to suit the demands of politics, religion, and education. The Romans used man's physical skill for military conquest; the age of Asceticism, in its attempt to separate physical and mental functions, fostered not only a disregard for health but the actual abuse of physical welfare; later eras recognized the physical nature of man but neglected provisions for physical education or health. Programs of physical *training*, with emphasis on muscular development and gymnastic coordination were initiated during the latter part of the 18th century. Modern programs of education emphasize the close interrelationships between mental and physical health, the necessity for education for leisure, and the contributions of physical education, health, and recreation to a well-balanced life.

Physical education

A primary factor of significance derived from Ancient Greek education is the acceptance of physical activity as an important aspect of total education. Vigorous play activity was developed on an organized basis by the Greeks, and their program consisted of running, jumping, throwing, wrestling, dancing, and sport activities as well as military training. The concept of physical education as a contribution to preparation for war was developed highly in Greece, although it was not the primary concept, as it was in the early Roman programs.

The programs after the fall of Rome were very limited and during the feudal period in Europe any physical instruction given was closely related to military preparations. The play of children was largely games of chase. Some play and recreation were related to religious and local festivals and celebrations.

The development of new educational ideas in the 18th century was accompanied by a recognition of the need for a return to the Greek ideal of a total program of education, including physical education. These ideas developed slowly, although programs combining many different physical activities were introduced into the German schools. Soon after 1800 the acceptance of physical education as a desirable part of education for girls was a significant development.

German programs devoted to body development resulted in activities that later became generally known as German gymnastics. The use of apparatus and the formation of sports and athletic clubs was a significant movement. Again, however, an important influence of this physical training was the preparation of German youth for war. In addition to gymnastics similar to those developed in Germany, Swedish physical educators included scientific analysis and remedial physical education as a part of their programs. Sports were emphasized during this period in England and many modern games were devised or originated. The English love of sports has been influential in the advancement of sports in this country.

Developments in the United States prior to the War Between the States were scattered and limited, although there was some recognition of the need for physical education in the schools. Sports were carried on outside of the schools and the school programs were copied from the European systems of gymnastics. American leaders soon began to adapt and modify these systems. Soon after 1900 a new concept of physical education developed, based on more free play, individual participation, and the inclusion of sports, games, and dancing in the program. The favorable progress of programs of sports and competition in schools and colleges resulted in a general acceptance of the need for physical education by 1920. State legislation requiring physical education followed World War I, and the preparation of teachers and leaders moved forward rapidly.

Scientific advancements have resulted in more general knowledge of the relationships between physical and mental health and the need for adequate programs of physical education. The change in emphasis on the functions of education has created an accompanying demand for men and women leaders who are capable of conducting programs of physical education that help prepare students for responsible citizenship.

Health education

Although the importance of health was recognized in ancient times, health instruction, sanitation, and personal hygiene were first given prominence in the writings of John Locke and others in the 17th century. Little development was made in the United States until after 1850.

Among the factors that have influenced the development of health education in the United States are the child study and temperance movements.[1] Educators began an intensified study of the child and his needs during the latter part of the 19th century. The importance of health and physical needs was sufficiently apparent to justify special provisions for them in school programs. The temperance movement was influential in promoting legislation directed toward teaching the harmful physiological effects of alcohol and narcotics. This legislation resulted in the inclusion of instruction in physiology and hygiene in the school curriculum. Medical examinations and follow-up programs were introduced after 1900 and have developed into the present health counseling programs. The physical condition of draft-age men examined during World War I and World War II created concern about the health and fitness of school children. Subsequent studies of the health status of school children have resulted in recommendations designed to improve health practices and programs.

The development of professional associations has been influential in promoting health education. Those interested in health education joined with the American Physical Education Association in 1937 to form the American Association for Health and Physical Education. Other groups formed included the American Public Health Association, an outgrowth of earlier child health groups. The influences of the Kellogg Foundation, the World Health Organization, and other health agencies have contributed to the establishment of strong health programs.

The federal government has been active in the promotion and advancement of health through the Children's Bureau, the health and welfare activities of the Federal Security Agency, White House Conferences on Children and Youth, and, more

[1] Ruth Grout, *Health Teaching in Schools*, 2d ed. (Philadelphia: W. B. Saunders Co., 1953), pp. 13-21.

recently, through the newly created Department of Health, Education and Welfare.

The development of universal school health education has been given great impetus by increased medical and scientific knowledge. School health programs have been largely incidental to other subject areas, and health teaching has been carried on by teachers of physical education, science, or home economics. Many of the early leaders in physical education in this country were medical men and their influence helped in the development of health and the emphasis on health education. The status of school health education and its relationship to health service and sanitation has only recently been well established.

The professional preparation of health educators has developed an increasing number of leaders, and some states now require special courses in health and health education of all teachers. Many schools now separate health education classes in the school curriculum, as well as integrating health teaching with other classes.

Recreation

The growth of recreation has closely paralleled that of physical education. Man has played during his leisure time throughout the ages. Records of primitive man give evidence that his games, contests of skill, rhythm, and dramatic song are the sources of many of our modern sports, games, and dance. The first recorded Olympic Games in 776 B.C. represented many years of refinement of primitive games. Further developments of similar sports and games have resulted in present-day events and modern programs. Changing civilizations have brought new interests and many variations in earlier leisure-time pursuits as well as the development of new sports and games and different forms of dance.

The modern recreation movement began during the 19th century. The experiments of Froebel, which resulted in the kindergarten; the programs of gymnastics developed by the early German, Danish, and Swedish physical educators increased interest in public areas for indoor and outdoor play; and the widespread natural growth of sports and games among the English people all contributed to the growth of recreation. Early developments in the United States showed the influences of both European and English programs. German immigrants established Turnvereins in the United States about 1850, and by 1860 students in many colleges had formed athletic clubs. Physical education programs during this period were centered around gymnastics. The opening of sand gardens for children in Boston in 1866 marked an important step toward public recreation. These sand gardens were patterned after similar ones that had been established in the parks in Berlin.[2]

The success of the Boston sand gardens resulted in the establishment of similar play areas by many cities. Additional stimulus to this movement was given by the increasing recognition of the need for greater protection of children from the dangers of play in unprotected areas. Improved labor laws and additional leisure time further emphasized the importance of recreational opportunities for all ages.

Cities began to consider the problem of public recreation and the responsibility of municipal government for providing recreational facilities. The opening of the first public park with facilities for recreation in Chicago in 1876 marked the beginning of a significant program for public recreation. The establishment of the Charlesbank Outdoor Gymnasium in Boston in 1889 and of the Hull House playground in Chicago in 1894 inaugurated the practice of equipping recreational areas with apparatus, playing fields, and courts, and of providing supervision and leadership. New York City opened several school play yards in 1899 to provide additional public play space. Many cities began to develop play areas, to appropriate funds for the expansion of play spaces, and to provide equipment and leadership.

---

[2] For many of the facts and dates in this section the authors are indebted to Elmer D. Mitchell and Bernard S. Mason, *The Theory of Play*, rev. ed. (New York: A. S. Barnes and Co., Inc., 1948), chs. i, ii.

Organized camping, which began in 1880 with the first boys camp, developed until there were 24 camps in 1900. Youth organizations were beginning to start programs of recreation. The Young Men's Christian Association, which had started in London in 1844 and in Boston in 1851, developed programs of play activities toward the latter part of the century. The Young Women's Christian Association, organized in London in 1861 and in Boston in 1866, started a limited program of recreation as early as 1877.

The 20th century marked the beginning of extensive development of parks and other public recreation areas in the United States. Chicago assumed municipal leadership by appropriating $10,000,000 for park playgrounds and by providing both indoor and outdoor recreational facilities, including extensive playing fields, wading and swimming pools, tennis courts, gymnasiums, and auditoriums, and other recreation areas. Other cities followed suit with large appropriations and extensive development of recreation areas.

The present National Recreation Association, formed in 1906 as the Playground and Recreation Association of America, has contributed greatly to the development of recreation programs throughout the country. It has also developed standards for recreation leaders and has brought together a national membership of professional workers and public-spirited persons interested in the development of recreation. Publications, clinics, and consultation and field services are some of the means through which this organization has served to promote recreation.

Youth organizations such as the Boy Scouts of America, organized in 1910, and the Camp Fire Girls and Girl Scouts organized in 1912, have also been active in furthering sound programs of recreation for boys and girls. Organized camping, the development of athletic programs in high schools and colleges, and the growth of recreation programs in industry have all contributed materially to improved opportunities for recreation.

Recognition of the importance of recreation has resulted in the sponsorship and financing of recreation programs by state and federal legislation. Millions of dollars have been and are being spent annually on areas, equipment, facilities, and leadership for recreation. The organization and administration of recreation has become highly specialized; municipal, industrial, commercial, semipublic, and private recreation agencies all conduct special programs. Many thousands of volunteer workers have made possible this broad spread of recreation programs. National standards for the preparation of recreation leaders have guided the development of the professional curriculum in numerous colleges.

PROFESSIONAL PREPARATION

The development of schools to prepare professional leaders in physical education can be traced to about 1800. In 1804, in Denmark, Franz Nachtegall was instrumental in starting the first college for physical education teachers. Ten years later, in Sweden, Per Hendrick Ling established a school for teachers of physical education which later became the Royal Institute of Gymnastics. It was not until about 1850 that such work was begun in the United States, when the Cincinnati Turnverein organized classes for teachers of gymnastics. The first professional school in this country was formed by Dio Lewis as the Normal Institute for Physical Education in Boston in 1861.[3] Although it did not last long it did graduate several small groups of teachers and stimulate efforts toward the preparation of teachers in the field of physical education.

A second school was established in New York by the Turnerbund in 1866. This school was later moved to Milwaukee where, under the leadership of George Brosius, hundreds of teachers were prepared.[4] The scope of the work in teacher education was enlarged through Brosius's adaptation of the work of the Turnverein groups for use in the public schools. In 1881 Dr.

[3] E. A. Rice, *A Brief History of Physical Education* (New York: A. S. Barnes and Co., 1930), p. 264.

[4] Norma Schwendener, *A History of Physical Education in the United States* (New York: A. S. Barnes and Co., 1942), p. 104.

Dudley Sargent began preparing physical education teachers in his classes for women at Harvard; through this work he was influential in stimulating the teacher-education movement. He was also responsible for developing the Harvard Summer School for Physical Education Teachers (1887 to 1932), which contributed to the preparation and inspiration of many outstanding leaders in physical education.

A fourth center was started by William G. Anderson in 1886 at Adelphi College in Brooklyn, and it was also through the efforts of Mr. Anderson that the Brooklyn Normal School for Physical Education was founded. The Brooklyn Normal School was moved to New Haven as the New Haven School of Gymnastics and later became Arnold College of Physical Education. In 1887 the Young Men's Christian Association added a department of physical education to prepare leaders at the International Young Men's Christian Association College at Springfield, Massachusetts. Many of the leaders in physical education in this country are graduates of this school.

Growth in numbers of schools

By 1914, when 24 schools in the United States were preparing teachers of physical education, fewer than 2,000 major students were enrolled. Courses leading to certificates or degrees in physical education were also being given in colleges and normal schools by this time. As a direct result of the renewal of interest in physical conditioning and physical fitness that took place during World War I, many states passed legislation requiring the teaching of physical education in the public schools. This legislative action greatly stimulated program development in physical education and created a demand for qualified teachers. By 1921 there were 4,890 major students in 81 schools.[5] This number had grown to nearly 100 by 1925.[6]

As a result of World War I emphasis on physical condition

---

[5] Wilbur P. Bowen, "Seven Years of Progress in Preparing Teachers of Physical Education," *American Physical Education Review*, 27:64, February 1922.
[6] E. A. Rice, *op cit.*, p. 266.

and the resultant state legislation, teacher-education programs that had been carried on largely in private schools and endowed colleges were introduced into state universities and state teachers colleges. The period of preparation was lengthened to four years in the majority of institutions by 1921. Cultural studies, basic sciences, and educational theory were gradually coordinated with the technical study of physical education. Major trends reported in 1932 were an increase in the number of colleges offering professional preparation and an increase in enrollments. At that time there were 210 schools offering a four-year major, of which 63 were state colleges and universities, 70 were teachers colleges, and 77 were private schools.[7] By 1940 there were nearly 400 schools preparing specialists in physical education and related areas, and according to recent estimates there are now more than 600 such schools.

Professional preparation of health education and recreation specialists has been a recent development. Early programs of professional preparation in these areas were included as a part of physical education preparation, owing to the interrelationships of the three areas. Recognition of the increasing complexity of preparation has resulted in the development of special programs. The number of such programs specifically designed to prepare health educators and recreation specialists has increased greatly in the last decade.

Health education

Health specialists have included doctors, nurses, and sanitary engineers who have transferred into public and school health from their original professions. Specialization in health now starts early in college and requires an undergraduate major followed by graduate study to qualify for such highly technical aspects of health work as administration, supervision, and college teaching.

[7] Clifford L. Brownell, "The Present Status of Professional Preparation of Teachers of Physical Education," *Research Quarterly of the American Physical Education Association*, 3:107-117, May 1932.

Although early emphasis on health in colleges and public schools was fostered by Horace Mann in 1879, this did not develop as a major influence until after 1920, when health education became accepted as an important part of the school program. Special certification requirements for health educators have been established by a number of states and it is to be anticipated that certification requirements will be adopted by the majority of states within the next few years. Physical education teachers have been permitted to teach health education without additional certification in many states in the past. Since the responsibility for health instruction has frequently rested upon physical educators, professional curriculums have customarily included some provision for basic courses. These courses make it possible for physical education majors to secure a minor in health education although a major in health education may not be offered.

Recreation

Professional preparation in recreation is possible in a number of colleges and universities, and more institutions are establishing major programs each year. Although certification standards have not been adopted, the problem of certification for recreation workers has been widely discussed among educators and recreation specialists. Increasing emphasis on recreation education, on the values of recreation in therapeutic treatment of emotionally disturbed individuals, and in the rehabilitation of victims of certain diseases and incapacitating accidents has created a growing demand for qualified recreation leaders. This demand may be expected to result in rapid growth in the number of professional programs for the preparation of recreation leaders.

PHILOSOPHY AND AIM

It is customary for a person to act in accordance with his own standards of conduct—he does things or refrains from doing things because of his own principles and ideals. In this way an individual develops a personal philosophy by which he lives. A professional group also develops a philosophy to govern the way it functions. Personal principles are often based on emotions or prejudices; a profession develops its principles only after careful investigation of facts, and uses them to guide the action taken by the profession, individually or in groups.[8]

Philosophy

The beliefs held regarding the functions of physical education, health education, and recreation represent a philosophy which is similar in nature to the philosophy of education. The fundamental difference is that while educational philosophy applies to education in the broadest sense, the philosophies of physical education, health education, or recreation must be interpreted in relation to their unique contributions to education.

The belief that certain achievements are ideal or worth working for automatically sets up a goal. Such a goal may never be fully realized, since each new accomplishment tends to extend it to a higher level. In medicine, for example, each new discovery calls forth greater efforts to find still better means of protecting health, of preventing illness and of fighting disease.

Everyone preparing to teach or work in a professional field must develop a personal philosophy. He must also develop concepts of the aims and objectives in his field and must prepare or accept a statement of the aims of his area of work. Physical education, health education, and recreation have many aspects in common and are interrelated to a high degree in their philosophy and aims. Each, also, is closely related to the total program of education.

[8] Jesse Feiring Williams and Clifford L. Brownell, *The Administration of Health Education and Physical Education,* 4th ed. (Philadelphia: W. B. Saunders Co., 1951), pp. 26-27; A. S. Barr, W. H. Burton, and L. J. Brueckner, *Supervision,* 2d ed. (New York: D. Appleton-Century Co., Inc., 1948), pp. 43-44; Agnes R. Wayman, *A Modern Philosophy of Physical Education* (Philadelphia: W. B. Saunders Co., 1938), pp. 70-71.

Aim

It is necessary to take some form of action to reach a goal. What that action will be and how it will be carried out depends upon the philosophy, principles, and standards which have been adopted. Progress toward an aim, or goal, is made by planning and taking definite steps toward the desired outcome. Each step brings the goal more nearly within reach.

A practical illustration of the operation of step-by-step achievements toward an aim is found in college life. A student who plans to teach has a number of objectives to realize—primarily graduation from college, certification as a teacher, and placement in a teaching position. His accomplishments are usually determined by his degree of success in mastering knowledge and developing proficiency in his professional field. When he has been granted a diploma and certification and has secured a position, his immediate objectives have been achieved. Obviously, these accomplishments represent only preliminary steps in his plans for the future and the aim he has for his life's work.

Philosophy of physical education

The American Association for Health, Physical Education and Recreation has stated the meaning and purposes of physical education as an introduction to its *Platform for Physical Education:*

> Physical education is a *way* of education through physical activities which are selected and carried on with full regard to values in human growth, development, and behavior. Because it is a phase of the total educational program, physical education aims for the same general goal that gives purpose to all the other learning experiences in the school—well rounded development of all children and youth as responsible citizens of our democratic society.[9]

[9] W. K. Streit and Simon A. McNeeley, "A Platform for Physical Education," *Journal of Health, Physical Education and Recreation*, 21:136, March 1950. (Reprinted by permission.)

Any definition of physical education must include recognition of its basic purpose in providing sound health, physical development, and skill in physical activities. An interpretation of the meaning of physical education must also indicate its responsibility for contributing to total education. From this standpoint, the following definition proves particularly acceptable:

> Physical education is the accumulation of wholesome experiences through participation in large-muscle activities that promote optimum growth and development.[10]

The aim of physical education

The aim of physical education is such that there will always be new achievements possible to improve the accomplishments that have been made. Many leaders in physical education have stated the aim; the most widely known and accepted statement is that made by Williams:

> Physical education should aim to provide skilled leadership and adequate facilities which will afford an opportunity for each individual or group to act in situations which are physically wholesome, mentally stimulating and satisfying, and socially sound.[11]

Since the aim indicates desired outcomes, it is essential that a profession devote itself to the purpose of realizing its aim. Thus it becomes apparent that physical educators must concentrate efforts to accomplish desirable outcomes in terms of:

1. Physical fitness
2. Social and motor skills
3. Knowledges and understandings
4. Habits, attitudes, and appreciations.[12]

[10] Clifford L. Brownell and E. Patricia Hagman, *Physical Education—Foundations and Principles* (New York: McGraw-Hill Book Co., Inc., 1951), p. 17. (Reprinted by permission.)

[11] Jesse Feiring Williams, *The Principles of Physical Education.* 5th ed. (Philadelphia: W. B. Saunders Co., 1949), p. 242. (Reprinted by permission.)

[12] By permission from Brownell and Hagman, *op cit.,* p. 183.

A Platform for Physical Education illustrates the importance of each of these four outcomes as follows:

Physical education provides a wealth of experiences which, along with other opportunities in the curriculum, are particularly important in helping each child and youth to:

1. Develop and maintain maximum physical efficiency. A physically efficient person enjoys sound functioning of the bodily processes, is free of remediable defects, possesses such qualities as strength, endurance, speed, a sense of balance, agility, and good posture and efficient body mechanics, and exercises these qualities according to his age and physical condition, maintaining a balance of activity, rest, work, and recreation. One who has unremediable defects learns to adjust to and compensate for his infirmities and develop his capabilities in order to live a happy and useful life.

2. Develop useful skills. In this sense, a skillful person is proficient in many fundamental skills, such as walking, dodging, gauging moving objects, and lifting, which are essential to living safely and successfully, and has abilities in a variety of activities, such as team and individual sports, swimming, and dancing, that contribute to physical and social efficiency at each stage of his life.

3. Conduct himself in socially acceptable ways. A person who behaves desirably, among other things, acts in a sportsmanlike manner, works for the common good, and respects the personalities of his fellows (team games and other group activities offer many opportunities to practice these qualities). He enjoys, contributes to, and is at ease in a variety of wholesome social situations (co-educational sports, dancing, swimming and other such activities help to provide learning experiences in such cases), exercises self-control in activities which are mentally stimulating and often emotionally intense, reacts quickly and wisely under pressure, is courageous and resourceful. Games, contests, and other competitive sports help to bring out these qualities when there is good leadership.

4. Enjoy wholesome recreation. A person who engages in wholesome recreation includes in his daily living activities that bring deep satisfaction, that are often creative, relaxing or stimulating, and draws upon a fund of recreational interests, knowledges, appreciations, and *skills*.

The intelligent physical educator makes the most of his many opportunities to help boys and girls, youth and adults, gain these values. As a teacher, his job is to select, organize, and guide activities suited to the needs, capacities, and interests of everyone taking part.[13]

In order to realize these outcomes it is essential that provisions for physical education assure:

1. A sufficient amount of activity for each child each day in accordance with his needs, abilities, and interests to develop physical skills and bodily fitness for the demands of everyday life.

2. The protection of the health and welfare of children and youth so that normal growth and development may take place without physical handicaps.

3. The teaching and guidance of the handicapped child so that he may learn recreational activities adapted to his limitations, and develop skills related to the play of normal children in order to participate in some capacity within the limits of his disability.

4. The learning of motor and social skills basic to enjoyable participation in the sports, games, and dances engaged in by others of the same age.

5. The establishment of knowledges, attitudes, and appreciations which contribute to recreational participation in physical activities.

6. Leaders capable of helping children and youth develop desirable attributes such as self-reliance, initiative, self-control, leadership, good sportsmanship, and responsibility to the group.

7. The equipment and facilities necessary for an adequate program.

8. A safe and healthful environment.

All phases of the program of physical education should contribute to the aim, and should be evaluated in terms of physical skills, social and emotional growth, attitudes and understandings. Keeping the aim in mind, teachers customarily set up specific objectives to insure the outcomes they desire. For example,

[13] Streit and McNeeley, *A Platform for Physical Education*, pp. 136-137. (Reprinted by permission.)

a teacher planning to teach a team game prepares statements indicating that the purpose of the lesson is to:

1. Teach pupils skills used in the game.
2. Help them learn how to play various positions and understand the values of teamwork.
3. Teach pupils a knowledge of the game, its playing areas and rules, and the use and care of equipment.
4. Guide the development of desirable social and emotional behavior.
5. Stimulate continued enjoyment in playing the game.

The purposes of a lesson are related both to the aim for the program and to the outcomes that are possible to accomplish during the specific instructional period. The results attained each day, week, or year add to the possibility of achieving the aim of physical education.

Philosophy of health education

Many interpretations have been made of the meaning of health education. When health is misconstrued to mean freedom from disease, for example, little attention is given to the positive aspects of health. When health is viewed as the means by which a person lives fully, a new and broader meaning of health education is possible. In this sense, the definition of health that states "Health is optimal personal fitness for fine living" [14] implies much for the educational program. A further description of personal health, which establishes three main divisions of fitness, is presented by Hoyman. His divisions are physical fitness, motor fitness, and mental and emotional fitness. Chart 4 shows these three phases of personal health as an interrelationship of various factors contributing to health.

It is necessary to recognize that the optimal fitness of any person is dependent on several factors—heredity, which determines the basic elements of personal makeup; environment, which includes such factors as community influences, nutrition,

[14] H. S. Hoyman, *Functional Health Teaching*, 2d ed. (Goshen, Indiana: McConnell School Map Co., 1950), p. 18. (Reprinted by permission.)

and housing; and behavior, which is the result of education and consists of the health habits and attitudes acquired by the person. Heredity and environment are strong influences that cannot

Chart 4

THREE THINGS DETERMINE PERSONAL HEALTH

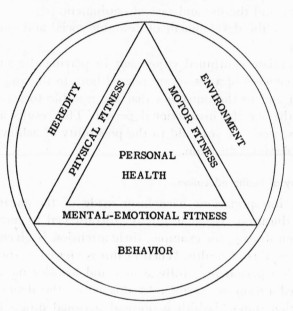

Three things determine personal health: heredity, environment, and behavior. Good health teaching is aimed at bringing about actual behavior changes in boys and girls that promote optimal personal health through healthful living. (Chart by Robert Osborn. Reproduced by permission from H. S. Hoyman, *Your Health and Personality*, copyright, 1948, by Harcourt, Brace and Company, Inc.)

be completely controlled or entirely changed. What a person does (his behavior) can be modified through education.

Health education, although directed toward the individual person, must also go beyond him to the relationships he has with others. From this point of view the following definition may be considered to include the total pattern.

Health education is the process of providing learning experiences for the purpose of influencing knowledge, attitudes, or conduct relating to individual, community, or world health.[15]

Aim of health education

The aim of all health programs is to improve the level of health. This may be accomplished through health service; prevention of disease by vaccination and other means; examinations to detect defects and disabilities; correction of remediable defects; and improvement of the environment through sanitation, good housing, adequate welfare services, and programs of education, physical education and recreation. It is essential to human welfare that specific and positive efforts be made to help people live longer and better. People must be shown how to develop lifelong habits and attitudes toward health. Instruction should teach people:

1. To improve their health and appearance through the hygienic care of the body and special sense organs.
2. To prevent, or to detect and correct, physical defects through the use of adequate medical and dental services.
3. To help prevent and control communicable diseases.
4. To help prevent and control noncommunicable diseases.
5. To help prevent accidents and to learn how to administer first aid and home-nursing care of the injured and sick.
6. To develop and maintain physical and motor fitness adequate for occupational, recreational, military, and health purposes.
7. To select and enjoy a diet conducive to optimal growth, development, and health.
8. To help promote and maintain a sanitary environment and a healthful community.
9. To direct affection and the sex impulse as constructive forces in wholesome living.
10. To become intelligent consumers of health services and products.
11. To understand the subjective basis of many personal health beliefs and practices and the need for objective standards.

15 Charles C. Wilson, ed., *Health Education*, Joint Committee Report, National Education Association and American Medical Association, 4th ed. (Washington, D. C.: National Education Association, 1948), p. 4. (Reprinted by permission.)

12. To develop ability to deal effectively with personal, family, and community health problems.

13. To face daily problems and to participate in social living in such a way as to improve emotional stability and mental health.

14. To develop a real desire to be healthy through participation in healthful daily living that minimizes fatigue and strain, avoids harmful "escape mechanisms," and links health with the achievement of high ideals.[16]

The platform suggested for health education represents the cooperative efforts of health specialists in major national and state associations, and it illustrates the total pattern of health education. It involves health service, healthful environment, and health instruction based on the needs of students. The objectives of this platform represent a statement of purposes and outcomes.

Objectives

Since the health of every individual is basic to his effective functioning as a member of society and to his personal happiness and success, every community should have, for all of its citizens, a total health education program.

The objectives of this program should be to improve the health behavior of every individual and to stimulate collective action, in accordance with democratic principles, to provide the community with needed health facilities and resources. Such a program would:

1. Make it possible for every person to attain the maximum health of which he is biologically and physiologically capable.

2. Help to develop mature individuals who possess the knowledge and philosophy to build not only healthier communities but a healthier world.[17]

The complete platform appears in Appendix C, pp. 353-355.

Philosophy of recreation

Concepts of recreation have been expressed by many leaders in the field of recreation from Joseph Lee, the recognized father

[16] H. S. Hoyman, *Health Guide Units for Oregon Teachers* (Ann Arbor: Edwards Bros., 1946), pp. 11-12. (Reprinted by permission.)

[17] "Suggested Platform for Health Education," *Journal of the American Association for Health, Physical Education and Recreation,* 18:436, 557, September 1947.

of recreation, to G. Ott Romney, George D. Butler, and C. K. Brightbill, present-day leaders. Among the prominent ideas are: that any activity which occupies leisure time is recreation; that recreation is a basic element in the lives of all people; that recreation is necessary as a change from the requirements of a job. The keynote in all recreation is enjoyable activity. It may be active or passive, but it is activity chosen by the individual for his own reasons. The following definition by Butler expresses the ideas of most present-day recreation leaders:

> Thus recreation is activity that is satisfying and engaged in for its own sake. In recreation the individual finds opportunity for self-expression, and from it he derives fun, relaxation, or pleasure.[18]

In determining the nature of recreation it must be recognized that recreation is a powerful social influence and that it has important contributions to make to modern life. The most important of these are the happiness and satisfaction an individual derives from recreational activity. In addition to these, there are health and physical values to be gained from many recreational activities. Other factors contribute to an understanding of the place and meaning of recreation in our present day social structure and way of living. Among these are technical and scientific developments which have created leisure time in ever increasing amounts, the patterns of urban and rural living, earlier retirement, and the potential usefulness of recreational activities as therapeutic measures and in the control of juvenile delinquency.

Aim of recreation

Recreation should provide facilities and programs to make possible individual choice of leisure-time interests for everyone. It must provide opportunities for self-expression, instruction,

[18] By permission from George D. Butler, *Introduction to Community Recreation*, 2d ed. (New York: McGraw-Hill Book Co., Inc., 1949), p. 5.

organization of activities and groups, and professional leadership. The components of this aim of recreation are:

1. Happiness	8. Citizenship
2. Satisfaction	9. Character
3. Balanced growth	10. Development of talents
4. Creativeness	11. Socialization
5. Competition	12. Individualization
6. Learning	13. Prevention and care
7. Health	14. Democracy [19]

The recreation platform set up by national recreation groups establishes the means by which such outcomes can be realized. The preamble to this platform states the basic purposes and concepts agreed upon by the groups:

Preamble: Recreation is a basic need for living in a democratic society. It may be an organized or a spontaneous activity under governmental, voluntary, or private auspices. For the individual, recreation may be any wholesome leisure experience engaged in solely for the satisfaction derived therefrom. It includes games and sports, camping, hiking, dancing, picnics, discussion groups, drama, music, arts and crafts, and other activities of personal choice. Recreation may be an individual hobby or an experience shared with others. It is man's principal opportunity for enrichment of living.

The present mechanized age and its prospect of increased leisure demands comprehensive planning for recreation. In every community there should be a citizens' recreation council representing all interested groups, and, in addition, a board or commission officially responsible for direction of a tax-supported public recreation program. As part of the complete community plan the voluntary and private agencies can provide significant opportunities for individual and group recreation.

The modern community supports education, health, recreation, welfare, and related services as essential to the individual and society. The provision of these services is a responsibility of the entire community including public, private, and voluntary agencies.[20]

[19] Harold D. Meyer and Charles K. Brightbill, *Community Recreation* (Boston: D. C. Heath and Co., 1948), pp. 24-28. (Reprinted by permission.)

[20] "Recreation—An Essential Community Service," *Journal of Health and Physical Education,* 17:368, June 1946. (Reprinted by permission.)

The complete statement of the platform appears in the appendix.

All recreation programs and activities, whether public, private, or individual, should be evaluated in terms of the aim and the outcomes listed above. The best results in recreation are dependent upon competent professional leadership directed toward achievement of the aim.

CONTRIBUTIONS OF PHYSICAL EDUCATION, HEALTH EDUCATION, AND RECREATION

Education must provide for the carryover of established ideals, customs, and knowledge from one generation to the next. Educational programs should place emphasis on the individual person and his basic needs, and must recognize the changing nature of society and the democratic way of life. Since the individual exists in a social group as a part of society, education has the obligation to help him understand his personal responsibilities and limitations, as well as his rights and privileges, in that society.

Provisions for vigorous physical activities; opportunities to develop physical, social, and emotional skills; recreational interests; and personal health activities are responsibilities of expert teaching and leadership. Education must equip each individual with the skills, strength, endurance, and coordination needed to carry out daily work and recreation. The well-educated person understands the importance of health and the need for maintaining his health at the highest possible level, and the need for recreation skills for leisure time. In addition, a well-educated person realizes the influence exerted by good personal appearance and grooming, social poise, and emotional control, both on his personality and on the opinions others have of him. Expert leadership in physical education, health education, and recreation helps to bring about all these desirable qualities.

It has been found that a child's social and emotional relationships are directly influenced by his ability to take an active and skillful part in the play of children of his own age.[21] Boys and girls learn more quickly when they are skillfully taught and when they have an opportunity to learn a variety of games, sports, and dances. A carefully planned program of physical education that provides for the interests and abilities of children of varying ages and abilities is necessary, since all children

Courtesy of University of Illinois

cannot become equally skillful in the same activities. In such a program, expertly directed, boys and girls learn to accept decisions, to play in a sportsmanlike manner, and to accept the responsibility of team or group membership.

Physical education is closely related to health education in many ways. Physical health and emotional adjustment are improved by a well-conducted activity program which may include incidental health instruction pertinent to the particular activity. Well-selected exercise and recreation help develop total

[21] Arthur I. Gates *et al.*, *Educational Psychology*, 3d ed. (New York: The Macmillan Co., 1950), pp. 70-76.

health by stimulating bodily activity, releasing strains and tensions, and by providing a change from the pattern of general school work.

The health education program contributes to an understanding of sound nutritional practices, the need for medical care, personal hygiene, home and family living, mental and emotional stability, and safety. A basic knowledge of scientific health facts, and the relationships of these facts to common fads and fallacies concerning health, is another benefit of such a program. Health education should develop concepts of community and national health and an awareness on the part of all persons of their broad responsibilities for the health of others. The total health needs of the community, the nation, and the world, as well as personal habits and attitudes are concerns of health education.

Recreation programs provide for the wise and effective use of leisure time which contributes directly to happiness, satisfaction, and the other objectives of recreation. Education for leisure time prepares a person for wise planning of his recreation, and recreational activities bring relief from the tensions of daily living. The person on the golf course who is interested in his game and his companions, or the person who is concentrating primarily on improving his shots has little time to think of problems in the office. His attention is shifted from himself and his problems to the activity in which he is participating.

The present social structure is complicated and places a problem of choice of leisure activity directly on the individual. Education for leisure and the provision of opportunities for recreation contribute the foundation for personal choices which must be made. Specific contributions of recreational activities are those related to physical and mental health, social adjustment, and character.

> The individual who has a rich recreation life is more likely to be a healthy, well-balanced, law-abiding citizen than the person who is deprived of recreational opportunities.[22]

[22] George D. Butler, *Community Recreation*, p. 17. (Reprinted by permission.)

Leadership is an attribute that the physical education teacher and recreation leader, in particular, strive to teach and encourage boys and girls to attain. Many boys and girls seem to be natural leaders; others can acquire the qualities of leadership; still others seem to have little capacity for or interest in leadership. All areas of school and recreation programs should contribute to opportunities for leadership development.[23]

> The leaders appear to excel their fellow students more or less in many mental, social, and physical traits. They are usually more intelligent than the average, they get better marks, they are taller and heavier, they are in better health, they are a bit older than the average, they come from a slightly higher socio-economic background, their athletic abilities are higher, and their social adjustment is better. These characteristics apply, of course, to leaders as a group; not all of them are true of any individual.[24]

Physical education, health education, and recreation have unique contributions to offer in terms of education for effective living. Participation in socially accepted activities is important, and the related educational contributions are vital, to living in a democracy.

THE ROLE OF PROFESSIONAL LEADERSHIP

The ability of leaders to provide an effective program of physical education, health education, and recreation determines the degree to which the aims of the program are realized. The content of the program, the adequacy of available facilities and equipment, the provisions made for health and safety, and the amount of time allotted for these activities are factors having a bearing on the desired results.

The teacher or leader must first of all accept his responsibility to the child. He must strive to understand the child, his personality, his capacity, his needs, and his attitudes, as well as the factors involved in growth and development, maturation, social

---

[23] Luella Cole, *Psychology of Adolescence*, 3d ed. (New York: Rinehart and Co., Inc., 1948), pp. 255-256; and Arthur I. Gates, *Educational Psychology*, p. 154.

[24] Cole, *op. cit.*, p. 234. (Reprinted by permission.)

contacts and interrelationships, emotional balance, and the physiological and psychological aspects of personality. The primary problem is to understand each child as he is and to help each child develop his potentialities.

The job of the teacher or leader is one of service to others; it provides constant challenges and new situations. The larger responsibilities in a position of leadership are reflected in the willingness of the leader to go beyond the immediate requirements of his job. Capability in giving personal guidance and in counseling individuals represent important aspects of leadership.

The leader who conducts an effective program:

1. Knows his subject thoroughly with respect to its techniques, its contributions to the avowed purposes of general education, and its unique qualities.

2. Establishes relationships with students that are cordial, democratic, and helpful.

3. Conducts himself as a teacher of students, first of all, rather than as a specialist in a given subject.

4. Exemplifies high ideals of professional behavior, including emotional stability and social maturity.

5. Takes a broad view of problems confronting education, instead of a narrow, personal, or departmental view.

6. Understands, and utilizes in his teaching, the problems confronting students in the home, school, and community.

7. Helps students formulate their own ideas, to develop their own skills, and to express their ideas and skills with clarity, efficiency, and sincerity.

8. Encourages students to participate in, and to take responsibility for, the evaluation or appraisal of their own acts and progress.

9. Gives careful attention to long-range planning and to preparation for the work of each day.

10. Provides intelligent guidance to students who may enter the teaching profession.

11. Participates in the affairs of the school and community as responsible citizens.

12. Appreciates the magnitude of his profession; cherishes the profound conviction that successful teaching benefits society as

a whole through the responsible leadership of individual youths during their formative years.[25]

Relationships in physical education, health education, and recreation

The relationships established by teachers and leaders should create an atmosphere which stimulates cooperative planning, initiative, and problem-solving. Wise guidance and leadership are essential if boys and girls are to develop capabilities for self-direction and responsible, intelligent, democratic action. It is imperative that the characteristics that are desirable in children and youth be understood, and that consistent efforts be made to help them achieve those qualities. The acceptance or rejection of a person by his own group may have far-reaching consequences in relation to his social and emotional adjustment.

Intergroup relationships and the problems of discrimination and prejudice are particularly important. The physical educator and recreation leader are in a position to provide guidance in these areas. Sports and games offer excellent opportunities for intergroup education and participation. The teacher or leader should know how to make democracy function and keep functioning through sports and other recreational activities.

The importance children give to physical skill creates two specific problems. First, well-skilled boys and girls must be taught to accept their accomplishments and the prestige granted them with modesty and an understanding of their relative values. Second, the poorly skilled child should be given more leadership responsibilities, and more chances to develop the other qualities that contribute to satisfactory relationships with his own group, than his skill alone might seem to merit. The program should be designed to provide opportunities for all.

In addition to relationships with children, it is also important that the teacher and leader establish satisfactory relationships

[25] Clifford L. Brownell and E. Patricia Hagman, *Physical Education—Foundations and Principles* (New York: McGraw-Hill Book Co., Inc., 1951), p. 298. (Reprinted by permission.)

with the community at large. Persons employed in these positions should be willing to participate freely in all community educational and recreational projects that need their services. There is a need for coordination of physical education, health education, and recreation activities in all communities. The leader in these programs should work for cooperation in the leadership and services of all three areas.

The program

Program planning requires familiarity with the modern concept of education which states that education is concerned with all experiences in and out of the school. Moreover, intelligent provisions for varying degrees of individual ability must be made in planning program content. All aspects of the program should be based upon adequate standards for the protection and welfare of the children and young people included in the program.

Physical Education. The physical education program must be planned for the needs of individuals as well as of groups. Some boys and girls benefit from a vigorous program of activities; others require modified or restricted activities designed specifically to meet their needs. The program should provide for a daily period of physical education for every school child. Activities should be intelligently selected according to their suitability for the groups to be taught, and should provide for the development of motor coordination, agility, strength, endurance, and bodily poise. Social and emotional learning should be recognized as desirable outcomes of the physical education program and should be provided for as a normal part of the experiences in physical education.

The well-balanced program of physical education includes instruction, opportunities for practice, participation in cocurricular programs, and provision for adequately organized, carefully supervised, and well-regulated intramural and extramural competition. A well-planned program of physical education in-

cludes a progressive development of rhythmic, group, individual, and team activities involving a variety of motor skills, social relationships, and recreational experiences. Although boys

Courtesy of University of Illinois

and girls are customarily taught in separate classes in the upper
grades and high school, co-physical education and corecreation
should be introduced at these levels wherever it is suitable. The
progressive development of activities is indicated in the accompanying lists.

1. PROGRAM ACTIVITIES

AQUATICS

Aquaplaning	Games and Stunts	Swimming	Water Ballet
Canoeing	Life Saving	Synchronized	Water Polo
Diving	Rowing	Swimming	Water Skiing

DANCE

Ballet	Folk	Modern	Social
Clog and Tap	Gymnastic	Rhythms	Square

GAMES, RELAYS, CONTESTS, TESTS

Goal Games	*Simple Team Games*	*Relays*	*Self-Testing* Accuracy
Club Snatch	Alley Soccer	Obstacle Relays	Throwing Balance Beam
Dare Base	Captain Ball	Overtake Relays	Tests Goal-Kicking
Midnight	Hit Pin Base-ball	Simple Relays	Goal-Shooting Pull-ups
Red Rover	New Comb	Shuttle Relays	Punting Push-ups
Group Games	*Tag Games*	*Contests*	Stunt Tests
Dodge Ball	Group Tag	Hand Wrestle	Target-
End Ball	Partner Tag	Indian Wrestle	Pitching
Kick Ball	Simple Tag	O'Leary	
Long Base	Team Tag	Tug of War	

GYMNASTICS, MARCHING, TUMBLING

Apparatus	Corrective	Marching	Stunts
Baton-Twirling	Free Exercises	Mimetics	Trampoline
Conditioning	Gymnastics	Remedial	Tumbling

INDIVIDUAL AND DUAL GAMES AND SPORTS

Aerial Darts	Croquet	Paddle Tennis	Rope-Twirling
Archery	Deck Tennis	Pistol	Skating
Badminton	Fencing	Riding	Squash
Billiards	Floor Tennis	Rifle	Table Tennis
Bowling	Golf	Ring Golf	Track and Field
Casting	Horseshoes	Rope-Jumping	Wrestling

TEAM SPORTS

Basketball	Field Hockey	Six-Man Football	Speedball
Baseball	Football	Soccer	Volleyball
Field Ball	Ice Hockey	Softball	Touch Football

OUTING ACTIVITIES

Bicycling	Hiking	Ice-Skating	Skiing
Camping	Hosteling	Nature Trailing	Tobogganning
Fishing	Hunting	Nature Craft	Woodcraft

2. PHYSICAL EDUCATION PROGRAM

The program of physical education is based upon certain fundamental skills of locomotion, body control, and control or handling of objects or equipment. The development of skill in dance, games, sports, gymnastics, and other activities is dependent upon skill in fundamental activities.

FUNDAMENTAL SKILLS

Locomotor Skills	*Body Control*	*Object Control*
Walking	Balancing	Handling
Running	Climbing	Rolling
Hopping	Hanging	Bouncing
Jumping	Swinging	Tossing
Leaping	Dodging	Throwing
Sliding	Pulling	Catching
Skipping	Pushing	Hitting
Galloping	Resisting	Kicking
Whirling	Relaxing	Batting

RHYTHMICAL ACTIVITIES

Fundamental Skills	*Rhythm Skills*	*Dance Forms*
Locomotor Movements	Dance Movements	Rhythms
Body Control	Steps and Patterns	Traditional Dances
Rhythmic Coordination	Composition	Current Dance Forms

GAMES, SPORTS, GYMNASTICS

Games	*Sports*	*Gymnastics*
Goal and Group	Aquatic	Apparatus
Simple or Modified Team	Individual and Dual	Corrective
Relays and Contests	Team	Conditioning
Stunts and Self-Testing	Winter and Outing	Tumbling

3. PHYSICAL EDUCATION PROGRAM—ELEMENTARY SCHOOL

Progressive development of physical education activities for elementary school children in a well-balanced program of instruction.

GRADES 1-3   GRADES 4-6

FUNDAMENTAL ACTIVITIES

1. Fundamental skills involving simple coordination in various activities.

2. Combinations of fundamental skills used in game and rhythmical activities.

1. Fundamental skills requiring increasingly difficult coordination and control.

2. Combined skills of locomotion, body control, and object-handling in games and rhythms.

Physical Education Program—Elementary School (cont'd)

Grades 1-3	Grades 4-6

RHYTHMICAL ACTIVITIES

1. Emphasis on fundamental skills in childhood rhythms and dances.	1. Folk, square, and social dances of increasing difficulty.
2. Dramatic and interpretative dance movements.	2. Combinations of movement requiring increasing skill.

GAMES, SPORTS, GYMNASTICS

1. Circle, group, and tag games and simple contests involving fundamental activities. Simple rules and equipment used.	1. Games and contests requiring skill. Modified team play and selected team games involving increasing skill and accuracy.
2. Gymnastic activities, including marching, stunts, simple forms of tumbling, and apparatus play on jungle gym equipment, balance beams, and boxes.	2. Stunts and selected tumbling activities. Elementary trampoline stunts.

RECREATION

1. Supervised play activities.	1. Supervised recreation.
2. Camping and outdoor education.	2. Camping and outdoor education.

COMPETITION

1. Lower grade intraschool play days involving group games and simple contests.	1. Play days within the school and with other local schools.
	2. Intramural competition in selected team games and individual sports.

4. PHYSICAL EDUCATION PROGRAM—JUNIOR AND SENIOR HIGH SCHOOL

The program of physical education for junior and senior high school boys and girls, including recreation and competition.

GRADES 7-9	GRADES 10-12

FUNDAMENTAL ACTIVITIES

1. Increasingly skillful performance of fundamental activities stressed.	1. Skillful performance and coordination emphasized through all activities in the program.
2. Coordination of skills required through games, sports, rhythms.	2. Increasingly skillful control and coordination involving accuracy, speed, and agility.

RHYTHMICAL ACTIVITIES

1. Various forms of dance, knowledge of steps and figures.	1. Wide variety of rhythmical activities. Skill standards requiring increasing ability.

Physical Education Program—Junior and Senior High School (cont'd)

Grades 7-9   Grades 10-12

RHYTHMICAL ACTIVITIES (CONT'D)

2. Square, folk, social and modern dance for both boys and girls.

2. Emphasis on social values of square, social, and folk dance in co-physical education classes. Modern dance for girls, and for both boys and girls in club and elective classes.

GAMES, SPORTS, GYMNASTICS

1. Introduction to a wide variety of team and individual sports.
2. Selected tumbling activities suitable to physical development. Selected gymnastic and apparatus exercises.

1. Development of skill in team and individual sports.
2. Development of increasing skill in tumbling. Perfection of skill in gymnastic and apparatus activities.

RECREATION

1. Supervised and student-led recreation activities.
2. Camping and outdoor programs.

1. Supervised and student-organized and -led recreation programs.
2. Camping and outdoor programs.

COMPETITION

1. Play days for boys and girls.
2. Intramural competition for boys and girls.

1. Play days for boys and girls.
2. Intramural competition for boys and girls.
3. Interscholastic competition for boys under careful supervision.

5. PHYSICAL EDUCATION PROGRAM—ALL GRADES

Activities and provisions that should be included in the program of physical education for all grades and for all school children.

INSTRUCTION

Recreational games and sports
Swimming (when facilities are available in school or community)
Outdoor education and camping
Co-physical education activities
Modified and restricted programs for physically handicapped children; body mechanics for all children
Health and safety

RECREATION

Supervised recreation
Supervised swimming
Camping out, camp activities
Over-night camping, day camping
School camping
Outing activities
Corecreational programs
Adapted recreational activities
Supervision and control of health and safety

The welfare of the individual is the teacher's fundamental consideration in selecting and conducting activities. The problems of body-contact sports, such as football and boxing for boys, and of interscholastic events for grade-school and junior-high-school boys and girls should be carefully evaluated. The American Association for Health, Physical Education and Recreation, in conjunction with health educators and medical consultants, has prepared standards for adequate programs and has formulated recommendations regarding interscholastic athletics for the elementary and secondary schools. The National Section for Girls' and Women's Sports has established standards for athletics for girls and women. Standards for programs of instruction, recreation, and interscholastic athletics have been determined by state and national groups as guides for the intelligent conduct of activities.

Educational practice indicates that instructional, intramural, and extramural activities should be incorporated in one coordinated program. The instructional program provides for learning, knowledge, and skill development in a wide variety of physical activities; the program of intramurals offers opportunities for voluntary participation of a recreational and competitive nature; the extramural program involves competition with and against pupils from other schools. Each part of the physical education program should be planned and conducted as an educational experience.

Health Education. The health needs of boys and girls are affected by their home background, nutritional status, provision for adequate medical and dental care, and other factors. Health education programs must provide for both individual and community requirements, and complete programs involve the cooperation of school, community, state, federal, and private-agency groups. The school health education program is usually composed of health service, efforts to provide and maintain a healthful school environment, and health instruction based on the needs of students. The list on p. 260 illustrates the pattern of school health education programs.

HEALTH EDUCATION [26]

SCHOOL HEALTH EDUCATION

Healthful School Living	*Health Services*	*Health Instruction*
1. SCHOOL ENVIRONMENT	1. APPRAISAL	1. Teaching of principles and facts of healthful living.
Lighting, heating, ventilation, cleaning, fire protection, safety, seating, water supply, and housekeeping.	Health examinations, tests and measures of health and development.	Presentation of the facts of science and the art of living.
2. SCHOOL ORGANIZATION	2. REMEDIAL	
Schedules, rest and activity periods, time allotments, overcrowding, school lunch, individual differences.	Follow-up services, correction of remediable defects.	2. Integration of health knowledge with actual living and personal achievement.
	3. PROTECTIVE	
3. PUPIL-TEACHER RELATIONSHIPS	Immunizations, first aid, control of contagion through medical and non-medical procedures, sight-conservation and adjustment service for mental, emotional and physical disturbances.	Facts are not enough. There must be the motive to live at one's best, to use the facts, and to live the knowledge.
Discipline, fatigue, home work, pressure.		3. Guidance of children in healthful living in school, home and community with opportunity for growth in self-direction....

The problems of medical and dental service as a part of school programs, of payment for treatment of school children, of the direct responsibility for health instruction, of the content of health courses, and of providing for more health specialists in school systems are receiving attention by health educators. The eventual solution of these and other problems will make possible greater advancements in school health education.

Recreation. Recreation programs should meet the needs and interests of everyone from the preschool child playing in the sand box to the seventy-year-old on the horseshoe court, from the industrial worker to the housewife, and from the handicapped person to the highly skilled person. An adequate community recreation program should provide a variety of recreational activities such as those in the accompanying list.

[26] Jesse Feiring Williams and C. L. Brownell, *The Administration of Health Education and Physical Education,* 4th ed. (Philadelphia: W. B. Saunders Co., 1951), p. 17. (Reprinted by permission.)

RECREATION PROGRAM

A recreation program provides for instruction, leadership, self-organized groups, and the organization of tournaments, meets, and other special events.

ARTS AND CRAFTS

Basketry	Jewelry	Plastic Craft
Ceramics	Leather Work	Sculpturing
Drawing	Metal Craft	Wood-Carving
Design	Painting	Wood-Working

CAMPING, OUTING, NATURE STUDY

Adult Camping	Hiking and Climbing	Wildlife Study
Family Camping	Hunting and Fishing	Woods Lore
Youth Camping	Nature Trailing	Woodcraft

CLUB GROUPS

Adult Clubs	Organization Clubs	Youth Clubs
Boys' and Girls' Clubs	Special-Interest Clubs	Young People's Clubs
Business Clubs	Social Clubs	Octogenarian Clubs

DANCE, SPORTS, GYMNASTICS

Aquatics	Individual and Dual Sports	Tournaments
Dance	Team Sports	Meets
Games	Outing Activities	City-wide League Play
Gymnastics	Turnverein Clubs	Special Events
Rehabilitation	Sport Clubs	Health Classes

DRAMATIC AND LITERARY

Book Review Groups	Play-Acting	Speech Correction
Dramatic Production	Radio	Television
Language Study	Stagecraft	Verse-Reading

HOMEMAKING

Baby-Sitting Clubs	Food Preparation	Family Clinics
Child Care	Home Planning	Family Living
Child Clinics	Interior Decoration	Family Recreation
Costume Design	Landscaping	Social Life

MUSIC

Conducting	Instrumental Music	Voice Study
Community and Group Singing	Choir and Glee Clubs	Concerts
Music Appreciation	Orchestra and Band	Recitals

SOCIAL ACTIVITIES

Card Parties	Dances	Hoedowns
Community Picnics	Game Parties	Social Events

Planning a program of recreation for a community or for a school requires the cooperation of a large number of people. The recreation program for a school should include such activities as dramatics, recreational music, arts and crafts, interest clubs devoted to language study, science, photography, nature study, and social activities—as well as a variety of active sports, games, and dancing.

Facilities and equipment

The lack of adequate facilities and sufficient equipment necessitates modifications and adaptations. The teacher or leader must be capable of developing a well-balanced program within the limitations of the available space and equipment. The provisions for physical education and recreation in well-planned, modern school buildings represent great strides toward a satisfactory solution of the needs for suitable indoor and outdoor space for physical education activities. In contrast, many schools, both old and new, still have insufficient space, poorly planned areas, or an entire lack of facilities for physical education. The vision, energy, and enthusiasm of young teachers of physical education must be directed toward securing the best possible facilities and equipment in the schools of tomorrow. Even though recreation facilities provided by community, state, and federal agencies are becoming increasingly important to community welfare, bigger and better-equipped playgrounds, parks and other facilities are still needed. Cooperation and coordination are essential in making all of the facilities of public and private agencies available for educational and recreational programs of all types.

SUMMARY

Professional leadership in physical education, health education, and recreation involves a recognition of the meaning and purposes of the programs. It is acknowledged that all are important parts of education. Every person employed in these fields is responsible for providing the kind of leadership that will result in the realization of the purposes of education and in more effective living.

College life and student activities, as well as professional study, contribute to leadership qualifications. Each student should accept every opportunity to enrich his understandings of people, develop social and emotional maturity, and acquire leadership experience. The well-qualified teacher and leader knows his subject thoroughly, is capable of establishing good relationships with children, knows how to plan and conduct a well-rounded program, is able to make effective use of available facilities and equipment, and recognizes that his profession is an integral part of education.

The leader in physical education, health education, or recreation who makes a real contribution to his profession possesses a combination of knowledge, experience, and imagination. He is prepared to see beyond details and daily routine and to develop ideas and new procedures. He provides democratic leadership and encourages cooperative participation by other staff members and by boys and girls in the planning and conduct of the program. Aware of the future and of long-range objectives, he does not lose his perspective in his concern with immediate problems.

In the final analysis the determining factor governing what is accomplished must be sought in the person who is doing the job. The leader who is trained, competent, and convinced of the value of his work can and does make available a program based on individual needs and on a philosophy directed toward the maximum good of all participants.

SUGGESTED PROBLEMS

1. Write a statement expressing your own philosophy of your profession, what you believe it means, and what you feel it should accomplish. You may include all three areas or select the one in which you are specializing. Start your statement with the words: "I believe that physical education . . . ."

2. Make a list of the objectives you believe were set up for your high-school health and physical education programs. Indicate the provisions that you believe were made for:
   a. Health and safety
   b. Skill development
   c. Leadership
   d. Social and emotional development

3. Get opinions from five people who are not professional leaders on the values of the services rendered through programs of physical education, health education, and recreation. Summarize these opinions and state in your own words whether you believe they are based on fact and complete information.

4. Write a statement on the function of leadership.

5. What is the educational role of programs in physical education, health education, and recreation?

6. What health guidance should be given through a physical education program?

7. Study professional physical education curriculums to determine how much health preparation is included.

8. Observe several physical education classes and report the health and safety practices followed by students.

9. Find several definitions of health and health education. Write in your own words a definition that incorporates the most significant points of those you have selected.

10. Study an elementary-school child and list his health practices and observable attitudes.

11. What is the relationship of health education to other objectives of education?

12. Do you believe that recreational education should be included in an elementary-school program? If so, what activities would you include in the program? If not, state specifically why you hold that opinion.

REFERENCES

Ainsworth, Dorothy A., "Contributions of Physical Education to the Social Service Agency," *Journal of the American Association for Health, Physical Education and Recreation,* 21:325, June 1950.

Allen, Catherine, "Training Student Leaders in Group Recreation," *Journal of the American Association for Health, Physical Education and Recreation,* 20:315, May 1949.

Anderson, George F., "Psychological Aspects of Teaching Physical Education," *Journal of the American Association for Health, Physical Education and Recreation,* 21:152, March 1950.

Bennett, Bruce L., "Physical Education and Learning in the Secondary School," *Journal of the American Association for Health, Physical Education and Recreation,* 20:452, September 1949.

Brace, David K., "The Contribution of Physical Education to Total Education," *Journal of the American Association for Health, Physical Education, and Recreation,* 20:635, December 1949.

Brightbill, C. K., and H. D. Meyer, *Recreation: Text and Readings.* New York: Prentice-Hall, Inc., 1953.

Brownell, Clifford, *Principles of Health Education Applied.* New York: McGraw-Hill Book Co., 1949.

Bucher, Charles A., *Foundations of Physical Education.* St. Louis: The C. V. Mosby Co., 1952.

———, with Tim Cohane, "Little League Baseball Can Hurt Your Boy," *Look,* 17:74, August 11, 1953.

Corbin, H. Dan, *Recreation Leadership.* New York: Prentice-Hall, Inc., 1953.

Cowell, Charles A., "Guidance Functions and Possibilities of Physical Education," *Journal of the American Association for Health, Physical Education and Recreation,* 20:238, April 1949.

Davis, E. C., and John D. Lawther, *Successful Teaching in Physical Education,* 2d ed. New York: Prentice-Hall, Inc., 1948.

Duggan, Anne Schley, "The Place of Dance in the School Physical Education Program," *Journal of the American Association for Health, Physical Education and Recreation,* 22:26, March 1951.

Duncan, Ray O., "It's Important to Win that Game," *Illinois Education,* 37:161, January 1949.

Forsythe, Charles E., *Administration of High School Athletics,* 2d ed. New York: Prentice-Hall, Inc., 1948.

———, and R. O. Duncan, *Administration of Physical Education.* New York: Prentice-Hall, Inc., 1951.

Gloss, George M., "Physical Education—The Total Approach," *Journal of the American Association for Health, Physical Education and Recreation,* 21:288, May 1950.

Grout, Ruth E., *Health Teaching in Schools,* 2d ed. Philadelphia: W. B. Saunders Company, 1953.

Grubb, Lena, "Camping is Education," *Journal of Health and Physical Education,* 14:266, May 1943.

Hodgkins, Jean, "Making Use of Student Leaders," *Journal of the American Association for Health, Physical Education and Recreation,* 21:222, April 1950.

Hoyman, H. S., H. A. Gordon, and P. F. Ervin, *Functional Health Teaching.* Goshen, Indiana: McConnell School Map Co., Inc., 1950.

Hughes, William L., "The Place of Athletics in the School Physical Education Program," *Journal of the American Association for Health, Physical Education and Recreation,* 21:23, December 1950.

Johnson, Sara M., "Physical Education Program in the Elementary School," *Journal of the American Association for Health, Physical Education and Recreation,* 20:380, June 1949.

Kendig, Robert C., "A Physical Education Program for All Students," *Journal of Health and Physical Education,* 18:170, December 1947.

Mack, Barbara, "A Dance Approach to Education," *Journal of the American Association for Health, Physical Education and Recreation,* 20:640, December 1949.

Nash, Jay B., "The Contributions of Physical Education to Recreation," *Journal of the American Association for Health, Physical Education and Recreation,* 22:53, October 1951.

————, F. H. Moench, and J. B. Saurborn, *Physical Education: Organization and Administration.* New York: A. S. Barnes and Co., 1951.

Nixon, Eugene W., and Frederick W. Cozens, *An Introduction to Physical Education,* 3d ed. Philadelphia: W. B. Saunders Co., 1952.

Oberteuffer, Delbert, "Some Contributions of Physical Education to an Educated Life," *Journal of Health and Physical Education,* 16:3, January 1945.

————, "Sportsmanship—Whose Responsibility?," *Journal of Health and Physical Education,* 19:543, October 1948.

"The Place of Camping in Education," *Journal of the American Association for Health, Physical Education and Recreation,* 21:5, January 1950.

Rogers, James E., "Physical Education in Education," *Journal of Health and Physical Education,* 19:560, December 1940.

Rugen, Mabel, "Physical Education's Contribution to Health Education," *Journal of the American Association for Health, Physical Education and Recreation,* 22:25, June 1951.

Scott, Harry A., *Competitive Sports in Schools and Colleges.* New York: Harper and Brothers, 1951.

Staley, S. C., *Curriculum in Sports.* Champaign, Illinois: Stipes Publishing Co., 1940.

Van Dalen, D. B., E. D. Mitchell, and B. L. Bennett, *A World History of Physical Education.* New York: Prentice-Hall, Inc., 1953.

Wilson, Charles C., ed., *Health Education* (Joint Committee Report of the National Education Association and American Medical Association), 4th ed. Washington, D. C.: The Association, 1948.

Wilson, Julie, "Dance Education for the Growing Child," *Journal of Health and Physical Education,* 19:326, May 1948.

Wolfson, Bernice J., "Dance—A Medium of Education," *Journal of the American Association for Health, Physical Education and Recreation,* 21:50, September 1950.

RECOMMENDED STANDARDS AND POLICIES

"Cardinal Athletic Principles," *Journal of Health and Physical Education,* 18:435, September 1947.

The National Conference on Undergraduate Professional Preparation in Health Education, Physical Education and Recreation. Chicago: The Athletic Institute, 1948.

National Facilities Conference, *A Guide for Planning Facilities for Athletics, Recreation, Physical and Health Education*. Chicago: The Athletic Institute, 1947.

"A Platform for Physical Education," *Journal of the American Association for Health, Physical Education and Recreation*, 21:136, March 1950.

School Athletics, Problems and Policies. Washington, D. C.: Educational Policies Commission, National Education Association and the American Association of School Administrators, 1954.

Standards for Guiding Competition by Girls and Women in Various Sports. Washington, D. C.: National Section for Girls' and Women's Sports of the American Association for Health, Physical Education and Recreation, 1948.

Standards in Athletics for Boys in Secondary Schools. Prepared by the Joint Committee on Standards for Interscholastic Athletics of the National Association of Secondary School Principals, National Federation of State High School Athletic Associations. Washington, D. C.: American Association for Health, Physical Education and Recreation, 1949.

Standards in Athletics for Girls and Women, rev. ed. Washington, D. C.: National Section for Girls' and Women's Sports of the American Association for Health, Physical Education and Recreation, 1948.

"Suggested School Health Policies (Part III) ," *Journal of Health and Physical Education*, 17:144, March 1946.

Sampson, F. H., ... [partially illegible header text]
... Enterprises, Inc., Publishers ... Chicago, Illinois,
1954, pp. 129.

A Program for Physical Education ...

Courtesy of MacMurray College

CHAPTER NINE

The nature
of a profession

The term *vocation* has been used to indicate an occupation requiring educational preparation in contrast to occupations in which it is possible to perform acceptable work with little or no preparation. An intelligent choice of a vocation may be based on special aptitudes which provide a means of earning an acceptable living or of accumulating wealth. Equally intelligent selection may result from interests and abilities which represent opportunities for making significant contributions to society. Some vocations are dignified as professions by virtue of the standards they represent, the qualifications of their members, and the services they render.

In order to become recognized as a profession an occupation must meet certain qualifications that have become established as characteristics of the standards of professional groups of people. Few professions meet all of the requirements. The degree to which teaching and leadership meet professional standards is presented briefly in this chapter.

CHARACTERISTICS OF A PROFESSION

The characteristics that distinguish a profession from other occupations include the following points:

1. The members of a profession are motivated by an ideal of service to others.

2. The ability to practice a profession is dependent upon intellectual learning, mastery of a specific body of knowledge, and

the development of skill in personal performance and in the use of equipment and other materials essential to professional services.

3. The completion of a specified period of preparation in supervised study, learning, and practice are requirements for membership in a profession. As a member of a profession a person is permitted to conduct professional work under his own direction.

4. The professional group has responsibility for recruiting prospective members, determining qualifications for membership, and improving standards of competency.

5. The group must enjoy an economic and social status sufficient to attract and hold persons of high intellectual and personal qualities to permanent careers in that profession.

6. A profession has a code of ethics that is observed by the majority of its members.

7. A profession is officially recognized by the government of the people it serves.

8. The profession maintains effective relationships with other groups in society, particularly in shaping public policy relating to the services of the profession.[1]

The degree to which any group meets the qualifications will determine its status as a profession. Many groups not recognized as professions meet a number of the specifications. Some profes-

---

[1] For further information see the following references:

Elmer D. Mitchell, "Physical Education as a Profession," *The Physical Educator,* 2:98-101, February 1942.

George E. Hill, "The Teaching Profession and the Public," *School and Society,* November 21, 1948, p. 56.

Alan Krim, "Recreation, A Developing Profession," *Recreation,* 38:300, September 1944.

Robert H. Morrison, "Teaching *Is* a Profession," *Journal of the National Education Association,* 39:202, March 1950.

Harry A. Scott, "Physical Education, Health Education, and Recreation as Professions," *Lecture* (New York: Teachers College, Columbia University, 1948).

R. Bruce Raup, Kenneth D. Benne, and R. Freeman Butts, *Summary of Topics: Vocation in Human Development* (New York: Teachers College, Columbia University, 1948).

Harold H. Titus, *Ethics for Today* (New York: American Book Company, 1947), pp. 296-298.

sional bodies that meet requirements sufficiently to be granted professional standing need improvements to raise the standards of the group to the highest possible level.

THE SIGNIFICANCE OF TEACHING AND LEADERSHIP

Teaching is one of the oldest of the learned professions. The first teachers were the primitive people who instructed the young in the ways of their society, and taught them survival skills. The first physical educator was the parent who taught his son to run, throw, protect himself, and engage in feats of daring and strength. The initiation of young people into the adult activities of the tribe was accomplished by the older men and women.

As civilization developed, scholars guided young men toward achievement in literature, science, the arts, and government. The influence of the early philosophers, artists, and scientists was extended through their pupils. The great Greek scholars gathered a few youths around them and instructed them in the mysteries of philosophy, astronomy, and medicine. When instruction in the arts, sports and music, games, and physical beauty became a part of the education of young citizens of ancient Greece, the foundations were laid for later systems of education and teaching.[2]

Recreation is as old as man and man's leisure time has always been devoted in part to sports and games.[3] Similar games are played in all parts of the world. The games of the ancient oriental countries, those of the South American Indians, and those of the modern European countries are all strikingly similar. The toys and playthings of the children are universal. Recreation as

[2] Jesse Feiring Williams, *The Principles of Physical Education*, 5th ed. rev. (Philadelphia: W. B. Saunders Co., 1949), pp. 3-4; Eugene W. Nixon and Frederick W. Cozens, *An Introduction to Physical Education*, 4th ed. (Philadelphia: W. B. Saunders Co., 1952), p. 271; R. Freeman Butts, *The College Charts Its Course* (New York: McGraw-Hill Book Co., Inc., 1939), pp. 20-28.

[3] Elmer D. Mitchell and Bernard S. Mason, *The Theory of Play* (New York: A. S. Barnes & Co., Inc., 1949), pp. 11-35.

a community and public activity, however, is comparatively recent.

Teaching has occupied a place of esteem in every era of civilization in which cultural advances have been made. It has been recognized as one of the traditional fields of service to man, in company with medicine, law, and theology. Recently other fields of work have become recognized as professions. The growth of new professions is shown by the fact that in 1870 approximately three-fourths of all professional workers were engaged in either teaching, medicine, law, or the ministry. In 1940 these areas of work included only about one-half of the people engaged in professions.[4] Professional leadership in recreation has paralleled technological developments since 1900, reflecting the relation between technical and scientific advances and increased leisure. The National Recreation Association was founded in 1906. Organized recreation programs requiring specialized professional leadership have become firmly established in the past 40 years, and college preparation of recreation leaders has developed since 1930.[5]

It is reasonable to question the effect of increased opportunities for professional work on the status of teaching and leadership. Surveys indicate that, in spite of the wide number of fields from which to select careers, teaching and leadership rank high in the opinion of the public as professions for young men and women. A nationwide study made in 1950 showed that teaching ranked second only to nursing as a recommended choice for women. A companion survey indicated that teaching as a profession for men rated seventh, below medicine, engineering, business, ministry, law, and government careers.[6] Recreation

4 Cora E. Taylor, "Current Issues in Education for the Professions," *Current Issues in Higher Education 1950* (Washington, D. C.: Department of Higher Education, National Education Association, 1950), p. 87.

5 Gerald B. Fitzgerald, "Recreation as Your Career," *Journal of the American Association for Health, Physical Education and Recreation*, 23:27, November, 1952.

6 George Gallup, "Nursing, Teaching Rated Number 1 and 2 in Professions," syndicated report appearing in *The* (Bloomington, Illinois) *Pantagraph*, July 15, 1950.

leadership as a profession is historically so new that it is difficult to evaluate its status in relationship to other professions.[7]

THE STATUS OF TEACHING AND PROFESSIONAL LEADERSHIP

The degree to which teaching and leadership meet the qualifications for a profession is best determined by an investigation of their standards and purposes as compared to the requirements for a profession.

Service to people

Education and recreation affect the daily lives of people, their work, and their recreational and cultural activities. Leaders and teachers are concerned with helping young people to learn to take their places in society, to realize their own capabilities, and to become good citizens. The individual teacher or leader must possess the ideal of service if he is to contribute to the development of children, the improvement of educational opportunities for all, and the betterment of society.

Mastery of knowledges and skills

The education of teachers and leaders involves wide areas of knowledge in the methods and techniques of teaching, and the processes through which learning takes place. Personal skill in activities, the ability to demonstrate, and the effective use of the materials and equipment associated with the particular field are necessary qualifications. In addition, teachers and leaders need an intelligent grasp of cultural and scientific developments and an understanding of the democratic principles of our society to carry out effectively the functions of education and recreation.

Preparation required for qualification

A minimum of four years of undergraduate work in an accredited institution is required for full certification of teachers.

[7] Harold D. Meyer and Charles K. Brightbill, *Community Recreation* (Boston: D. C. Heath and Co., 1948), pp. 663-674.

In some states teachers may secure a provisional teaching certificate since the shortage of teachers has made it necessary to employ teachers who lack adequate professional preparation. The certification standards for *all* teachers should include the minimum of four years of college work, special preparation in professional education, student teaching, and a Bachelor's degree.[8]

Standards for recreation leaders have been developed and are becoming more and more specific. There has been no actual provision for certification as yet, but a trend in that direction can be noted. Many of the larger cities have established civil service examinations and qualifications for employment as recreational leaders. The basic requirement is graduation from an approved four-year recreation curriculum in which attention has been given to all phases of a recreation program. Field work and practical experience are generally required.

Responsibility for recruitment and certification

The problem of interesting capable young men and women in the profession is recognized as a responsibility of the members of the teaching profession. The standards for the selection of prospective workers have been recommended by professional groups and are acknowledged as a direct concern of the profession. The desirable qualities in teachers have been determined, and educational programs have been developed to prepare competent teachers and leaders.[9] In-service programs provide advanced study and experimentation as a contribution to professional competencies.

The certification of teachers is a joint responsibility of the state and the profession. Standards proposed for accrediting institutions preparing teachers are in keeping with consistent efforts of the profession to secure more adequate preparation for

8 James H. Griggs, "Current Problems in the Preparation of the Elementary and Secondary Teachers," *Current Trends in Higher Education, 1949,* pp. 76-77.
9 Warren C. Lovinger, "General Education for the Prospective Teacher," *Current Trends in Higher Education, 1948,* pp. 93-95.

all prospective teachers.[10] It is unfortunate that standards for certification of teachers vary widely and in some states are below those recommended by the profession. It was estimated that only about 60 per cent of the teachers in the United States had Bachelor's degrees as recently as 1950, and that less than 25 per cent of the states required a Bachelor's degree and professional preparation for elementary-school teaching, although almost all states required the Bachelor's degree for certification to teach in the secondary schools.[11] In respect to certification the teaching profession needs definite improvement.

The professional preparation of recreation leaders has developed as an individual effort on the part of faculties of colleges and universities. Accreditation and certification procedures are lacking but national recreation groups are beginning to recommend standards for preparation and certification of recreation leaders.

Code of Ethics

The code of ethics of the National Education Association has been developed as a result of years of effort by national leaders in education. The majority of states and Hawaii and Puerto Rico have officially adopted either the NEA code or ones similar to it. Special codes of ethics or statements of procedure have been prepared by physical education, health education, and recreation groups.[12]

Education, public welfare, and recreation a government concern

Although the terms *education* and *school* do not appear in the Constitution of the United States, the responsibility of government for education has long been recognized. The Tenth Amendment to the Constitution made the function of education

---

10 American Association of Colleges for Teacher Education, *Third Year Book, 1950*, p. 114.

11 Earl Armstrong, "Current Issues in the Preparation of Teachers for the Elementary and Secondary Schools," *Current Issues in Higher Education, 1950*, pp. 94-95.

12 See Appendix B for codes of ethics.

the responsibility of the individual states. The total program of education must be considered a national system of education since all of the agencies concerned with education form an educational undertaking on a nationwide scale.

The United States Office of Education is the official educational agency of the federal government. This office is responsible for collecting facts about schools, disseminating information of value to people engaged in educational work, and promoting the cause of education. Special appropriations for the support of vocational education and vocational rehabilitation and for land-grant colleges are distributed through the Office of Education.[13]

State and local governments appropriate money for school purposes, including the salaries for teachers and the funds for retirement programs. The responsibility of the state to promote and finance adequate educational opportunities in local districts is acknowledged universally. Great improvements are needed in the way of more and better schools, better salaries for teachers, and more adequate retirement programs.

Recreation has become accepted as a basic need of all people. Individuals have always participated in recreational activities on a personal basis, but recently government agencies have taken a part in the promotion and conduct of recreation programs. The federal and state governments, through the provision of parks, forests, and playgrounds, have accepted a responsibility for recreation, and municipalities have assumed a major role through tax-supported programs of recreation.[14]

Economic and social status

Teachers' salaries were among the lowest paid to professional groups until the educational crisis following World War II awakened the public, the press, and the government to the need

---

[13] Chris A. DeYoung, *Introduction to American Public Education* (New York: McGraw-Hill Book Co., Inc., 1950), pp. 23-26.

[14] George D. Butler, *Introduction to Community Recreation* (New York: McGraw-Hill Book Co., Inc., 1949), pp. 10-76; Harold D. Meyer and Charles K. Brightbill, *Community Recreation* (Boston: D. C. Heath & Co., 1948), pp. 59-125.

for providing economic security for teachers. Many teachers and recreation leaders failed to return to their regular work following service in the armed forces, work in industry, or research duties on government projects during the war. The resulting shortages, combined with increased school enrollments and enlarged recreation programs, have endangered the progress of education and recreation throughout the nation. In order to encourage young men and women to enter these professions and stay in them, salaries, tenure, working conditions, and retirement provisions have been improved, and all these factors show indications of further advancement.[15] The public has realized to what extent teachers and recreation leaders are responsible for the welfare of the youth of the country, and the importance of these fields to the democratic way of life.

The social status of members of the professions of teaching and recreation has improved with the recognition of the worth of educational and recreational programs.[16] The popular attitude toward teachers is well expressed in the following quotation:

> So let us look with renewed respect on those teachers who are sticking to their profession. In them rests the full responsibility for a growing generation's understanding of our Bill of Rights— and of the teachings of Washington, Jefferson, Lincoln, and our other great, great, men. To our teachers, then, in whose hands lie some of the work of holding the peace, may I express an entire Nation's heartfelt thanks.[17]

Relationships with other groups

Teachers, leaders, and professional organizations are taking an increasingly active part in the affairs of public life. Members

[15] Benjamin W. Frazier, *Teaching as a Career,* Bulletin 1947, No. 11, Federal Security Agency, Office of Education (Washington, D. C.: Government Printing Office, 1947), p. 21.

[16] "The Status of the Teaching Profession," *Research Bulletin of the National Education Association,* 18:49, March 1940.

[17] Don Ameche, as quoted in E. E. Samuelson *et al., You'd Like Teaching* (Ellensburg, Washington: Central College of Washington, 1946), p. 9. (Reprinted by permission.)

are concerned with the problems of the communities in which they work, and in promotional programs for the advancement of education, public welfare, and recreation. Employees as a group contribute time, energy, and leadership to programs of Parent-Teacher Associations, welfare organizations, and agencies concerned with youth programs, to community programs of education and recreation for out-of-school youth and adults, and to many other civic undertakings.

The following conclusions may be drawn about the professional status of teaching and leadership:

1. Both fulfill many of the conditions established as characteristics of a profession.

2. Certification of persons who have not met minimum standards of preparation and employment of poorly prepared teachers lower the professional quality of the work.[18]

3. Inadequate salaries, areas in which tenure and retirement provisions are nonexistent or insufficient, and social restrictions imposed by some communities tend to discourage capable young men and women from entering these professions. Great improvements are needed in these areas.[19]

4. Prospective teachers, teachers in schools, recreation leaders and groups, and educational organizations must continue to maintain professional standards and promote an understanding by the general public of the professional nature of their work. Constant effort must be expended by teachers and leaders toward improving all aspects of teaching and leadership and the preparation for these professions. All have a definite responsibility for encouraging capable young men and women to enter the profession.

5. Institutions offering professional programs must provide the kind of curriculum that will prepare prospective teachers and leaders to enter the field with high qualifications. College

18 Earl Armstrong, "Current Issues in the Preparation of Teachers," p. 94.

19 For further information on points 3, 4, and 5 see report by the Commission on Teacher Education, Karl W. Bigelow, director, *The Improvement of Teacher Education* (Washington, D. C.: American Council on Education, 1946), pp. 263, 73-75, and 107, 112 respectively.

and university teachers should be well qualified through experience and advanced study to carry on the program of professional
education.[20]

STATUS OF PHYSICAL EDUCATION,
HEALTH EDUCATION, AND RECREATION

The professional areas of physical education, health education,
and recreation meet the requirements of a profession as a part
of the total field of teaching and social service. In addition, they

Courtesy of University of Illinois

make specific contributions to the teaching profession and possess certain attributes of their own that fulfill many of the requirements for professional standing. The intellectual compre-
hension of a definite body of knowledge and mastery of specific

[20] *Higher Education for American Democracy*, Report of the President's Commission on Higher Education (New York: Harper and Bros., 1949), vol. i, pp.
77-89, and vol. ii, p. 60; Harold D. Meyer and Charles K. Brightbill, *Community
Recreation* (Boston: D. C. Heath & Co., 1948), pp. 669-670.

skills, methods, equipment, and materials are required before
a person is qualified to teach physical education and health education or to conduct recreation programs. Physical education,
health, and recreation programs, whether conducted for schools
or for out-of-school groups, are important and require expert
leadership.

National committees, working cooperatively with other educational groups, have developed standards for undergraduate
preparation and graduate study in physical education, health
education, and recreation.[21] Local and state physical education
groups work closely with state departments of education on certification requirements. Reputable teacher education departments aid in fulfilling certification requirements through constant study and improvement of the curriculum for teachers.
Recreation personnel work cooperatively through the National
Recreation Association, The American Recreation Society, and
state groups to develop standards for employment and professional work. The stated purposes of the American Recreation
Society include the following:

1. To unite in one organization all recreational workers in
America.

2. To foster and to maintain high standards of professional
qualifications.

3. To foster and to maintain high standards of professional
ethics.

4. To encourage and promote adequate programs of professional training for recreation workers.[22]

In keeping with the professional nature of the organization,
the American Association for Health, Physical Education and
Recreation has adopted the Code of Ethics for Teachers of the

21 *National Conference on Undergraduate Professional Preparation in Physical
Education, Health Education, and Recreation* (Chicago: The Athletic Institute,
1948); *Graduate Study in Health Education, Physical Education, and Recreation*
(Chicago: The Athletic Institute, 1950); Participants in National Recreation
Workshop, *Recreation for Community Living: Guiding Principles* (Chicago: The
Athletic Institute, 1952).

22 *Everyone Needs Recreation,* Bulletin of the American Recreation Society,
Inc. (Washington, D. C.: 1953), p. 2.

National Education Association and has prepared a code of ethics for physical education teachers.[23] The Association and affiliated organizations, in cooperation with other educational groups and the United States Office of Education, promote a program of international relations to create better opportunities and understandings among nations.[24] The basic principles of the United Nations Educational, Scientific and Cultural Organization have been accepted by the Association. The Pan-American Institute of Physical Education [25] and the International Congress on Essentials of Physical Education for Youth represent accomplishments in international cooperation.

Physical education, health education, and recreation fulfill many of the characteristics of a profession and meet the same requirements of professional status as the total teaching profession. As educational opportunities are increased, as economic and social provisions for all teachers and leaders improve, the professional status of physical educators, health educators, and recreation leaders will be strengthened.

THE TEACHER AND LEADER

The strength of a profession lies in its individual members, and in their contribution to the professional growth of the entire group. Teachers of physical education or health education and recreation leaders become qualified by virtue of their preparation for membership in their profession. As a teacher or coach in a school or college; as a leader in community, camp, youth organization, hospital, or industrial recreation programs; as an educational or recreational worker in the military services, the individual member exerts an influence that affects the professional standing of the group he represents.

[23] "Suggested Code of Ethics for Teachers of Physical Education," *Journal of the American Association for Health, Physical Education and Recreation,* 21:323, June 1950.

[24] "Conference on International Relations," *Journal of the American Association for Health, Physical Education and Recreation,* 21:25, November 1950.

[25] "Pan-American Institute of Physical Education," *Journal of the American Association for Health, Physical Education and Recreation,* 22:30, March 1951.

The teacher serves as a key person in relationships within the school and in the community. The teacher of physical education or health education is concerned with the entire school program and with environmental influences as they affect the boys and girls he teaches. Contacts with children, youth, and adults create many opportunities for leadership and guidance. Teaching influences the attitudes, skills, social and emotional development, and physical and mental health of every person with whom the teacher works. As a professional person the teacher in the physical education and health areas holds an important place in the life of the school and the community, and is responsible for upholding the highest standards of the teaching profession.

The recreation leader provides the professional leadership necessary to bring together all the efforts of governmental agencies, voluntary groups, and individuals contributing to the total program of community recreation. The leader works for a broader concept and acceptance of recreation on the part of all people and seeks to secure greater understanding of the need for recreation in daily living. The professional leadership provided through personal efforts and through encouragement of public assistance is responsible for the place of recreation in American life.

SUMMARY

The professional nature of teaching and leadership becomes apparent when its characteristics are compared with the qualifications for professions. Teaching touches upon all areas of human life in its service to people, and is devoted primarily to school experiences. The importance of teaching to the American way of life and to the preservation of democracy requires high standards of professional preparation and the ability to perform professional duties with competence. Recreational leadership contributes greatly to the ever-increasing out-of-school and leisure hours of young and old.

The outlook for these professions is promising. The public is aware as never before of the necessity for increasing the security of teachers and leaders through improved salaries, tenure, and retirement provisions. Community acceptance of teachers and leaders as professional persons has resulted in the removal of social restrictions in the large majority of situations. It has been recognized that the future in these areas must be made more attractive in order to interest the most capable young men and women.

Teachers of physical education and health education and recreation leaders have a twofold responsibility. They must accept the standards of their profession and meet the requirements and qualifications established for them. In addition, they are also members of a professional group, and must be capable of making the specific contributions unique to these areas of service.

Many improvements are needed before teaching and recreation leadership will reach the highest possible status as professions. In the meantime, the teachers and leaders of today continue to carry on the traditions of professional work that are as old as man and through which man retains the culture of previous generations and passes on his own accomplishments to those who follow.

SUGGESTED PROBLEMS

1. Read the sportsmanship codes in Appendix B. How do they relate to ethical conduct? Present several examples.

2. Study the purposes and pledge of the Future Teachers of America in Appendices B and C. In what way does this organization promote professional standards for teachers? Why is it important for prospective teachers to understand and accept professional standards?

3. Study the Code of Ethics for Teachers of the National Education Association in Appendix B. Indicate the points that affect the personal relationships between members of the teaching profession. In what ways have your teachers shown professional courtesy toward each other?

4. What statements apply particularly to professional growth of teachers? In what ways?

5. Study the platform and statement of policy of the major recreation associations (see Appendix C). How do these statements reflect the items listed on pp. 269-270 as essential to a profession?

6. What are some of the things that each undergraduate student preparing to become a teacher or recreation leader should start practicing in order to insure meeting professional standards? How can you gain experience and skill in the use of such standards in college?

7. Is it important to future teachers to understand the professional nature of teaching? Why?

REFERENCES

Committee on Vocational Guidance, "Physical Education as a Profession," *Research Quarterly of the American Association for Health, Physical Education and Recreation,* 13:131, May 1942.

DeGroot, Dudley S., "Are We Ignoring Coaching as a Profession?," *Journal of the American Association for Health, Physical Education and Recreation,* 21:30, December 1950.

Department of Classroom Teachers and Research Division, National Education Association, *Ethics for Teachers,* Discussion Pamphlet No. 5. Washington, D. C.: The Association, 1945.

————, *Salary Scheduling,* Discussion Pamphlet No. 8. Washington, D. C.: The Association, 1946.

————, *Teacher Leaves of Absence,* Discussion Pamphlet No. 7. Washington, D. C.: The Association, 1945.

————, *Teacher Tenure,* Discussion Pamphlet No. 1 (rev.). Washington, D. C.: The Association, 1947.

Fitzgerald, Gerald B., "Recreation as Your Career," *Journal of the American Association for Health, Physical Education and Recreation,* 23:27, November 1952.

Future Teachers of America Yearbook. Washington, D. C.: National Education Association, published annually.

Hill, George E., "The Teaching Profession and the Public," *School and Society.* 56:36, November 21, 1948.

Kauffman, Earl, Jr., "Is Recreation a Profession?," *Journal of the American Association for Health, Physical Education and Recreation.* 20:515, October 1949.

Krakower, Hyman, "Recognition of Physical Education as a Profession," *Journal of the American Association for Health, Physical Education and Recreation.* 20:578, November 1949.

Krim, Alan, "Recreation, A Developing Profession," *Recreation,* 38:300, September 1944.

Life Magazine: Special Education Issue, 29:16, October 16, 1950.

Lindsay, Margaret, "Ask Yourself Some Questions," *Journal of the National Education Association.* 40:173, March 1951.

Meyer, Harold D., and Charles K. Brightbill, *Community Recreation,* pp. 7-59, 663-676. Boston: D. C. Heath and Company, 1948.

Mitchell, Elmer D., "Physical Education as a Profession," *The Physical Educator,* 2:98, February 1942.

Rautman, Arthur L., "The Physical Education Teacher as a Personal Model," *Journal of the American Association for Health, Physical Education and Recreation*, 21:10, January 1950.

Uhler, William P., Jr., "On Being A Teacher of Physical Education," *Journal of the American Association for Health, Physical Education and Recreation*, 21:65, February 1950.

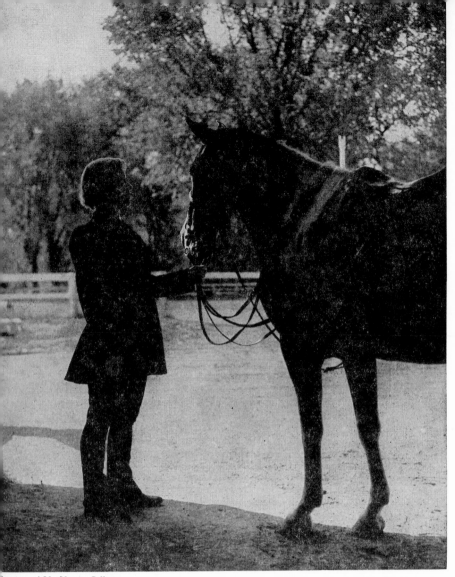

CHAPTER TEN

Looking ahead

Even though employment as a professional worker may seem a matter of the future, looking ahead to the possibility of securing a satisfactory position is actually a part of planning for your career. Permanent employment may be some years removed and dependent upon completing college requirements and qualifying for professional work. Summer work in camps, recreation centers, or youth agencies, and part-time work during the school year are immediate possibilities. Unforeseen emergencies occasionally necessitate dropping out of school for a year or two to work before returning to college to complete preparation. Intelligent planning includes consideration of all these possibilities.

The process of securing paid employment during college usually involves writing applications for positions and meeting prospective employers for interviews. Summer work and part-time or full-time employment may require a change of residence, with the accompanying problems of finding an acceptable place to live and adjusting to a new community or to changed living conditions. Employment as a qualified professional worker requires a knowledge of the responsibilities of the work, sufficient maturity to understand the importance of securing comfortable living quarters, and the ability to adjust satisfactorily to the community and its standards.

The following are the most common questions concerning employment:

1. Is there a demand for inexperienced camp counselors, summer recreation leaders, or part-time workers in health agencies, hospital recreation, or youth agencies?

2. How can information be secured about summer work, or part-time work, or permanent positions?

3. What types of positions are available for the inexperienced person?

4. Is it wise to register with a commercial agency?

5. Is it ethical, after having had an interview and an offer of a position, to return a contract unsigned and accept another position?

6. When is the best time to secure a position?

PLACEMENT OPPORTUNITIES

The opportunities for employment in various professional positions have been discussed in preceding chapters. The following discussion summarizes placement possibilities available to qualified persons. The requirements for placement in teaching include completion of work for a Bachelor's degree and certification to teach. Temporary certification may be secured in some states by taking a teachers' examination and meeting other requirements, which usually include completion of the first two years of college. Qualifications for employment in public health work and in youth agency work or in recreation departments are similar to those for teachers, with the exception of state certification. A civil service examination is customarily required to qualify for positions with public agencies. Employment in some of the areas related to physical education, health education, and recreation require specialization beyond the Bachelor's degree.

Summer and part-time employment

The greatest opportunities for summer employment in professional work for majors in physical education, health education, and recreation are camp counseling, recreation work, and work in welfare agencies that conduct play schools, rehabilitation programs for handicapped children, or summer camps. Some positions are available in summer resorts and in national park hotels or inns as recreation leaders. Part-time work or successful performance during professional laboratory assignments may result in full-time placement during summer vacations in positions with health agencies, hospitals, and youth or welfare agencies. Part-time employment in intramural, recreational, and student activity programs provides both professional experiences and assistance in financing a college education. It is important to recognize that such work experiences have value in preparation for future full-time professional employment. A person who has worked for three summers as a camp counselor or recreation leader has approximately the equivalent of a year's experience in his field.

Professional positions in physical education

The positions available to inexperienced teachers of physical education vary in different sections of the country. The distribution of population in urban and rural areas, the effectiveness of state school laws in physical education, and the ability of the state to provide adequate school funds are among the factors affecting placement in a given state. Many states maintaining adequate requirements for physical education in the public schools are unable to secure a sufficient number of qualified teachers from graduates of colleges to meet their demands. Teachers who are willing to change localities and move from a state with limited possibilities for employment increase their placement opportunities immeasurably.

Elementary School Positions. Positions in elementary schools in large cities may involve teaching in two or more schools, particularly in the lower grades. The classroom teacher is often responsible for a daily program of physical education with the assistance of the physical education teacher, who spends a certain number of hours a week in the school to organize the program, teach demonstration lessons, and act as a consultant. In other situations, the physical education teacher is responsible for the programs in several schools and teaches in a number of different schools each day.

The demand for both men and women teachers of physical

education on the elementary school level is great. The advisability of meeting requirements for both elementary and secondary school certification should be considered. The man physical educator in an elementary school usually teaches boys in the upper grades and conducts the athletic program. Some combinations of teaching and coaching include instruction in the upper grades and coaching in a junior or senior high school. Women teachers usually teach both boys and girls in the lower grades and upper-grade girls, supervise recreation during preschool and noon hours, and conduct intramural activities for girls. Positions in elementary schools often form the background for advancement to supervisory work.

Secondary School Positions. Positions in high schools vary from those in large city schools requiring a staff of several teachers to those in small town or rural high schools, where the physical education teacher is assigned to teach a combination of subjects. Men who are primarily interested in coaching often find that a position in a small high school offers good coaching experience that increases their possibilities of securing a position as a coach in a larger school.

The high school of small or medium size offers opportunities to secure excellent experience. Such schools often provide young teachers with more possibilities for original work and planning than do larger schools where programs are well established and older teachers assume the major responsibilities. Should a person find that he is dissatisfied, or has little chance for advancement, or that conditions in the school are not conducive to satisfactory relationships, the experience he has gained is no less valuable in securing another position. Many large high schools employ only teachers with two or three years of successful teaching experience, with the result that positions are often available in these schools to teachers who have previously taught in small high schools.

Coaching Positions. Men graduates who have been outstanding athletes have opportunities to secure head coaching positions in high schools and junior colleges. In fact, the man who has made a reputation as an outstanding athlete is frequently sought for such positions. A first coaching position may be in the capacity of an assistant to an experienced coach, or in a position combining teaching and coaching assignments. A few positions are usually available in small colleges, or in colleges employing part-time or assistant coaches on a graduate assistantship basis.

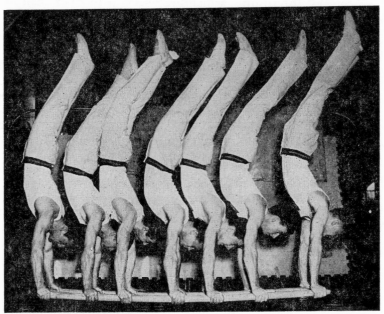

Courtesy of University of Illinois

High-school coaching opportunities have increased with the general expansion of sports interest. Where the athletic program formerly consisted of two or three major sports in the average high school, many competitive sports programs now include as many as ten or twelve different sports, with two or three teams representing the school in some of the sports.

College Positions. Although it is unusual for full-time positions in a college or university to be available to inexperienced teachers, openings do occur occasionally. A few graduate assistantships are available to qualified graduates without experience who have a high scholastic record as undergraduates and possess good recommendations. The majority of such positions require a year or more of successful experience since it is considered advisable to gain some professional experience before starting graduate study. The graduate assistant usually teaches approximately half-time and carries a reduced schedule of graduate courses. Internships, which are fewer in number than assistantships, customarily represent a concluding year of undergraduate preparation or additional specialization beyond the Bachelor's degree. Some outstanding students occasionally receive scholarships or grants as research assistants.

College and university positions in physical education offer a great variety of opportunities. In addition to required physical education, or what is often called the service program, most colleges and universities have programs of intramurals, recreation, and varsity athletics, all of which require competent leadership.

Professional positions in health education

Positions in health education are less numerous than those in physical education but there are opportunities for health educators in the larger public school systems, and as assistants to health education supervisors. A limited number of positions are available in junior colleges and, with some specialization, in college departments. Federal, state, and local health departments and private health agencies employ a number of health educators in various capacities. Numerous positions in junior and senior high schools require ability to teach health education and one or more other subjects. Some of the high schools in large cities employ health counselors whose duties include health instruction, coordination of health services, and responsibility for the entire health program of the school. Experience and advanced study are usually required for appointment to full-time positions on the college level, although some graduate assistantships are available.

Professional positions in recreation

The number of positions for qualified but inexperienced recreation leaders has increased greatly. There is a demand for leaders in municipal and industrial recreation departments and in youth organizations such as the YMCA, the YWCA, Boy Scouts, Girl Scouts, and Camp Fire Girls. Positions in recreational and occupational therapy usually require either specialization beyond the Bachelor's degree or graduation from an approved curriculum in recreational or occupational therapy. A limited number of positions for qualified recreation workers occur in children's hospitals. School camping and outdoor education programs have opened an entire new area of prospective employment for recreation leaders. A few positions in camping include year-round employment for experienced camp directors, who are responsible for camp administration during camp seasons and for employment of camp personnel, public relations, publicity, interviews with parents and prospective campers, and general promotion of the camp during the rest of the year. The recreation program of the American Red Cross requires a number of professional leaders who are qualified to conduct a variety of recreational activities. There is a trend toward the combination of school physical education and recreation positions to provide year-round employment for qualified persons. These employees give leadership to school physical education and sports programs, and conduct community recreation activities throughout the year. Full-time directors are being employed to organize and administer employee recreation programs in industries sponsoring recreation for their employees.

Positions in related fields

Qualified physical educators, health educators, and recreation leaders are often employed in work closely related to their professional fields. Professional preparation in these areas provides a background for specialization in therapeutics, corrective physical education, recreational therapy, and occupational therapy. The similarity between requirements for undergraduate majors makes it possible for a student to combine major and minor work or to arrange a double major and thereby increase his qualification for many positions.

Positions outside the United States

Placement opportunities outside the United States occur in a variety of locations. Teachers are needed in American schools in countries where industrial firms maintain large groups of workers and their families, and on permanent bases where the families of men in the armed services are located. A number of qualified young teachers and leaders are employed in the Canal Zone, for example, as physical education teachers and recreation program directors. The work of the YMCA and the YWCA in foreign countries provides a number of positions for capable physical educators and recreation leaders. The majority of these positions require previous experience and some knowledge of foreign languages.

PLACEMENT INFORMATION AND SERVICES

Information on available summer work in camps, recreation departments, and other agencies employing professional students during summer vacations is usually available through college departments of physical education, health, and recreation, or from instructors who teach professional courses in recreation and camp leadership. Camp directors and directors of municipal recreation programs frequently send notices of summer positions to faculty members of professional departments in nearby colleges. It is advisable to write to camp and recreation directors early in the year to inquire about work opportunities for the summer months. College placement offices are occasionally notified of summer work opportunities; Deans of Men and Women and faculty members who have previously served as camp counselors or recreation leaders may also have information regarding such positions. The best sources of information, as a rule, are direct contacts with employing officials and with the faculty members of a professional department staff.

School officials and agency administrators customarily list vacancies for full-time professional workers with college placement offices and commercial employment agencies. Friends, teachers, and school board members often hear of available positions and refer information to capable young people who are preparing to enter professional work. Occasionally, school or agency administrators who know a college student personally or are acquainted with his abilities inform him directly of a vacancy and suggest that he apply.

College placement services

Colleges and universities maintain placement offices to help graduates secure positions, and to help school and agency administrators find capable teachers and leaders. Professional leaders who are interested in changing positions also receive the advantages of the placement services of the colleges where they have studied as undergraduates or graduates.

Students usually receive information concerning registration with the college placement office sometime during their senior year. Each person who is interested in placement is responsible for meeting certain registration requirements. A small fee is generally charged by a placement office to cover the cost of preparing credentials. Credentials include such information as a record of college course work and marks, scholastic honors, personal information prepared by each candidate, and recommendations from college professors, high-school teachers and principals, and employers.

When notices of vacancies are received in a college placement office, efforts are made to recommend candidates whose credentials indicate that they are qualified for the positions to be filled. Candidates are then notified of available positions and are expected to write letters of application for those in which they are interested. It is not unusual for administrators to visit college placement offices in order to review credentials and interview candidates. As a result, a student may be requested to meet an employing official for an interview in the placement office on very short notice. The interview may result in the appointment of one of several students who have been interviewed. In such cases it is usually unnecessary to make any form of application, although an information form may be required as a record of qualifications and personal interests. It is important to notify the placement office and major department of the results of applications.

State placement agencies

A number of state departments of education and state teachers' associations and several state employment agencies maintain placement services. Information concerning registration, fees, and the filing of credentials should be secured directly from those offices.

Private placement agencies

Registration with reputable private or commercial agencies increases opportunities for placement, since the services of such agencies usually extend to a number of states. Some of these agencies maintain branch offices in various sections of the country that provide contacts throughout the United States. A nominal fee is charged for registration and a commission, which usually amounts to five per cent of the first year's salary, is payable to the agency if placement is secured through its services.[1]

Professional placement services

A placement exchange is maintained by the American Association for Health, Physical Education and Recreation without charge for members. The National Recreation Association main-

[1] National Association of Teachers' Agencies, 533 Genesee Valley Trust Building, Rochester, N. Y., or Office of Education, Department of Health, Education, and Welfare, Washington 25, D. C., will supply information concerning private agencies free of charge on request.

tains a Recreation Personnel Service to assist qualified recreation people in placement. Registration information supplied by applicants is sent to employers who have listed positions for which selected candidates seem to qualify. The exchange of information serves to introduce the employer to applicants; he may then contact them for further information and official credentials. Prospective members of the profession may benefit from these services at some time during their careers.

Organizations such as the YMCA, the YWCA, Boy Scouts, and Girl Scouts maintain placement offices. It is advisable for anyone who is interested in youth agency work to write to the national headquarters of the organization for information concerning registration with the placement office.

Placement through individual efforts

Although college placement officers make every effort to assist students to find positions, every person should plan to take an active part in securing placement. Principals and teachers of schools a person has attended and camp and recreation directors for whom he has worked should be kept informed of the progress he has made in college work, the time at which his preparation will be completed, and his interest in available positions. Since these persons have many contacts with administrators of school, recreation, and agency programs, they frequently hear of vacancies in other than their own localities. Friends and relatives also are usually interested in keeping in touch with possible openings if their aid is enlisted.

The desire to secure a position should be balanced by an intelligent application of professional ethics. Unsolicited applications, or applications made where no vacancy exists, are considered unethical and may place a candidate at a disadvantage should a position become available. Valid information indicating that a vacancy exists should be followed up by an inquiry regarding the position. An application should never be made for a position known to be held by another person.

REFERENCES AND RECOMMENDATIONS

The references listed and the recommendations written by college and high-school teachers, school principals, employers, and friends who are respected citizens in their communities form an important part of a set of credentials. It is customary to list as references the names of a number of persons to whom placement officers and agencies may write for statements regarding a candidate. These letters of recommendations form a valuable part of the credentials on file with a placement agency. Recommendations made directly to a placement office as confidential information are preferred to open letters given to applicants. It is of great importance that only those persons who really know an applicant and his qualifications should be selected as references. References are usually requested for summer and part-time positions also.

College placement offices usually suggest the number of faculty members from whom students should secure recommendations. Students may be given forms to distribute to teachers who have agreed to write recommendations for them, or a form may be sent from the placement office to each person listed as a reference. Courtesy requires that permission be secured from each person whose name is used as a reference before the recommendation is sent or given to him.

LETTERS OF APPLICATION

A letter of application may be the determining factor in whether an applicant is considered or rejected for a position. College placement offices customarily supply information concerning the letter of application and make suggestions relative to the construction and content. A person who realizes he has shortcomings in written English or in ability to phrase statements, or who is unfamiliar with the data to be included, should consult a placement official for assistance in formulating letters of application. College teachers of English, friends who are preparing to teach English, and faculty advisers may be contacted for advice. A teacher with experience in preparing letters of application often detects errors in grammatical construction, unnecessary information, and the omission of details that should appear in an application. A well-written application is important in securing part-time employment as well as in applying for a full-time professional position. Although the materials provided by college placement offices usually include suggestions on form, the following points may be helpful as guides in preparing a letter of application:

1. Secure the correct name, title, and address of the person to whom an application is to be directed.

   a. Be sure of the spelling of names and the correct initials.

   b. Write the title in full; do not abbreviate.

   c. Check the address carefully for all details.

2. Use good form in the introductory salutation and the closing signature.

   a. Refer to the suggestions prepared by the placement office.

   b. Confer with a placement officer if in doubt.

   c. Make the written signature neat and legible.

3. Prepare all letters on standard business-size stationery.

4. Enclose a self-addressed, stamped envelope for the reply.

5. Type the letter, being careful to avoid typing errors and erasures. Proofread all letters before enclosing them in envelopes.

6. Be specific about the position for which the application is made.

7. Enclose an application picture with the first communication if one is desired, or if a picture is not included with the credentials to be forwarded from the placement office or agency.

8. Make a concise, well-organized summary of the data presented relative to professional preparation and experience. Include:

   a. Camp counseling, recreation leadership, work with health agencies, certification and experience in American Red Cross life-saving and water safety, or first-aid programs.

    b. Youth leadership experiences.

    c. Work experience.

  9. Express interest in the position and the hope that the credentials will meet the qualifications required.

  10. State specifically whether credentials are being forwarded by a placement bureau or whether they will be sent on request from the prospective employer.

Timing is important in making an application. A letter of application should be sent promptly upon notification of a vacancy. Since notices of available positions are often sent to a number of placement offices, it is to be expected that there will be numerous applications for each position. Some time may elapse before a notice is sent to an applicant stating that he is under consideration or that the position has been filled. Unsolicited applications are not advisable. Although requests concerning the possibility of vacancies and unsolicited applications are usually acknowledged at the convenience of an employing official, such communications receive little favor.

THE PERSONAL INTERVIEW

Since many employers require an interview with candidates before making an appointment, an employer's request for a personal interview should not be considered as assurance of employment. The opportunity to make a personal contact with a possible employer should be welcomed as an indication that serious consideration has been given to the application. Experiences gained during interviews when applying for part-time work, or for summer camp and recreation positions, are often helpful when applying for full-time professional positions. The interview is an important factor in securing placement, and should be prepared for with care in order to create a satisfactory impression.

The available information concerning a position may be limited. The type of position, approximate salary, and general qualifications required should be determined before an interview. A person who has held the position to be filled and others who are familiar with the community and the position may be able to supply the necessary details. A realistic and objective description of the working conditions and information about the administrators and their expectations of employees is of value in preparing for an interview. An applicant should not be hesitant in requesting specific details, either before or during the interview, in order to make sure he does not accept a position for which he is unsuited.

Preparing for the interview

The following suggestions may assist in making an interview a pleasant and satisfactory experience.

1. Determine the time and place of the interview.

a. Plan to arrive in sufficient time to look around the community and to see the working location if possible before the time of the appointment.

b. Arrange to arrive promptly at the time indicated.

2. Present the best possible appearance.

a. Select clothing with care. Dress in a manner in keeping with a professional business contact. Campus clothes are seldom appropriate.

b. Be sure that clothing, nails, hair, and skin are clean and well-groomed.

c. Take precautions against body and breath odors.

d. Recognize that good posture in standing, walking, and sitting represents personal attributes and assists in creating a favorable impression.

3. Determine to be courteous, attentive, and pleasant.

a. Plan to refrain from making adverse comments relative to any drawbacks that become apparent in the position or working conditions.

b. Be prepared to give information about personal habits, church preference, and professional preparation without resentment or self-consciousness.

c. Prepare a statement of personal philosophy and be ready to present it simply and sincerely.

4. Allow sufficient time to visit the school or agency if asked to do so, and indicate interest in future plans for the program.

The interview

During interviews the candidate may meet several persons with whom he will be expected to work if he is appointed to the position. The manner in which an applicant conducts himself, the poise he shows in meeting officials, and his attitude during the conference may determine the outcome of the interview. A candidate has a definite responsibility to help make the interview a satisfactory occasion.

A few things each person can do to contribute to the success of a conference with a prospective employer merit consideration. Although any meeting between two people creates a unique situation, the following points may be helpful in interviews:

1. Be tactful, honest, and sincere.

2. Avoid unsolicited suggestions about procedures followed. If changes are recommended for the program by an employing official, they should be accepted for consideration without debate or challenge.

3. Answer questions as simply and directly as possible. An employer needs to find out a great many things about an applicant's attitudes, interests, ability to express himself, knowledge of his professional field, and personal philosophy.

4. Refrain from exhibiting the full extent of the knowledge possessed on topics under discussion. If the answers are satisfactory, there should be no need for elaboration.

5. Show modesty about personal accomplishments.

6. Recognize the point at which the interview is to be terminated.

    a. Allow the person conducting the conference to indicate that it is concluded, but be alert to the situation and be prepared to leave without delay.

    b. Show the same courtesy and poise that would be correct in any other business contact.

c. Express appreciation for the consideration shown in making the interview possible.

7. Avoid evidence of concern if no decision is made. Notification of the decision may be deferred until a number of other applicants are interviewed.

Follow-up contacts

A letter expressing appreciation for the opportunity of meeting and conferring with the person who conducted the interview may be sent to that person shortly after the interview. The letter should reaffirm the applicant's interest in the position and indicate the hope that his qualifications will be considered favorably. No further effort to re-establish contact with the employer should be made unless the candidate has been asked to notify him before accepting another position. When an applicant is notified of his appointment he should either accept or reject the position immediately. Delay inconveniences the employing official and other candidates.

CONTRACTS

The contract represents a working agreement; its provisions and stipulations are equally binding to both employer and employee. It serves to protect the interests of both parties to the contract. The employee is given security by the provisions made for salary, tenure, and retirement, and the employer in return has a statement or implication of obligations on the part of the employee to fulfill his responsibilities as a professional worker. Laws governing the school contract vary in different states. Each prospective teacher should secure information concerning the state law on teaching contracts and the provisions made through teaching contracts for benefits in tenure and retirement.

When a person indicates his willingness to accept a position and a contract is sent to him for his signature, he should read the provisions carefully and make a notation of his rights and responsibilities under the terms of the contract. The procedure for signing and returning the contract should be followed accurately. The contract should be returned before the expiration of the time limit indicated, whether it is accepted or rejected.

Contract agreements may take a number of forms. A formal contract is customary for teaching positions, but a written notification of an appointment stipulating the conditions of employment serves as the contract in some localities. Verbal agreements often represent job appointments in business and industry, and may be used for part-time employment or summer work in camps and recreation departments. A written statement of the terms of appointment is preferable to a verbal statement under most circumstances, since it usually stipulates the salary and the nature of responsibilities. Verbal acceptance of a position should be considered as a form of contract, and should be maintained as an agreement unless a release is granted for valid reasons.

Contract ethics

Professional ethics should be observed in all matters related to the acceptance of a contract. Obviously it is highly unethical to accept a contract in one situation for security while actively engaged in attempting to secure a more attractive position elsewhere. When a contract is signed, applications for all other positions should be withdrawn. It is unfair to other applicants and to employers to allow them to continue to consider a person who has already accepted another position.

Release from contract

Situations may arise which make it necessary or advisable to request a release from a contract. A family emergency that makes it impossible for an employee to continue with previous plans, personal illness, and disability are acknowledged as just cause for resignation. A definite professional advancement or an offer of a position in a locality where it is possible for a husband and wife to work in the same school or department may warrant a request for a release from a signed contract. An honest statement of the conditions usually results in a cooperative attitude on the part of an employer.

PLANNING AHEAD

When a position is accepted information about specific responsibilities should be determined. Certain provisions also should be made to assure a successful start. For example, if a position is accepted as a counselor in a summer camp, the following information is essential:

1. Date and time counselors are expected to arrive at camp.

2. Dates camp will be in session.

3. Responsibilities that are expected in relation to campers and program activities.

4. Working conditions—hours, free time, restrictions, counselor privileges, and camp facilities.

5. General camp regulations.

6. The total program of the camp and the philosophy of the camp director regarding the purpose of the camp and its service to campers. Descriptive pamphlets published about the camp, its program, and its purpose, together with communications from the director, usually supply this information.

7. Clothing and personal equipment recommended for counselors.

Plans for the work should include preparations necessary for efficient work on the job:

1. Secure all required and suggested camp equipment and program materials and make sure that it is at the camp on the specified date.

2. Become thoroughly familiar with camp literature and other available information about the camp.

3. Plan program activities connected with the counseling appointment.

4. Arrange transportation to coincide with the specified time of arrival for counselors.

5. Carry out all preseason activities suggested by the director. If responsibilities include meeting a group of campers and

traveling with them to camp, all preliminary arrangements should be made well in advance.

Whether the work is camp counseling or summer recreation work, part-time employment during the school year, or a full-time position in a professional field, planning ahead is essential to success as a worker on the job.

Adjustment to professional work

The emphasis placed on adjustment to working conditions merits serious attention since success in adjusting to responsibilities and the ability to develop pleasant personal relationships affects satisfaction with a career, the enjoyment of professional activities, and a healthy personality.[2] Pleasant working conditions, good personal health, comfortable living quarters, a sincere interest in professional advancement, and stimulating personal interests are important factors in adjustment.[3] Intelligent efforts should be made to adopt an attitude that will make professional work and community relationships enjoyable and worth while. A large part of the success of a beginning teacher or leader is his ability to become a professional person, to show sincere interest in all activities of the school or agency, and to become an active member of the community.[4]

Living accommodations

The availability of housing, the attitude of the community toward "proper" accommodations for young teachers, desirable neighborhoods in which to live, and the possibilities of living near work are considerations affecting the selection of a place to live. School and agency administrators usually help newcomers in a community select appropriate housing. It is of great

---

[2] Norman Fenton, *Mental Hygiene in School Practice* (Palo Alto, California: Stanford University Press, 1943), pp. 289, 329; Herbert A. Carrol, *Mental Hygiene* (New York: Prentice-Hall, Inc., 1947), pp. 204-210.

[3] *Ibid.*, pp. 326-329.

[4] Raleigh Schorling, *Student Teaching* (New York: McGraw-Hill Book Co., Inc., 1940), pp. 290-301; Paul A. Witty and Charles E. Skinner, eds., *Mental Hygiene in Modern Education* (New York: Farrar and Rinehart, Inc., 1939), pp. 520-524.

importance that women should find it unnecessary to pass through any area of a town having a questionable or unsavory reputation in order to reach their homes. Recreation employees are not as restricted as teachers in their choice of living accommodations.

In some communities a person has little trouble finding appropriate houses or apartments; in other localities, suitable apartments are rare or unavailable and it may be necessary to find accommodations in the homes of townspeople. When such an arrangement is necessary, several points should be considered in the selection of a room, or in making combined room and board arrangements.

1. The family should be respected by others in the community.

2. A reasonable amount of privacy and freedom should be assured the roomer. Questions to consider include:

a. Can the room assigned be reached without passing through the family living room?

b. Are keys to the house and room provided?

c. Is the landlady pleasantly formal? Emphasis on informality may result in unwelcome intrusion in personal affairs.

d. Is there restraint in discussing other roomers, aside from brief and friendly mention of them?

e. Is there recognition that children in the family should respect the free time and personal belongings of the roomer?

3. The cost should be comparable to similar situations in the same locality. A place with excellent recommendations is usually worth the additional expense unless the rent is excessive.

4. Definite arrangements should be made relative to the cost and time of serving meals. Light housekeeping privileges for breakfast and on weekends may be preferred by some people.

It should be unnecessary to comment on the fact that the privacy and rights of the home owner should be respected. Actions that would be unacceptable in one's own home, or that may result in impositions on the home owner's hospitality, should be avoided.

STARTING PROFESSIONAL WORK

It is a good plan to arrive in the community several days before duties begin in order to complete living arrangements, become familiar with the community, and prepare for the beginning of work. A high-school coach may find it necessary to report for coaching duties a week or more before other teachers arrive for meetings and the opening of the school. A recreation employee may also need more time to prepare for program activities.

Preparations

A new teacher will find that time spent in the school before class work begins gives him an opportunity to complete many details of preparation for the school year. This is particularly true in schools employing only one man and one woman teacher of health and physical education or in schools in which one person is responsible for the entire program. The recreation leader should also plan sufficient time to become familiar with the program for which he is responsible before assuming his duties.

While it is to be expected that the previous teacher, coach, or leader has left all records and supplies in good condition, the new employee will find many details to check. Records should be studied and information secured regarding equipment and inventory lists, the organization of office and storage space, the location of keys and locker combinations, and the provisions for the preparation and maintenance of facilities.

Planning conferences and meetings

Participants in professional laboratory experiences customarily attend some staff meetings of professional workers. Additional experiences with staff planning accompany camp counseling and recreation work. For example: the counseling staff of a summer camp meets at regular intervals to discuss the program and plan activities, and meetings of all full- and part-time employees in a recreation department or youth agency are held as a means of coordinating program plans or organization undertakings. Orientation meetings are an important part of the introduction of new staff members to their duties and serve to acquaint them with the cooperative relationships essential to good planning.

It is customary in well-organized schools to hold a general faculty meeting and arrange for planning conferences or group meetings before the first day of school. The purposes of the meeting are to introduce new teachers to the other members of the teaching staff, discuss policies, and changes in curriculum, and plan for the coming year. The new recreation employee may have the advantage of similar orientation meetings, or he may have the problem of adjusting to his work with little or no group planning. In many cases he is required to begin work in a program which is already in operation on a year-round basis.

While other meetings are held throughout the year at specified times, the first meetings create opportunities for new employees to learn many things about a school or agency, to become acquainted with other staff members, and to experience teamwork which stimulates enthusiastic participation.

Starting work

The first day of work is an important one. The professional worker is on his own and, for the first time, has the full responsibility for children, the working environment, and the effectiveness of his instruction and leadership. Fundamentally, he faces many of the same problems that he dealt with during professional laboratory experiences, but now he must rely upon his own ability to handle routine details and to conduct the program. He must provide work that is interesting and challenging for each group. The first impressions he makes may determine lasting attitudes of young people toward him as a leader and toward the activities he leads.

The wise leader learns to accept the fact that references will be made to his predecessor and shows respect for the feelings of loyalty and admiration expressed by children for that person. Professional ethics indicate that only favorable comments should be encouraged, and that practices a predecessor has established should not be ignored or changed without careful consideration. Criticism, or comparisons unfavorable to a former leader, should be discouraged.

PERSONAL ADJUSTMENT

The first few days or weeks of either part-time or full-time professional work involve numerous adjustments. Problems are centered in the area of human relationships, the change from student life to professional activities, and the strain of making a successful start in professional work. It is helpful when there are several other young people who have recently started professional work, since they are more apt to have interests in common with others near their own ages. They are frequently able to assist newcomers to establish contacts with the older professional persons or townspeople. The importance of contacts with parents and participation in school or agency and community activities has been emphasized previously. It is suggested that beginning employees temporarily restrict their activities outside of their work until they are well acquainted with their duties and responsibilities.

SUMMARY

Placement is a natural concern of prospective professional leaders and should be included in plans for a career. The procedures associated with securing employment during summer vacations and in part-time jobs are similar in many respects to those connected with obtaining placement in full-time professional work. The processes of securing placement at any time customarily involve an application, references, and a personal interview. Placement in full-time professional positions is usually accomplished with the assistance of a college placement office. The services of a placement office are available to students who indicate their desire for placement by registering with that office.

The responsibility for securing placement rests to a great extent with the person seeking employment. Appointment to any position normally requires a written application, an interview, and qualifications that meet the personal and professional requirements of a position. The role of a placement office is that of preparing official credentials, notifying applicants of vacancies, and assisting with arrangements for interviews. College placement offices also supply instructions for writing letters of application and procedures to follow in an interview.

Placement opportunities in teaching are more numerous for a teacher whose preparation certifies him for both elementary and secondary schools. A minor for which there is a demand may also increase opportunities for placement. Health education majors who are interested in work in health agencies should plan to meet any special requirements stipulated for agency employees. There are a great many placement opportunities for qualified recreation leaders in public and private agencies. It is possible to find employment in recreation in any locality or type of program desired.

Planning for a career extends beyond the point of securing a position to intelligent consideration of the factors affecting a successful start in the profession. The new teacher or leader looking forward to his first position should give attention to continued personal development, and to satisfactory adjustment to his work and the community.

SUGGESTED PROBLEMS

1. Consult the statement on Ethics for Teachers in Appendix B (pp. 338-342), and list the points that apply to ethical conduct in securing a position.

2. Write a letter of application to a director of a summer camp or a recreation department, or to a school superintendent. Indicate:

   a. The specific position for which your application is intended.

   b. Your personal qualifications, including age, physical characteristics, state of health, and special aptitudes in such activities as music, drama, arts and crafts, and nature study.

   c. Your professional qualifications based on preparation, experiences in child and youth leadership, and the activities you are capable of conducting.

d. Professional persons from whom recommendations may be secured.

e. School and home address and telephone number.

3. Make a list of the information you should have before applying for a position.

4. What would you like to know about a position before accepting a position or starting work?

5. What are some of the things you can do on your own initiative to assure satisfactory adjustment to professional work?

6. What would you like to have members of the community do for you?

REFERENCES

Department of Classroom Teachers, *Fit to Teach: Ninth Yearbook,* ch. iv. Washington, D. C.: National Education Association, 1938.

Dreese, Mitchell, *How to Get THE Job.* Chicago: Science Research Associates, 1946.

Fenton, Norman, *Mental Hygiene in School Practice,* chs. xv-xix. Palo Alto, California: Stanford University Press, 1943.

Frazier, Benjamin, *Suggestions for Securing Teaching Positions,* Circular No. 224, 8th Rev. Washington, D. C.: Federal Security Agency, Office of Education, 1948.

————, *Summary of Teacher Certification Requirements, 1947-48,* Circular No. 233, 5th Rev. Washington, D. C.: Federal Security Agency, Office of Education, 1948.

————, *Teacher Placement, Registration, and Related Services, 1948,* Circular No. 209, 7th Rev. Washington, D. C.: Federal Security Agency, Office of Education, 1948.

Gardiner, Glen L., *How You Can Get a Job.* New York: Harper and Brothers, 1938.

Gates, Arthur L., *et al., Educational Psychology,* ch. xxii. New York: The Macmillan Co., 1950.

Kozman, Hilda C., Rosalind Cassidy, and C. O. Jackson, *Methods in Physical Education,* rev. ed., chs. vii, viii. Philadelphia: W. B. Saunders Co., 1951.

Lyons, William J., "What the Community Expects of Its Teachers," *School Life,* 30:18-19, November 1947.

Mitchell, Elmer D., "Sign Posts for the Beginning Teacher of Physical Education," *Lecture,* 1952.

Schorling, Raleigh, *Student Teaching,* ch. x. New York: McGraw-Hill Book Co., Inc., 1940.

Stumpf, W. A., "Put Your Best Foot Forward," *Journal of the National Education Association,* 42:79, February 1953.

Witty, Paul, and Charles E. Skinner, eds., *Mental Hygiene in Modern Education,* ch. xxviii. New York: Farrar and Rinehart, Inc., 1939.

Wrinkle, W. L., and Robert S. Gilchrist, *Secondary Education for American Democracy,* Part IV. New York: Farrar and Rinehart, Inc., 1942.

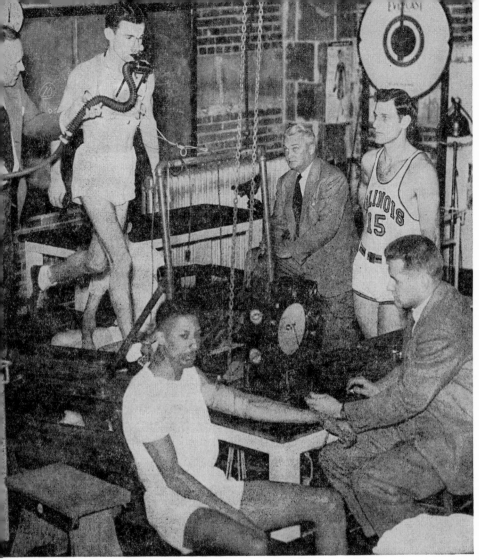

Courtesy of University of Illinois

CHAPTER ELEVEN

Professional growth

You, as a future member of a profession, face a responsibility to yourself and to your profession for growth as a person and as a professional worker now and in the future. Professional growth involves both attitude and performance, and is a strong influence in success during your career. Professional growth actually begins with the selection of a vocation and continues with efforts to meet the requirements of professional work. Plans which include provisions for realizing all possible benefits from college life and study, for securing additional experience through summer work in recreation and camp programs, and for the development of desirable personal characteristics form a background for both personal and professional growth.

The ability of a person to develop the qualities necessary for successful professional work, to improve his capabilities, to accept and carry out responsibilities, to show originality and creativeness in meeting problems, and to increase his knowledge and understanding of his work is a measure of his capacity for professional growth. Professional persons contribute to their own development through familiarity with professional literature, by study and experimentation, by writing for publication, by contributing to the undertakings of professional organizations, and by actively demonstrating their belief in standards of ethical conduct. A knowledge of contemporary affairs, wide cultural and recreational interests, travel experiences, and a well-balanced social life are considered valuable assets to professional people.

Many of the things professional people do to improve their qualifications can be started in college. For example, college

315

students can become familiar with professional literature, start
their personal libraries of reference material, take advantage of
opportunities to participate in professional activities, and develop varied avocational interests.

PROFESSIONAL LITERATURE

Reading assignments for professional courses usually include
references to the best available materials on the subjects being
studied. Library reference reading offers a good opportunity to
become a familiar with professional literature and to start making a bibliography of resource material that will be valuable
to you in your work.

Periodicals

Although limitations on time may prevent extensive reading in any one area of study, monthly journals on physical education, health education, and recreation contain a great deal
of valuable material. In addition to the articles written by professional leaders, these periodicals include committee reports,
reviews of new books, suggestions for new activities, and listings of free and low-cost materials available from such sources
as publishing companies, sporting goods manufacturers, health
agencies, insurance companies, and government agencies. State
and national education periodicals include such diversified subjects as professional ethics, educational platforms, suggestions
for conducting meetings, and ideas for bulletin board displays.

Student membership in the American Association for Health,
Physical Education and Recreation includes a subscription to
the *Journal,* which is published monthly during the school year.
Professional membership entitles members to both the *Journal*
and the *Research Quarterly*. The *Research Quarterly* is published four times a year and contains reports on outstanding
research in physical education, health education, recreation,
and related fields. Current and past publications of these periodicals are available in college libraries for reference reading.
Members of the Association customarily retain their copies, and

often have them bound in annual volumes for addition to their professional libraries.

Books, bulletins, and pamphlets

Books form one of the major sources of reference for professional work. A number of new books appear each year on most educational subjects. Many of the older books are revised and published in new editions at regular intervals. Although it is important to use good, up-to-date publications, many of the older books are of great value as references. It is always advisable to consult several authorities on a subject before drawing final conclusions. Different points of view, a variety of ideas, and several choices of method form a better background than a single source.

The general extent of the literature in physical education, health education, and recreation may be determined by consulting the catalog index in the college library. It is necessary to look under various topical headings to find all the references on any subject, since the title of a book, as well as the nature of its contents, is used as a guide in indexing the card. Unfortunately, it is almost impossible for the average college library to purchase all of the good books published, or to provide all pertinent bulletins and pamphlets.

Many outstanding books have been written on various areas of physical education, health education, and recreation. It is not unusual to find that it is necessary to refer to several books to secure the information and material needed for professional work. As a result, reference reading assignments are used to supplement classwork and assigned reading in required textbooks in the majority of professional courses.

Many important publications appear in the form of bulletins and pamphlets. Research studies and reports are found often in monograph form, and a variety of other material is available in small, unbound volumes. The National Education Association and its departments, including the American Association for Health, Physical Education and Recreation, issue bulletins and pamphlets on teaching and leadership, programs, activities, and various other subjects.

The well-informed person is familiar with the writings in his profession and with various sources of material. Catalogs of current books, lists of government publications, bibliographies, and library guides and catalog indexes supply a wide range of information on many subjects. Catalog listings are also available for audio-visual materials. Films, film strips, and other illustrative materials supplement the literature and supply excellent instructional aids. Free and low-cost publications supply another good source of information. These publications, which are available to individuals as well as to organizations, are produced by state and federal agencies, public and private organizations, and business firms.

Personal library of professional materials

A personal library of professional books and reference material is as essential to the teacher or leader as a set of fine tools is to a craftsman. You should start developing a professional library and securing other material related to your vocation. Many of your textbooks are suitable for later reference use in your professional work. It is advisable to consult instructors of professional courses about books to retain or purchase for your own library. Many free or low-cost publications are valuable additions to any collection of professional materials.

A bibliography of reference materials, notebooks prepared for professional courses, official guides and rule books, looseleaf files of articles on sports and other activities, pictures, and charts should be included in your library. Catalog listings of audio-visual materials and a bibliography of recommended films, film strips, and other instructional aids serve as useful references.

AFFILIATION WITH PROFESSIONAL ORGANIZATIONS

There are many benefits to be gained from affiliation with a professional organization. An exchange of ideas, cooperative work on professional studies and other activities, and stimulating associations with colleagues interested in similar professional problems tend to encourage the development of broad professional interests, improve the quality of work, and encourage participation in an increasing number of professional activities. Membership in an undergraduate professional club offers many opportunities for participation in professional activities.

Student membership in the American Association for Health, Physical Education and Recreation offers many advantages, including the subscription to the *Journal*. Student section meetings are a regular part of district and national conventions of the Association. Student members from various colleges plan the program for student meetings, serve on discussion panels with professional leaders, and have opportunities to meet and talk with well-known leaders and to hear addresses by outstanding authorities. Many of the other professional organizations for physical education, health, recreation, and therapy are affiliated with the American Association for Health, Physical Education and Recreation. As a result, leadership in all of these areas is represented at district and national conventions of the Association.

As a prospective member of the profession, you should be informed concerning your national association, its work and services, and the officers who are responsible for the progress and growth of the organization and the profession. As a member of the Association you should participate in its work, maintain its standards, and contribute to its growth and program.

As a teacher or leader you should look forward to affiliations with organizations actively concerned with education, health, and recreation, and to associations with colleagues in related areas of work. Organizations such as the National Education Association, the National Recreation Association, the American Recreation Society, and the American Public Health Association represent large professional groups who are contributing materially to many areas of education, health, and welfare.

CONTRIBUTIONS TO YOUR PROFESSION

There are a number of immediate and practical contributions you can make to your profession. For example, your reactions to the current rules for team sports are important, as are your suggestions regarding needed changes in rules. Even though rules are formulated by large committees of experienced persons and changes in current rules are usually the result of experimentation, suggestions from players are valuable. Rules discussions which result in well-formulated suggestions to a rules committee may prove a worthwhile contribution to that group.

Professional students who have planned and conducted workshops, clinics, sport days, and play days for high schools and grade schools have made definite contributions both to the school programs and to boys and girls. Among the successful clinics and workshops conducted by professional students those providing a combination of discussion, demonstration, and participation have proved most successful. You, and your fellow students, are capable of organizing and conducting similar events. The experience of working cooperatively with others, of participating in a professional undertaking, and of actively leading boys and girls increases your abilities and assurance in professional work.

Writing for publication may result in a contribution to your profession. Work on a college paper or yearbook or writing for a club publication is often a good background for professional writing. Written assignments, reports requiring original work, and committee work on class projects help to develop ability in writing. A number of excellent articles have been written by students for professional publications on such topics as student meetings at conventions, the values of attending professional meetings, and looking forward to professional work.

The ability to write well is a decided asset. Contributions to professional literature are of sufficient value to justify lighter teaching loads for faculty members who are engaged in writing books or a series of articles. The preparation of reference material, simplified directions for games, courses of study, and a variety of reports is a normal part of the work of most teachers, and of many recreation leaders and health specialists as well. Articles on successful programs, practical and effective devices used in teaching, youth leadership programs, and a variety of other program activities may result in definite contributions to professional literature. Teachers and leaders who have ability in writing gain personally and professionally from producing material of value to their professional fields.

Service on committees, participation in experimental studies, volunteer work with groups needing leadership, and cooperation with community groups in programs of physical education, health, recreation, and general welfare are among ways professional people contribute to the work and effectiveness of their profession. Every person aids his profession who, through his conduct, his standards, and his capability as a leader, helps his profession grow and improve its stature in the opinion of the community in which he works.

ADVANCED STUDY AND SPECIALIZATION

Although it is usually advisable to delay advanced study and specialization until you have had some professional experience, consideration for these aspects of your career should be included in your plans for the future. Your scholastic record as an undergraduate is an important factor in your acceptance as a graduate student, since it is often judged as evidence of your ability to conduct advanced study successfully. Several of the related areas of professional work require some degree of specialization beyond the Bachelor's degree for admission to the field, or for certification as a worker. A number of these fields require undergraduate science courses in addition to those included in the major curriculum for physical education, health education, or recreation. If you are looking forward to specialization requiring specific preparation in sciences, your plans should provide for a minor in sciences to include those forming the background for specialization.

Professional growth through advanced study is provided for teachers through leaves of absence. College teachers are granted sabbatical leave on partial salary at regular intervals for the purpose of graduate study, research, writing, and travel for educational purposes. The leading youth agencies make similar provisions for leaders to study while on leave from their posi-

Courtesy of University of Illinois

tions. Summer session courses, evening and weekend classes in colleges and universities, extension courses, coaching clinics, and workshops offer possibilities for advanced study during summer vacations or during free hours while on a regular job. The majority of graduate schools offer graduate assistantships, fellowships, or scholarships to qualified persons. A graduate assistant or fellow usually teaches part time or assists with research in addition to part time study, and receives a nominal salary or tuition expenses in remuneration for his services.

Advanced study is generally required for promotion. Some degree of specialization is often necessary for advancement to positions of responsibility. Many of the better positions are available only to persons who have earned a Master's degree, or who have done additional study beyond that degree. Supervisory and administrative positions customarily require the possession of a Doctor's degree as well as successful experience. Opportunities for placement in positions of responsibility that command high salaries are usually limited to applicants whose qualifications include experience, advanced degrees, and specialization.

TRAVEL

Travel, as an educational and recreational experience, is recognized as one of the most effective sources of information and enjoyment. Modern transportation has opened wide opportunities for travel, and has shown that few areas of the world are inaccessible to the average traveler. The wide use of educational field trips and tours by schools and colleges is further evidence of the value of travel. Such tours offer a wide choice of interesting experiences, recreation, and college credit at relatively low expense.

An example of a college tour is the trip to Mexico conducted regularly by a midwestern teachers college as one of a series of educational tours for undergraduate students. The trip is made in a large college bus and covers a period of about three weeks. At the time of registration for the last term of the school year, students who plan to take the trip register for credit for the trip as a part of their schedule of classes. Credit is given for required or elective courses in history, social studies, or Spanish under the direction of faculty members who accompany the tour. The trip coincides with spring vacation and extends a week or more into the regular school period following the vacation. Students who take the trip are excused from their classes on the campus, but are responsible for making satisfactory arrangements with their instructors for college work they miss during their absence. The trip itinerary includes visits to major cities, historical points of interest, native villages, and educational institutions; tours of factories, museums, and craft and art centers; and free time for side trips and recreation. The expense of the trip is low and many students who plan for it are able to save enough from their work during a summer vacation to enable them to take the tour the following year.

Summer travel with your family or friends can be both educational and recreational. Experiences that contribute to your knowledge of the country, of people, and of recreational opportunities are of value to you as a person and as a leader or teacher. Travel is a source of personal enjoyment, a means of broadening interests, and a way of learning at firsthand about a country and its people. Travel is a significant factor in the recreation of a professional person, since it provides a source of growth combined with vacation periods in an environment completely separated from work responsibilities.

Summer vacation periods during your college years may be combined travel and work vacations. Work in summer camps in different sections of the country offers opportunities to travel, to meet people from various areas, and to improve your professional abilities. Work at summer resorts and at inns and camp areas in national parks is available for college students and offers many vacation possibilities for combined travel, work, and recreation. Each summer a number of openings are available on travel cruises for college students who can lead social recreation, entertain, or play musical instruments.

Many colleges recognize the values of travel to professional workers by providing leaves for that purpose, and by including educational travel as one of several factors influencing promotion. A summer of travel and recreation is possible with little more expenditure than is involved in attendance at a summer session in a college. Many colleges are located in or near vacation areas and offer attractive recreation and trip opportunities in connection with course work, or as a part of the summer recreation program. College tours to foreign countries may be planned to coincide with Olympic Games, dance festivals, health meetings, and international sports events. Such provisions make it possible for professional workers to engage in advanced study, travel, enjoy a variety of recreational activities, and return to their work refreshed and stimulated by their summer activities.

AVOCATIONAL INTERESTS

Recreational interests, hobbies, and social activities are essential to sound mental and physical health. The significance of recreation in modern life is sufficient to warrant vast programs involving extensive governmental and private expenditure, the reservation of large areas of public lands, and the employment of thousands of professional workers to direct activities. Physical educators, health educators, and recreation leaders should be aware of the values of avocational interests in their personal lives as well as in the lives of the people whom they teach and lead.

It has been found that people tend to engage in the recreational interests they have developed in their youth rather than to learn new avocational skills. Your present interests are assets that should be developed and maintained, and your abilities in areas not connected with your profession are also important as both immediate and future recreational skills. It is natural that your interests in sports, swimming, dance, and outdoor activities will be followed during college years, but you should also plan to devote some time to other interests you have developed. Arts and crafts, music, reading, dramatics, photography, and many other avocational interests offer lifelong recreational enjoyment and the opportunity to increase your range of friends.

Physical educators, health educators, and recreation leaders who are responsible for teaching others the values of well-rounded recreational interests should be aware of the importance of avocational activities; and of their professional obligation to develop similar interests for themselves. Time must be planned for recreation in the life of every person if he is to enjoy a happy, rich personal life and maintain enthusiasm and zest for his profession.

SUMMARY

Professional growth is a combination of personal and professional development which starts with intelligent planning, continues during your preparation, and extends throughout your career. Among the many factors contributing to your growth are a professional attitude, conscious improvement of personal characteristics and abilities, and increasing knowledge of professional affairs. Familiarity with professional literature, the accumulation of personal resource materials, active participation in professional organizations, and contributions to your profession are practical steps toward growth as a professional person. Advanced study and specialization and educational travel also improve your qualifications for professional advancement and broaden your interests and understandings. The cultivation of avocational interests is essential to a well-balanced, happy life and to enthusiastic, creative professional work.

SUGGESTED PROBLEMS

1. Discuss the activities in which you engage that you believe contribute to your professional growth.

2. What plans do you have for your professional advancement following graduation?

3. List the periodicals you read for college courses in education, physical education, health education, and recreation.

4. Make a list of the professional books and other reference material you have already acquired. What other references do you plan to add to your collection?

5. Consult current issues of the *Journal of the American Association for Health, Physical Education and Recreation* for information concerning the names, positions, and accomplishments of the national officers of the Association. Secure the same information for the officers of your district and state associations.

6. List information that you have, or find information concerning current camps and workshops specializing in such activities as:
   a. Modern, folk, square, and social dance.
   b. Hockey, football, tennis, archery, golf, and boating.
   c. Health and safety.
   d. Outdoor education, camp, and recreation leadership.

7. Write a short article on your experiences or interests in travel. Indicate books you have read or films you have seen that have increased your interest in travel, and the plans you hope to realize for future travel.

8. What hobbies or recreational interests do you have that are not directly related to your major? What new interests would you like to develop?

REFERENCES

Cassidy, Rosalind, "New Directions in Physical Education," *Journal of Health and Physical Education,* 19:10, December 1948.

Commission on Teacher Evaluation, Association for Supervision and Curriculum Development, *Better Than Rating: New Approaches to Appraisal of Teaching Services.* Washington, D. C.: The Association, 1950.

Committee on Tenure and Academic Freedom, National Education Association, *Teacher Tenure: Analysis and Appraisal.* Washington, D. C.: The Association, 1947.

De Groot, Dudley, "The Teaching Profession and the Public," *School and Society,* November 21, 1948, p. 56.

Department of Classroom Teachers and Research Division, National Education Association, *Ethics for Teachers,* Discussion Pamphlet No. 5. Washington, D. C.: The Association, 1945.

————, *Salary Scheduling,* Discussion Pamphlet No. 8. Washington, D. C.: The Association, 1946.

————, *Teacher Leaves of Absence,* Discussion Pamphlet No. 7. Washington, D. C.: The Association, 1945.

————, *Teacher Rating,* Discussion Pamphlet No. 10. Washington, D. C.: The Association, 1946.

————, *Teacher Tenure,* Discussion Pamphlet No. 1, rev. Washington, D. C.: The Association, 1947.

Hewitt, Jack E., "The Graduate Major in Physical Education," *Research Quarterly of the American Association for Health, Physical Education and Recreation,* 13:252, May 1942.

Manley, Helen, "Experience First, or a Master's Degree," *Journal of the American Association for Health, Physical Education and Recreation,* 21:76, February 1950.

Miller, Ben W., "The Role of the Professional Organizations," *Journal of Health and Physical Education.* 16:551, December 1945.

National Education Association, "Status of the Teaching Profession," *Research Bulletin of the National Education Association,* 18:49, March 1940.

Nixon, Eugene W., and Frederick W. Cozens, *An Introduction to Physical Education,* pp. 199-210. Philadelphia: W. B. Saunders Co., 1952.

Nordly, Carl L., "Improvement of Personnel," *Journal of Health and Physical Education,* 19:650, December 1948.

————, "Quantity vs. Quality," *Journal of Health and Physical Education,* 19:319, May 1948.

Prall, Charles E., and C. L. Cushman, *Teacher Education In-Service.* Washington, D. C.: American Council on Education, 1944.

"Proposed Report on the Educational Qualification of Health Educators," *American Journal of Public Health and Nation's Health,* 33:998, 1943.

Schorling, Raleigh, *Student Teaching,* pp. 304-313. New York: McGraw-Hill Book Co., Inc., 1940.

Shaw, John H., and George E. Krablin, "Extra Pay for Extra Services," *Research Quarterly of the American Association for Health, Physical Education and Recreation,* 21:195, October 1950.

"Shine and Rise," *Journal of the American Association for Health, Physical Education and Recreation,* 21:15, November 1950.

Streit, W. K., and Simon A. McNeeley, "A Platform for Physical Education," *Journal of the American Association for Health, Physical Education and Recreation,* 21:135, March 1950.

Studebaker, John W., "Contrasts in Education," *Journal of the National Education Association,* 27:240, October 1948.

"Suggested Code of Ethics for Teachers of Physical Education," *Journal of the American Association for Health, Physical Education and Recreation,* 21:323, June 1950.

Tyler, Ralph, "Adult Education for Teachers," *Illinois Education,* 38:56, October 1948.

Uhler, William P., Jr., "On Being a Teacher of Physical Education," *Journal of the American Association for Health, Physical Education and Recreation,* 21:65, March 1950.

Unruh, Adolph, "An Ingenuity Quotient," *Journal of the National Education Association,* 38:188, March 1949.

Williams, Jesse Feiring, and Clifford L. Brownell, *The Administration of Health, and Physical Education,* 4th ed., pp. 42-59. Philadelphia: W. B. Saunders Co., 1951.

Wolffe, Joseph B., "New Horizons in Health, Physical Education and Recreation," *Journal of Health and Physical Education,* 18:699, December 1947.

Appendixes

A. A Guide for Re-evaluating Your Choice of Career ... 331

B. An Athlete's Creed 335
   The Code of the Sportsmanship Brotherhood 336
   A Code of Sportsmanship for Fans 336
   Future Teachers of America Pledge 337
   Bill of Rights for Teachers 338
   Code of Ethics 338
   Suggested Code of Ethics for Teachers of Physical
     Education 342
   A Suggested Code of Ethics for Recreation Personnel . 343

C. Purposes of the Future Teachers of America
    Movement 346
   Platform for Physical Education 347
   Suggested Platform for Health Education 353
   Suggested Platform for Recreation 355

D. Cardinal Athletic Principles (Boys) 357
   Desirable Practices in Athletics for Girls
    and Women 359

E. Professional Associations 364
   Youth Agencies (Sources of Information) 365

Appendix A

A GUIDE FOR RE-EVALUATING YOUR CHOICE OF CAREER

ASK YOURSELF SOME QUESTIONS

I. HOW DO YOU RATE?

1. *Appraise your qualifications*

a. How do your attributes compare with those required for success in professional work?

b. Are you developing new interests and skills that will help you as a teacher and leader?

c. Are you interested in working with boys and girls, or would you rather develop more skill in your own performance?

2. *Evaluate your health*

a. Are you able to meet the demands of study, campus activities, and extra activities in your major without being tired out?

b. Do physical activities demand more endurance than you have?

c. Do you make an effort to live intelligently, maintain good health habits, get sufficient sleep, eat regular meals, and take time for social recreation?

3. *Examine your interests*

a. Are you interested in learning new activities, how to organize and manage programs, and how to coach and officiate, or do you prefer to spend your time engaging in sports you already know?

b. Are you interested in learning new activities, and in improving your skill in the ones you already know?

c. Do you enjoy working on laboratory experiments in science and in learning how the human body works?

d. Would you like to work as a counselor or recreation leader during the summer months?

e. Have you continued to develop your special talents, or have you dropped your previous interest in such activities as music, dramatics, art, or news writing?

4. *Estimate your accomplishments*

a. How do you stand in scholastic accomplishment? What subjects are hardest for you, and why?

b. Are you doing well in professional courses? What are your weaknesses, and what can you do about them?

c. What is your status with other majors in the department? Are you considered a leader? Do others depend on you to get things done?

d. Are you considered a good prospect for professional work by other students? By your major professors?

e. Are you average or above average in professional courses and in activities in your major field?

II. WHAT ARE YOUR PROSPECTS?

1. *Investigate all opportunities*

a. Have you found out about opportunities in physical education, health education, recreation, and allied fields?

b. Do you know the new opportunities that are developing in schools, agencies, and institutions?

c. Are you familiar with requirements, personal qualifications, working conditions, and salaries in various areas of work?

2. *Evaluate your potentialities*

a. What are your greatest strengths in sports, dancing, biological sciences, and other areas of study?

b. How good is your leadership ability? What special activities do you feel able to lead?

c. In what areas have you secured leadership experiences, or work experience that should prove helpful in professional work?

d. For what kind of work do you seem best qualified? With what age groups have you been most successful?

e. What job opportunities interest you most?

III. WHAT ABOUT THE COST?

1. *Consider the financial outlay*

a. Have you considered the cost of a college education? Of additional specialization?

b. Are you disturbed about the cost of tuition, books, equipment, and personal supplies in physical education, health education, and recreation preparation?

c. Does the financial outlay seem worth-while? Are you willing to make necessary sacrifices for your preparation?

2. *Consider the immediate returns*

a. What immediate sources of income are available to undergraduate students of physical education, health education, and recreation?

b. Have you considered the possibilities of summer and part-time work while you are in college?

c. Do you believe it would be more practical to leave college and enter an occupation offering immediate financial independence?

3. *Consider future expenditures*

a. Have you considered the possibility that future advancement may require spending time and money to secure advanced specialization?

b. Have you considered the fact that professional workers must continue to purchase new books, personal equipment, and other professional materials as a part of their work?

IV. WHAT OF THE FUTURE?

1. Do positions in physical education, health education, and recreation offer the kind of income and security you want for yourself?

2. Are positions in physical education and recreation suitable for people beyond middle age?

3. Will *you* be able to continue working in your chosen career after you are no longer able to participate in strenuous sports?

4. Is it possible to change to another area of work within your profession if you find that your interests and abilities change?

5. Do positions in these fields offer future possibilities for improved salaries and working conditions?

6. Are the services of physical education, health education, and recreation significant to people and to the country?

V. HAVE YOU CHOSEN WISELY?

1. *Make sure your choice is a wise one for you*

    a. Do you really like the work in professional classes?

    b. Are you successful in the professional work you are doing as a major?

    c. Are you looking forward to the time when you will be a qualified member of your future profession?

2. *This is your lifetime work*

    a. Are you sure you want to spend your life in this work?

    b. Can you look ahead to continued enjoyment of your chosen work?

    c. Are you proud to be known as a major in your prospective professional work?

3. *Seek advice*

    a. Have you consulted others whose opinions you respect about the wisdom of your choice?

    b. Have you considered all of the suggestions made by friends, parents, and professional workers?

    c. What do professional leaders think of *your* possibilities for professional work?

VI. WHAT IS YOUR ANSWER?

You must make the final decision. If you decide you have chosen wisely, your career lies ahead of you in a carefully chosen field. The future offers great opportunities to you as a member of a growing, vital profession.

Appendix B

THE ATHLETE'S CREED [1]

Adopted by the National Federation of
State High School Athletic Associations

I BELIEVE...

It is a Privilege to play on a high-school team.

Adherence to Training Rules is a duty of each squad member.

Questionable Practices and borderline ethics are not profitable.

He Who Abides by the rules of the school deserves homage and respect.

The Greatest Satisfaction comes from giving one's best thru the season of preparation and during the game.

The Highest Type of enjoyment comes from working in a worthy cause.

Contests should engender goodwill between schools, and it is the duty of each player to promote this feeling.

The Proper Question for the athlete is "What can I do for the school?" instead of "What will the school give me if I win?"

The Success of an athletic department, school, or nation depends on the adherence of its members to the laws of the organization.

The Making and retaining of friends on the faculty, in the student body, among fans, and on opposing teams are among the most valuable assets of life.

---

[1] This and the following three selections were reprinted in the *1947 Report of the Professional Ethics Committee* (Washington, D. C.: National Education Association, 1947), pp. 18, 34, 64, and 32 respectively.

A CODE OF SPORTSMANSHIP

*Adopted by Kiwanis International and published in U. S. Office
of Education Intramural and Interscholastic Athletic Bulletin
No. 17, 1932*

1. I will cheer good plays by either team.

2. I will support the decisions of the officials.

3. I will respect the rules and encourage others to do so.

4. I will remember that to build character is more important than
   to win games.

THE CODE OF THE SPORTSMANSHIP BROTHERHOOD

*Published in U. S. Office of Education Intramural and Inter-
scholastic Athletics Bulletin No. 17, 1932*

1. Keep the rules.

2. Keep faith with your comrade.

3. Keep your temper.

4. Keep yourself fit.

5. Keep a stout heart in defeat.

6. Keep your pride under in victory.

7. Keep a sound soul, a clean mind, and a healthy body.

8. Play the game.

A CODE OF SPORTSMANSHIP FOR FANS

*Adopted by the Sportsmanship Brotherhood and published in
U. S. Office of Education Intramural and Interscholastic Athletics
Bulletin No. 17, 1932*

1. I will consider my athletic opponents and the officials as my
guests and will treat them as such.

2. I will cheer both teams as they come on the field of play.

3. I will applaud good plays made by either team.

4. I will not applaud errors.

5. I will not "razz" the players of either team nor anyone officially connected with either team.

6. I will consider the officials as the proper authorities to make decisions and I will accept their decisions.

7. I will not attempt to disturb any player or official.

8. I will not stir up unfriendly rivalry among the fans or players.

9. I will consider it my privilege and duty to encourage players and authorities to live up to the spirit of the rules of the association governing their athletic competition and to appreciate the privilege of membership.

10. I will consider it my privilege and duty to exemplify and promote the adoption of "A Code of Sportsmanship for Fans" everywhere.

FUTURE TEACHERS OF AMERICA PLEDGE [2]

The good teacher requires:

PHYSICAL VITALITY. I will try to keep my body well and strong.

MENTAL VIGOR. I will study daily to keep my mind active and alert.

MORAL DISCRIMINATION. I will seek to know the right and to live by it.

WHOLESOME PERSONALITY. I will cultivate in myself good will, friendliness, poise, upright bearing, and careful speech.

HELPFULNESS. I will learn the art of helping others by doing helpful things daily in school and home.

KNOWLEDGE. I will fill my mind with worthy thoughts by observing the beautiful world around me, by reading the best books, and by association with the best companions.

LEADERSHIP. I will make my influence count on the side of right, avoiding habits that weaken and destroy.

These Things Will I Do Now That I May Be
Worthy The High Office Of Teacher

This FTA Pledge is taken by all who become members of FTA groups.

[2] *Future Teachers of America: Ninth Yearbook, 1949* (Washington, D. C.: National Education Association, 1949), p. 229.

A BILL OF RIGHTS FOR TEACHERS [3]

by Raleigh Schorling, University of Michigan

1. The right to teach classes that are not too large—in general from ten to twenty pupils.

2. The right to have time in the school day for planning.

3. The right to a 45 hour week.

4. The right to an adequate amount of helpful and constructive supervision.

5. The right to adequate compensation for the full year of fifty-two weeks.

6. The right to have good materials and enough of them.

7. The right to work in a room that, with the help of the students, can be made pleasant and appropriate to the tasks to be learned.

8. The right to the same personal liberties which other respectable citizens assume for themselves as a matter of course.

9. The right to an internship.

10. The right to a realistic program of in-service education.

11. The right to participate in modifying the curriculum and methods, and in formulating school policies.

12. The right to keep from being lost in the profession.

CODE OF ETHICS [4]

We, the members of the National Education Association of the United States, hold these truths to be self-evident—

—that the primary purpose of education in the United States is to develop citizens who will safeguard, strengthen, and improve the democracy obtained thru a representative government;

—that the achievement of effective democracy in all aspects of American life and the maintenance of our national ideals depend upon making acceptable educational opportunities available to all;

---

[3] From the *N.E.A. Journal*, November 1946, p. 478. Reprinted in the *1947 Report of the Professional Ethics Committee* (Washington, D. C.: National Education Association, 1947), p. 18.

[4] National Education Association, *Code of Ethics*, 1952. (Reprinted by permission.)

—that the quality of education reflects the ideals, motives, preparation, and conduct of the members of the teaching profession;

—that whoever chooses teaching as a career assumes the obligation to conduct himself in accordance with the ideals of the profession.

FIRST PRINCIPLE:

The primary obligation of the teaching profession is to guide children, youth, and adults in the pursuit of knowledge and skills, to prepare them in the ways of democracy, and to help them to become happy, useful, self-supporting citizens. The ultimate strength of the nation lies in the social responsibility, economic competence, and moral strength of the individual American.

In fulfilling the obligations of this first principle the teacher will—

1. Deal justly and impartially with students regardless of their physical, mental, emotional, political, economic, social, racial, or religious characteristics.

2. Recognize the differences among students and seek to meet their individual needs.

3. Encourage students to formulate and work for high individual goals in the development of their physical, intellectual, creative, and spiritual endowments.

4. Aid students to develop an understanding and appreciation not only of the opportunities and benefits of American democracy but also of their obligations to it.

5. Respect the right of every student to have confidential information about himself withheld except when its release is to authorized agencies or is required by law.

6. Accept no remuneration for tutoring except in accordance with approved policies of the governing board.

SECOND PRINCIPLE:

The members of the teaching profession share with parents the task of shaping each student's purposes and acts toward socially acceptable ends. The effectiveness of many methods of teaching is dependent upon cooperative relationships with the home.

In fulfilling the obligations of this second principle the teacher will—

1. Respect the basic responsibility of parents for their children.

2. Seek to establish friendly and cooperative relationships with the home.

3. Help to increase the student's confidence in his own home and avoid disparaging remarks which might undermine that confidence.

4. Provide parents with information that will serve the best interests of their children, and be discreet with information received from parents.

5. Keep parents informed about the progress of their children as interpreted in terms of the purposes of the school.

THIRD PRINCIPLE:

The teaching profession occupies a position of public trust involving not only the individual teacher's personal conduct, but also the interaction of the school and the community. Education is most effective when these many relationships operate in a friendly, cooperative, and constructive manner.

In fulfilling the obligations of this third principle the teacher will—

1. Adhere to any reasonable pattern of behavior accepted by the community for professional persons.

2. Perform the duties of citizenship, and participate in community activities with due consideration for his obligations to his students, his family, and himself.

3. Discuss controversial issues from an objective point of view, thereby keeping his class from partisan opinions.

4. Recognize that the public schools belong to the people of the community, encourage lay participation in shaping the purposes of the school, and strive to keep the public informed of the educational program which is being provided.

5. Respect the community in which he is employed and be loyal to the school system, community, state, and nation.

6. Work to improve education in the community and to strengthen the community's moral, spiritual, and intellectual life.

FOURTH PRINCIPLE:

The members of the teaching profession have inescapable obligations with respect to employment. These obligations are nearly always shared employer-employee responsibilities based upon mutual respect and good faith.

In fulfilling the obligations of this fourth principle the teacher will—

1. Conduct professional business through the proper channels.

2. Refrain from discussing confidential and official information with unauthorized persons.

3. Apply for employment on the basis of competence only, and avoid asking for a specific position known to be filled by another teacher.

4. Seek employment in a professional manner, avoiding such practices as the indiscriminate distribution of applications.

5. Refuse to accept a position when the vacancy has been created through unprofessional activity or pending controversy over professional policy or the application of unjust personnel practices and procedures.

6. Adhere to the conditions of a contract until service thereunder has been performed, the contract has been terminated by mutual consent, or the contract has otherwise been legally terminated.

7. Give and expect due notice before a change of position is to be made.

8. Be fair in all recommendations that are given concerning the work of other teachers.

9. Accept no compensation from producers of instructional supplies when one's recommendations affect the local purchase or use of such teaching aids.

10. Engage in no gainful employment, outside of his contract, where the employment affects adversely his professional status or impairs his standing with students, associates, and the community.

11. Cooperate in the development of school policies and assume one's professional obligations thereby incurred.

12. Accept one's obligation to the employing board for maintaining a professional level of service.

FIFTH PRINCIPLE:

The teaching profession is distinguished from many other occupations by the uniqueness and quality of the professional relationships among all teachers. Community support and respect are influenced by the standards of teachers and their attitudes toward teaching and other teachers.

In fulfilling the obligations of this fifth principle the teacher will—

1. Deal with other members of the profession in the same manner as he himself wishes to be treated.

2. Stand by other teachers who have acted on his behalf and at his request.

3. Speak constructively of other teachers, but report honestly to responsible persons in matters involving the welfare of students, the school system, and the profession.

4. Maintain active membership in professional organizations and, thru participation, strive to attain the objectives that justify such organized groups.

5. Seek to make professional growth continuous by such procedures as study, research, travel, conferences, and attendance at professional meetings.

6. Make the teaching profession so attractive in ideals and practices that sincere and able young people will want to enter it.

SUGGESTED CODE OF ETHICS FOR TEACHERS OF PHYSICAL EDUCATION [5]

PREAMBLE

Believing that the strength of our American Democracy and its influence upon the course of events everywhere in the world lies in the physical, mental and moral strength of its individual citizens; believing that the schools of America possess the greatest potential for the development of these strengths in our young citizens; believing that the teachers of physical education have a unique opportunity, as well as responsibility, to contribute greatly to the achievement of this potentiality; believing that all teachers of physical education should approach this great responsibility in a spirit of true professional devotion, the American Association for Health, Physical Education and Recreation proposes for the guidance of members of the profession these [principles of ethics.]

[5] "Suggested Code of Ethics for Teachers of Physical Education," *Journal of the American Association for Health, Physical Education and Recreation,* 21:323, June 1950.

PRINCIPLES OF ETHICS

1. Inasmuch as teachers of physical education are members of the teaching profession, the American Association for Health, Physical Education and Recreation endorses without reservation the Code of Ethics for Teachers, adopted by the National Education Association.

2. The aim of physical education is the optimum development of the individual. To this end teachers of physical education should conduct programs and provide opportunities for experiences which will promote the physical development of youth and contribute to social, emotional and mental growth.

3. In a democratic society every child has a right to the time of the teacher, the use of the facilities, and a part in the planned activities. Physical education teachers should resist the temptation to devote an undue amount of time and attention to the activities of students of superior ability to the neglect of the less proficient.

4. The professional relations of a teacher with pupils require that all information of a personal nature shall be held in strict confidence.

5. While a physical education teacher should maintain a friendly interest in the progress of pupils, familiarity should be avoided as inimical to effective teaching and professional dignity.

6. The teacher's personal life should exemplify the highest ethical principles and should motivate children to the practice of good living and wholesome activities.

7. To promote effective teaching, the teacher of physical education should maintain relations with associates which are based on mutual integrity, understanding and respect.

CODE OF ETHICS FOR PROFESSIONAL RECREATION PERSONNEL IN CALIFORNIA [6]

PREAMBLE

Believing that recreation is a constructive force in the world; believing that in modern living the individual finds many oppor-

[6] David Gray, "A Suggested Code of Ethics for Recreation Personnel," *Journal of the American Association for Health, Physical Education and Recreation,* 24:26, October 1953.

tunities for mental and emotional stimulation, relaxation, physical development, and creative experience in recreation; believing that the primary purpose of the recreation movement is to multiply the opportunities for happiness in our society; and believing recreation leaders are charged with a great public responsibility, the California Recreation Society proposes for the guidance of its members these principles of ethics.

PRINCIPLES OF ETHICS

I. Responsibility to Participants

To fulfill his responsibility to the participant, the recreation leader:

1. Respects people as individuals and willingly serves them impartially.

2. Is worthy of trust and withholds confidential information except as required otherwise by law or a responsible agency.

3. Serves all of his participants according to their needs and avoids spending an undue proportion of his time with any individual or group to the exclusion of others.

II. Responsibility to Society

To fulfill his responsibility to society, the recreation leader:

1. Is loyal to his employer, community, state, and nation.

2. Promotes, through organized recreation, understanding of the privileges and responsibilities of American democracy.

3. Strives to improve community life through recreation.

4. Respects the primary responsibility of parents for children and develops among his participants respect for wholesome family relationships.

III. Responsibility to the Profession

To fulfill his responsibility to the profession, the recreation leader:

1. Honors, dignifies, and supports recreation leadership by giving his best effort to it.

2. Realizes the profession is only as good as its individual members and through professional growth and active membership in professional organizations, contributes to its advancement.

3. Accepts his profession as a life work and does not engage in

outside employment which adversely affects his primary service or standing in the community.

4. Seeks employment in a professional manner and on the basis of competence only.

5. Recognizes the value of the profession and promotes its future by inspiring promising young people to prepare for it.

6. Recognizes the responsibility of the professional group for the conduct of the members.

IV. Responsibility to Self

To uphold his responsibility to himself, the recreation leader:

1. Maintains relationships with associates based on mutual integrity, understanding, and respect.

2. Maintains his health and physical fitness.

3. Is honest in making recommendations.

4. Attempts to think clearly and maintains an objective point of view in controversial questions.

5. Practices intellectual honesty and willingly credits borrowed ideas.

V. Responsibility to Employer

To fulfill his responsibility to his employer, the recreation leader:

1. Shows he has a position of special trust and adheres to the standard of personal conduct acceptable for professional persons in the community.

2. Understands the requirements of effective organization and willingly works through channels.

3. Gives and expects due notice before termination of employment.

4. Absents himself from duty only for good reason.

5. Cooperates in the development of policies and maintains a professional level of service.

Appendix C

PURPOSES OF THE FUTURE TEACHERS OF AMERICA MOVEMENT [1]

1

To develop among young people who are preparing to be teachers an organization which shall be an integral part of state and national education associations.

2

To acquaint teachers in training with the history, ethics, and program of the organized teaching profession.

3

To give teachers in training practical experience in working together in a democratic way on the problems of the profession and the community.

4

To interest the best young men and women in education as a lifelong career.

5

To encourage careful selection of persons admitted to schools which prepare teachers, with emphasis on both character and scholarship.

6

To seek thru the dissemination of information and thru higher standards of preparation to bring teacher supply and demand into a reasonable balance.

[1] *Future Teachers of America: Ninth Yearbook, 1949* (Washington, D. C.: National Education Association, 1949).

PLATFORM FOR PHYSICAL EDUCATION [2]

Its Place

Physical education helps people satisfy age-old needs—physical and social—in present day living.

In earlier and perhaps simpler times, our forefathers' needs for physical activity were met to a great extent in everyday living. Today, many of us, because of progress in science and social organization, perform our daily tasks and earn a livelihood with little expenditure of physical energy. Yet, everyone needs physical activity to grow properly or keep healthy. A person develops as he exercises his body and mind, as he gains new ideas and skills and as he applies his knowledge and skill effectively.

Our kind of society has brought severe demands upon emotional and nervous stability. To live fully today, one must be able to get along with others, control his emotions, and find outlets of self-expression. More people have more leisure today than ever before. Many need guidance in using their leisure hours constructively.

Individuals who possess vigor, strength, and character are in normal times the greatest resources of a nation. They are indispensable in times of emergency. Physical education contributes to the total FITNESS of all citizens who in their accumulated strength guarantee the SECURITY OF THE UNITED STATES OF AMERICA.

Its Meaning and Purposes

Physical education is a *way* of education through physical activities which are selected and carried on with full regard to values in human growth, development, and behavior. Because it is a phase of the total educational program, physical education aims for the same general goal that gives purpose to all the other learning experiences of the school—the well-rounded development of all children and youth as responsible citizens in our democratic society.

Physical education provides a wealth of experiences which, along with other opportunities in the curriculum, are particularly important in helping each child and youth:

2 W. K. Streit and Simon A. McNeeley, "A Platform for Physical Education," *Journal of the American Association for Health, Physical Education and Recreation*, 21:137, 186-87, March 1950.

1. Develop and maintain maximum physical efficiency
    A physically efficient person
    enjoys sound functioning of the bodily processes,
    is free of correctable defects,
    possesses such qualities as strength, endurance, speed, a sense
    of balance, agility, and good posture and efficient body
    mechanics,
    exercises these qualities according to his age and physical
    condition, maintaining a balance of activity, rest, work
    and recreation.
    One who has un-correctable defects learns to adjust to and
    compensate for his infirmities and develop his capabilities
    in order to live a happy, useful life.

2. Develop useful skills
    In this sense, a skillful person
    is proficient in many fundamental skills, such as walking,
    dodging, gauging moving objects and lifting, which are
    essential to living safely and successfully,
    has abilities in a variety of activities, such as team and in-
    dividual sports, swimming, and dancing, that contribute
    to physical and social efficiency at each stage of life.

3. Conduct himself in socially-acceptable ways
    A person who behaves desirably, among other things,
    acts in a sportsmanlike manner, works for the common good,
    respects the personalities of his fellows,
    (Team games and other group activities offer many op-
    portunities to practice these qualities.)
    enjoys, contributes to, and is at ease in a variety of whole-
    some social situations,
    (Co-educational sports, dancing, swimming and other such
    activities help provide learning experiences for this.)
    exercises self-control in activities which are mentally stimu-
    lating and often emotionally intense, reacts quickly and
    wisely under pressure, is courageous and resourceful,
    (Games, contests and other competitive sports help bring
    out these qualities when there is good leadership.)

4. Enjoy wholesome recreation

> A person who engages in wholesome recreation
>> includes in his daily living activities that bring deep satisfaction, that are often creative, relaxing or stimulating,
>> draws upon a fund of recreational interests, knowledges, appreciations and *skills*.

The intelligent physical educator makes the most of his many opportunities to help boys and girls, youth and adults gain these values. As a teacher, his job is to select, organize and guide activities suited to the needs, capacities, and interests of everyone taking part.

Its Platform

FOR EVERY PERSON THERE SHOULD BE OPPORTUNITY TO GAIN THE VALUES OF PHYSICAL EDUCATION BY TAKING PART IN ACTIVITIES SELECTED ACCORDING TO HIS INTERESTS AND ACCORDING TO HIS NEEDS—AS SHOWN BY A MEDICAL EXAMINATION AND OTHER WAYS.

Everyone should be encouraged to take part regularly in a variety of activities appropriate to his age, physical condition, abilities, and social interests. Participation should be aimed toward achievement of the values discussed in the section on Meanings and Purposes.

A thorough medical examination should be one of the main bases for the selection of physical activities for all persons. Children and adults should have a medical examination every year, if possible. The school health program should call for a periodic examination at a minimum of every three years with additional provisions for special examinations of those who seem to need additional medical attention, and of participants in vigorous competitive activities. Proper use of results of these examinations should bring about the maximum physical development of each child and youth and the maintenance of fitness of the adult.

IN EVERY COMMUNITY ALL POSSIBILITIES FOR PHYSICAL EDUCATION SHOULD BE DEVELOPED. Good schools, in making the most of the educational opportunities of physical education, provide guidance, a well-balanced varied program, and indoor and outdoor facilities, equipment and other "teaching tools" adequate for full participation. Community and school facilities for recreation should supplement each other, should be adequate in amount, and should be used efficiently to serve the needs of all child, youth, and adult groups in a constructive program of activity. The program should be carried out in accordance with sound principles of physical education. The physical education environments should be established and maintained with full regard for the health and safety of those who use them.

THROUGH THE ELEMENTARY SCHOOLS, EVERY CHILD—IN THIS FORMATIVE PERIOD OF HIS DEVELOPMENT—SHOULD HAVE THE ADVANTAGE OF A WELL-PLANNED, WELL-CONDUCTED PHYSICAL ACTIVITY PROGRAM. Teachers who understand the place of physical education in child development, and who are competent in guiding the learning, provide ample time and individualized instruction in skills and techniques of a variety of activities. These activities include modified athletic games, stunts, tumbling, creative rhythms, folk dancing, and simple games for large and small groups. Proper attitudes and understanding are sought and may be increased by encouraging children to assist in planning and carrying out the program. Instruction is supplemented by other physical education opportunities during recess, supervised play, intramural sports, and other curricular activities.

NO BOY OR GIRL IN JUNIOR AND SENIOR HIGH SCHOOL SHOULD BE DEPRIVED OF THE PHYSICAL AND SOCIAL DEVELOPMENT TO WHICH PHYSICAL EDUCATION CONTRIBUTES SO MUCH. Every high school student has a right to a daily period of *instruction* in such activities as team sports, individual and partner sports (like tennis, badminton, handball, golf), stunts, folk, square, social and creative dancing, swimming, and many more, or, if he is handicapped, modified activities that bring him as much of the full program as his condition permits.

Length of periods, credit, methods of grading, and other qualities should be comparable to those of other phases of the curriculum. Maximum values in the time devoted to physical education are achieved when there is selected grade placement of activities and groupings for efficiency in learning. There should be, also, adaptation of instruction to activity needs and interests at various age levels, and student participation in planning and carrying out the program. Furthermore, encouragement should be given to participation in intramural, recreational, and athletic activities as outlined in subsequent paragraphs.

EFFECTIVENESS AND EFFICIENCY OF COLLEGE STUDENTS SHOULD BE DEVELOPED AND MAINTAINED THROUGH A COORDINATED CAMPUS-WIDE

PROGRAM WHICH INCLUDES PHYSICAL EDUCATION EXPERIENCES FOR ALL STUDENTS. The college or university has a two-fold responsibility. The first is for providing a full program of physical activity to help each student achieve and maintain a high level of personal and social competence. The second is for educating teachers and other leaders in physical education who will be capable of advancing the high standards of the profession.

SUPPLEMENTING INSTRUCTION IN PHYSICAL ACTIVITY, THERE SHOULD BE AMPLE OPPORTUNITIES FOR ALL BOYS AND GIRLS TO PARTICIPATE IN INTRAMURAL AND OTHER RECREATIONAL ACTIVITIES. The total needs for activity cannot be met feasibly in the instructional periods alone. Neither can all other values be realized. Elementary and secondary schools, and colleges should provide opportunities for every student voluntarily to participate in wholesome intramural activities on a level of competition appropriate to ability, size, and degree of maturity. Schools and colleges should also provide for participation in sports and other activities, through clubs and similar means, on a basis other than that of organized competition.

SO THAT ALL THE EDUCATIONAL VALUES OF INTERSCHOLASTIC ATH-LETICS MAY BE SECURED FOR YOUTH, ATHLETICS SHOULD BE ADMINIS-TERED AND CONDUCTED BY SCHOOL OFFICIALS AND TEACHERS WHO ARE PRIMARILY CONCERNED ABOUT THE WELFARE OF THE PARTICIPANTS. As an outgrowth of a good program of instruction for all and intra-murals for many, interschool competition may offer valuable educa-tive experiences for the well-skilled. Full regard must be given to the factors of age, sex, size, degree of maturity, condition of health, skill, ability, social and psychological development, and personal and professional competency of the leaders.

UNITED THROUGH PROFESSIONAL ASSSOCIATIONS ON NATIONAL, DIS-TRICT, STATE AND LOCAL LEVELS, LEADERHIP IN PHYSICAL EDUCATION SHOULD REPRESENT THE FINEST IN PROFESSIONAL PREPARATION, PER-SONAL INTEGRITY, AND SOCIAL CONSCIOUSNESS. Because of the tremen-dous possibilities for good that are latent in physical education and because the nature and appeal of the activities magnify the influ-ence of the leader, especially when dealing with impressionable youth, those who presume to educate through physical activities should be equal to their trust.

The staff selected to conduct the program of physical education should meet the standards of certification and professional preparation of other members of a school's teaching staff. There should be adequate, defined certification standards set by the respective state departments of education for teachers, supervisors, and administrators of physical education.

If the accepted pattern of organization of the elementary school delegates the responsibility for physical education to the classroom teacher, basic training in this field should be adequately incorporated in elementary teacher preparation. Both consultative and supervisory services should be available to classroom teachers through persons fully qualified in physical education who are employed within the school system.

STATES AND LOCAL COMMUNITIES, ASSISTED WHERE NECESSARY BY THE FEDERAL GOVERNMENT, SHOULD PROVIDE SUFFICIENT SUPPORT FOR A QUALITY PROGRAM OF PHYSICAL EDUCATION. Physical education is an integral part of the total education process. Within a good educational program physical education should be established with resources adequate to achieve its full purpose. Budgets of Boards of Education need to include such *educational necessities* as play areas, gymnasiums, sports equipment and supplies, shower, locker and towel facilities, and, not the least, salaries of supervisory and teaching personnel adequate in number.

AMERICA MUST REMAIN STRONG; ALL THOSE WHO LIVE BENEATH HER FLAG—ALL AGENCIES CONCERNED WITH THE HEALTH, PHYSICAL AND SOCIAL WELL-BEING OF HER PEOPLE—MUST WORK TOGETHER FOR NATIONAL SECURITY AND INTERNATIONAL GOODWILL THROUGH CITIZENS WHO POSSESS TOTAL *FITNESS*. National security and international good will can be achieved by citizens who "live most and serve best." The role of physical education in their development is not insignificant. The principles outlined in this Platform, integrated with those of the Platforms of Health Education and Recreation, if applied, will contribute much to the development of total FITNESS of the people of the U.S.A.

SUGGESTED PLATFORM FOR HEALTH EDUCATION [3]

OBJECTIVES

Since the health of every individual is basic to his effective functioning as a member of society and to his personal happiness and success, every community should have, for all of its citizens, a total health education program.

The objectives of this program should be to improve the health behavior of every individual and to stimulate collective action, in accordance with democratic principles, to provide the community with needed health facilities and resources. Such a program would:

1. Make it possible for every person to attain the maximum health of which he is biologically and physiologically capable.

2. Help to develop mature individuals who possess the knowledge and philosophy to build not only healthier communities but a healthier world.

PLATFORM

1. A program of health education, based upon accepted scientific facts, should be available to individuals of all ages, all races, and all creeds.

2. Emphasis should be placed on the functional use of scientific facts adapted to the educational level, interests and needs of the countless natural groups in every community.

3. School health education and community health education are essential parts of a well balanced program. Neither can function with full effectiveness without the other.

4. Every community should have an organization through which all health education activities are coordinated and in which all official, voluntary, industrial, and civic groups concerned with child or adult health, and the general public can plan together and carry into action a total health education program suited to the needs of all the people.

5. Trained leadership is necessary for efficient operation of a school or a community health education program. Qualification of persons responsible for community health education programs and

[3] "A Suggested Platform for Health Education," *Journal of Health and Physical Education,* 18:436, September 1947.

for elementary, secondary, college, and university health education should include professional training in health *and* education.

6.   One or more qualified educators or health coordinators should be available in every health department and every school system to work with all school and community groups, and similar workers should be available in other organizations such as the voluntary agencies, agriculture, and industry.

7.   Adequate medical, dental, and nursing services should be provided for all school children. The scope and administration of these services should be planned cooperatively by the official state and local agencies concerned with these programs. In the implementation of these services, particularly on the local level, there should be cooperative planning by school, public health, and other official agencies, the medical and dental professions, the non-official health agencies. The operation of these services should be coordinated with health teaching and should provide educational experiences for the child, parent, and teacher which result in changed behavior.

8.   Every child should attend school in a building which is safe, sanitary, pleasant, and healthful, and should have a daily schedule which is in accord with sound health practices.

9.   Advanced training in public health and education for persons especially interested in and fitted for the field of health education should be encouraged through the provision of fellowships or other financial assistance.

10.   All teachers in the elementary and secondary schools should have adequate preparation in the field of health so that they may teach effectively and contribute to a well integrated curriculum.

11.   Community health education is the responsibility not only of the health department, but also of the schools, voluntary agencies, and other groups such as agriculture, welfare, and industry.

12.   A major part of this program should be devoted to helping the people of a community organize in order to find and solve their own health problems in accordance with democratic principles.

13.   The community health education program should provide persons of all ages with accepted scientific facts adapted to their needs, interests, and educational levels.

14.   There should be continuous evaluation of all phases of the total health education program, including appraisal of the adequacy

of the program, and the effectiveness of the methods and materials used.

15. There should be a thorough analysis of existing health education tools and materials, followed by coordinated planning for their production, use, and evaluation on the part of universities, health and education departments, voluntary agencies, and commercial groups.

PLATFORM FOR RECREATION [4]

1. A program of recreation should be provided in every community, rural and urban, and for all people, children, youth, and adults.

2. Opportunities and programs for recreation should be available twelve months of the year.

3. A program of recreation should be planned to meet the interests and needs of individuals and groups.

4. Education for the "worthy use of leisure" in homes, schools, and other community institutions is essential.

5. Community planning for leisure requires cooperative action of public and voluntary agencies including civic, patriotic, religious, social, and other groups which have recreational interests and resources.

6. A recreation plan for the community should result in the fullest use of all resources and be integrated with long-range planning for all other community services.

7. Wherever possible, federal, state, and local agencies should correlate their plans for the planning, acquisition, and use of recreation facilities.

8. Recreation facilities, public and private, should be planned on a neighborhood, district, and regional basis to provide the maximum opportunities and services for all age groups.

9. Local planning boards, recreation commissions, boards of education, and park boards should cooperate in long-range planning for the acquisition, development, and use of recreation facilities.

10. Schools should serve as adequately as possible the education-

[4] "Recreation—An Essential Community Service," *Journal of Health and Physical Education*, 17:368, June 1946.

recreation needs of pupils and be planned so that they will be efficient centers for community use.

11. Parks should be planned wherever possible to include facilities for sports, games, and other recreation activities which are suitable for children, youth, and adults.

12. Recreation personnel should have professional training and personal qualifications suited to their specific services.

13. Civil service and/or state certification procedures should be adopted to insure the employment of professionally trained and qualified personnel in public recreation programs.

14. Each agency, organization, or group which has recreation functions and facilities should employ an adequate staff of qualified personnel to meet its share of the community needs.

15. Professional associations and societies on national, state, and local levels should cooperate in establishing and improving professional standards and in achieving the objectives of recreation.

16. Every state should create necessary and appropriate enabling legislation which permits every community to plan, finance, and administer an adequate public recreation program.

17. Public recreation programs should be financed by tax funds under a department of the local government.

18. Adequate financial support for the recreation services rendered by voluntary agencies should be provided by contributions.

19. A fundamental and continuing obligation of all responsible agencies is to develop a public awareness of the social significance of recreation by interpreting its needs, services, and opportunities.

20. Recreation services, actual and potential, should be evaluated continuously in terms of their contributions toward enriching individual and community life.

Appendix D

CARDINAL ATHLETIC PRINCIPLES FOR INTERSCHOLASTIC ATHLETICS [1]

Schools provide opportunity for each individual to develop himself to the limit of his capacity in the skills, appreciations, and health concepts which engender personal satisfaction and civic usefulness. A good school program includes the means for exploring many fields of activity. One such field is that which involves athletic performance. Participation in and appreciation of the skills in a sports contest is a part of enjoyable living. Ability to recognize degrees of proficiency in these skills is one important attribute of the well-balanced individual. The perfectly timed and coordinated activities by which an individual, or a team, strives to achieve a definite objective is an exemplification of coordination and efficiency. A good school program provides a mixture of benevolent restrictions and freedom, of mental growth and physical development, of liberties and restraints. Developing and maintaining a physically fit nation is one of its important aims.

For developing endurance, strength, alertness, and coordination, contests and conditioning exercises have been made a part of the school program. Nature wisely insured a degree of physical development and social adjustment by endowing the individual with a desire to play. Around this desire, as a nucleus, can be built a complete program of beneficial exercises in which healthful and satisfying habits and attitudes are stressed.

To be of maximum effectiveness, the athletic program will:

1. Be closely coordinated with the general instructional program and properly articulated with the other departments of the school.

2. Be such that the number of students accommodated and the

[1] "Cardinal Athletic Principles," *Journal of Health and Physical Education,* 18:435, September 1947.

educational aims achieved justify the use of tax funds for its support and also warrant the use of other sources of income.

3. Provide that the time and attention which is given to the collection of such funds is not such as to interfere with the efficiency of the athletic program or of any other departments of the school.

4. Confine the school athletic activity to events which are sponsored and supervised by the proper school authorities so that any exploitation or improper use of prestige built up by school teams or members of such teams may be avoided.

5. Be planned in such a way as to result in opportunity for many individuals to explore a wide variety of sports and to set reasonable season limits for each listed sport.

6. Be controlled in such a way as to avoid the elements of professionalism and commercialism which tend to grow up in connection with widely publicized "bowl" contests, barnstorming trips, and interstate or inter-sectional contests which require excessive travel expense or loss of school time or which are claimed to be justified by educational travel values.

7. Be kept free from the type of contest which involves a gathering of so-called "all-stars" from different schools to participate in contests which may be used as a gathering place for representatives of certain colleges or professional organizations who are interested in soliciting athletic talent for their teams.

8. Include educative exercises to reach all non-participating students and community followers of the school teams in order to insure a proper understanding and appreciation of the sports skills and of the need for adherence to principles of game ethics.

9. Encourage a balanced program of intramural activity in grades below the ninth to make it unnecessary to sponsor contests of a championship nature in these grades.

10. Engender respect for the rules and policies under which the school conducts its program.

DESIRABLE PRACTICES IN SPORTS
FOR GIRLS AND WOMEN [2]

Recommended by National Section for Girls' and Women's Sports,
American Association for Health, Physical Education and Recreation

We believe that, for the welfare of the girls and women who participate in sports, certain practices should be followed. We therefore, present the following suggestions for your guidance in conducting sports programs.

STANDARDS FOR DESIRABLE PRACTICES

The program of sports activities should:

1. Be based upon the recognition of individual differences (age, physique, interests, ability, experience, health) and the state of maturity (physiological, emotional, social) of the participants.

2. Be determined by:
   a) The evaluation of the activity in its present and future use.
   b) The classification of individuals in ability from beginner to expert.

3. Provide opportunity for each player to lead according to her merit and to follow according to her willingness and ability to adapt herself to others and to a common end.

4. Promote the acquisition of skill by using sound and varied methods.

5. Schedule regular play periods of limited length, at frequent intervals, at a time of day when energy is at a high level.

6. Provide for the selection of members of all teams so that they play against those of approximately the same ability and maturity.

7. Be taught, coached, and officiated, by qualified women *whenever* and *wherever* possible.

8. Provide officials whose decisions are sound, consistent, and impartial.

9. Include the use of official rules authorized by the National

---

[2] An Adaptation of *Standards in Sports for Girls and Women* (Washington, D. C.: National Section for Girls' and Women's Sports, American Association for Health, Physical Education and Recreation, 1949). The above statement (Rev. 1953) appears in flyer form for free distribution.

Section for Girls' and Women's Sports of the American Association
for Health, Physical Education and Recreation.

10. Stimulate the participants to play for the enjoyment of playing and not for tangible rewards or because of artificial incentives.

11. Include a variety of sports, both team and individual, and
provide opportunity for all girls wishing to participate to be a member of a team in those sports for which teams are organized.

12. Promote informal social events in connection with competition.

13. Secure written parental permission for minors engaging in
any extramural competition.

14. Provide guidance for girls and women concerning appropriate costume for sports.

15. Limit extramural competition to a small geographic area.

16. Provide safe transportation in bonded carriers.

17. Provide a program of competition for girls separate from that
arranged for boys (eliminating such events as double-header games
or "curtain raisers") except those activities in which boys and girls
are encouraged to play together on mixed teams.

18. Limit the total length of sports seasons and the maximum
number of practice periods and games to be played in a day or a
week. Specific recommendations pertaining to the above factors
may be obtained in "specific standards." [3]

LEADERSHIP

Administrators, teachers or coaches, and players should be primarily concerned with the outcomes of the program.

1. The Administrator is directly responsible for:
   a) Selecting qualified women to direct the program
   b) Providing facilities, equipment, and finances to carry on
      the program
   c) Providing equal use of facilities and equipment for boys
      and girls
   d) Providing health safeguards (see section on Health)
   e) Guiding publicity to emphasize the educational and rec-
      reational values of the program (see section on Publicity)

[3] Specific *Standards for Guiding Competition for Girls and Women* on the
various team and individual sports appear in the official guides on girls' and
women's sports.

2. The Teacher or Coach is responsible for:
   a) Having a thorough knowledge of the games and their rules and strategy
   b) Providing opportunity for all girls to play
   c) Encouraging skillful play for full enjoyment of the game
   d) Emphasizing the importance of health examinations
   e) Developing intelligent leadership and wise followership among the players
   f) Conducting activities on a sound competitive basis
   g) Exemplifying those traits which she tries to develop in others

3. The Player is responsible for her own conduct as shown through:
   a) Intelligent health practices
   b) Courtesy, fair play, and good sportsmanship
   c) High quality of leadership within her own group
   d) Emotional control in all game situations
   e) Playing to the best of her ability

HEALTH

Provision must be made for careful supervision of the health of all players.

1. Participants must have periodic health examinations.

2. Written permission from a physician should be required after serious illness or injury.

3. First aid supplies should be available at practices and games.

4. Participation during the menstrual period should be determined on the basis of individual differences.

5. Equipment and facilities should be hygienic and safe.

6. Players should be removed from activity if injured, over-fatigued, or showing evidence of emotional instability.

PUBLICITY

A planned program of publicity should present interesting information concerning the program, its standards, aims and outcomes. The publicity should be carefully interpreted to newspapers, parents, community leaders, players, and their associates. Publicity should stress:

1. The recreational and social values of sports rather than the winning of championships.

2. Achievements of the groups and teams rather than those of individuals.

TYPES OF COMPETITION

The method of organizing competition must be determined in terms of desirable outcomes. The guides to constructive competition are that the program of sports shall offer equal opportunity to all in terms of individual ability, that it shall be wide in range, that it shall be adapted to the needs and interests of the participants and that it shall be honestly and expertly led.

Intramural—Competition of groups playing one another within their school, within their industrial group, or within their organization. Intramural competition should have priority in regard to facilities, time and leadership because of its serving the greatest number of players.

Extramural—Competition involving a group or team from one school, industrial group, or organization playing with a group or team from another school, industrial group, or organization. Types of informal extramural competition are:

1. SPORTS DAYS—An event in which several schools, industrial groups, or organizations come together, often playing more than one activity and each school, industrial group, or organization bringing two or more groups of players.

2. PLAY DAYS—A very informal type of competition: in this players of the participating schools or clubs are divided up among color teams. This type of event is particularly suitable for high school groups and for individual sports activities.

3. TELEGRAPHIC MEETS—Teams compete with each other by establishing records against time, or for score, while performing in their own locations. Such records are sent to a central committee for comparison. Archery, pistol and rifle, swimming events, bowling, and track and field are adaptable to this plan.

4. INFORMAL EXTRAMURAL COMPETITION—Occasional games played toward the end of the intramural season. These may be between intramural winners or two teams selected from intramural players. In contrast is the "varsity type" in which a small, highly

selected group plays a series of games with similar teams from a number of schools.

No one type of competitive organization can be designated as the approved form. The method of organizing competition must be determined by the desirable possibilities it provides, not by the type into which it can be classified.

THE ONE PURPOSE OF SPORTS FOR GIRLS
AND WOMEN IS THE GOOD OF
THOSE WHO PLAY

Appendix E

PROFESSIONAL ASSOCIATIONS

American Association for Health, Physical Education and Recreation, 1201 Sixteenth Street, N.W., Washington, D. C.

American Association of Group Workers, 134 E. 56th Street, New York 22, New York

American Camping Association, 343 S. Dearborn Street, Chicago, Illinois

American Physical Therapy Association, 1790 Broadway, New York 19, New York

American Public Health Association, 1790 Broadway, New York 19, New York

American Recreation Society, 1101 M Street, N.W., Washington, D. C.

American School Health Asociation, A. O. DeWeese, Treasurer, Kent University, Kent, Ohio

American Social Hygiene Association, 1790 Broadway, New York 19, New York

Association for Childhood Education, 1201 Sixteenth Street, N.W., Washington 6, D. C.

National Collegiate Athletic Association, Walter Byers, Executive Director, Fairfax Building, 101 West 11th Street, Kansas City, Missouri

National Education Asociation, 1201 Sixteenth Street, N.W., Washington 6, D. C.

National Recreation Association, 315 Fourth Avenue, New York, New York

National Safety Council, 20 North Wacker Drive, Chicago 6, Illinois

National Tuberculosis Association, 1790 Broadway, New York 19, New York

YOUTH AGENCIES

American Youth Hostels, Inc., 6 East 39th Street, New York 16, New York

Boy Scouts of America, 2 Park Avenue, New York, New York

Boys' Clubs of America, 381 Fourth Avenue, New York, New York

Camp Fire Girls, Inc., 88 Lexington Avenue, New York, New York

Catholic Youth Organization, 31 E. Congress Street, Chicago, Illinois

4-H Clubs, Extension Service, United States Department of Agriculture, Washington, D. C.

Future Farmers of America, Office of Education, Department of Health, Education and Welfare, Washington, D. C.

Girl Scouts of the United States of America, 155 East 44th Street, New York, New York

Young Men's Christian Association, 291 Broadway, New York 7, New York

Young Men's and Young Women's Hebrew Associations, 135 East 32nd Street, New York, New York

Young Women's Christian Association, 600 Lexington Avenue, New York, New York

Bibliography

PHYSICAL EDUCATION

Ainsworth, Dorothy A., "Contributions of Physical Education to the Social Service Agency," *Journal of the American Association for Health, Physical Education and Recreation*, 21:325, June 1950.

Bennett, Bruce L., "Physical Education and Social Learning in the Elementary School," *Journal of the American Association for Health, Physical Education and Recreation*, 20:452, September 1949.

Berner, Leo, Arthur Tauber, and John E. Davis, "Physical Education in Medical Practice," *Journal of the American Association for Health, Physical Education and Recreation*, 24:32, November 1953.

Blanchard, Vaughn S., and Laurentine Collins, *A Modern Physical Education Program for Boys and Girls*. New York: A. S. Barnes and Co., 1940.

Boardman, Betty, "A Senior Looks at Student Teaching," *Journal of Health and Physical Education*, 19:168, March 1948.

Bovard, John F., "Recognizing Social and Cultural Values," *Journal of Health and Physical Education*, 12:131, March 1941.

Brace, David K., "The Contributions of Physical Education to Total Education," *Journal of the American Association for Health, Physical Education and Recreation*, 20:635, December 1949.

————, *Health and Physical Education for Junior and Senior High Schools*. New York: A. S. Barnes and Co., 1948.

Brown, Richard L., "Swimming—Activity for the Handicapped," *Journal of the American Association for Health, Physical Education and Recreation*, 24:14, April 1953.

Brownell, Clifford L., and E. Patricia Hagman, *Physical Education—Foundations and Principles*. New York: McGraw-Hill Book Co., Inc., 1951.

Bucher, Charles, *Foundations of Physical Education*. St. Louis: C. V. Mosby Co., 1952.

Careers in Service to the Handicapped, American Physical Therapy Association, American Occupational Association, American Speech and Hearing Association, and International Council for Exceptional Children. Chicago: The National Society for Crippled Children and Adults, Inc., n.d.

Cassidy, Rosalind, "Contributions of Physical Education to Democratic Citizenship," *Journal of the American Association for Health, Physical Education and Recreation*, 21:4, April 1950.

Cromwell, Dean B., "The History of the Olympic Games," *Athletic Journal*, 18:6, 75-76, September 1947.

Davis, Elwood C., and John D. Lawther, *Successful Teaching in Physical Education*, 2d ed. rev. New York: Prentice-Hall, Inc., 1948.

Forsythe, Charles E., and Ray O. Duncan, *Administration of Physical Education*. New York: Prentice-Hall, Inc., 1951.

Graduate Study in Health Education, Physical Education and Recreation. Chicago: The Athletic Institute, 1950.

Jackson, C. O., "Inspection Trips in Physical Education," *Journal of Health and Physical Education*, 19:319, May 1948.

Johnson, Ralph H., "Selection of Men Students for Professional Training in Physical Education," *Research Quarterly of the American Association for Health, Physical Education and Recreation*, 20:307, October 1949.

Kebric, Burt M., "Problems of Beginning Teachers of Physical Education in the High Schools of California," *Research Quarterly of the American Association for Health, Physical Education and Recreation*, 16:42, March 1945.

Kendig, Robert C., "A Physical Education Program for All Students," *Journal of Health and Physical Education*, 17:170, December 1947.

Kozman, Hilda C., Rosalind Cassidy, and C. O. Jackson, *Methods in Physical Education*, 2d ed. Philadelphia: W. B. Saunders Co., 1952.

Kretchmar, Robert T., "Corecreation for Major Students," *Journal of the American Association for Health, Physical Education and Recreation*, 21:174, March 1950.

LaSalle, Dorothy, *Guidance of Children Through Physical Education*. New York: A. S. Barnes and Co., 1946.

Leavitt, Norma M., and Hartley D. Price, *Intramural and Recreational Sports for Men and Women*. New York: A. S. Barnes and Co., 1949.

Mack, Barbara, "A Dance Approach to Education," *Journal of the American Association for Health, Physical Education and Recreation*, 20:640, December 1949.

Makechnie, George K., *Physical Education*, Vocational and Professional Monographs, No. 68. Boston: Bellman Publishing Co., Inc., 1946.

Manley, Helen, "Experience First, or a Master's Degree," *Journal of the American Association for Health, Physical Education and Recreation*, 21:76, February 1950.

————, "The Plight of Elementary School Physical Education," *Journal of Health and Physical Education*, 19:355, May 1948.

————, "The Girl Graduate," *Journal of the American Association for Health, Physical Education and Recreation*, 20:316, May 1949.

Mason, James G., "Recreation Leadership for Physical Education Majors," *Journal of the American Association for Health, Physical Education and Recreation*, 25:14, January 1954.

McNeeley, Simon A., and Elsa Schneider, *Physical Education in the School Child's Day*, Bulletin 1950, No. 14. Washington, D. C.: United States Government Printing Office, 1950.

Miller, Ben W., "The Role of the Professional Organizations," *Journal of Health and Physical Education*, 16:551, December 1945.

Mitchell, E. D., "The Question of Undergraduate Specialization in Physical Education," *Proceedings of the College Physical Education Association*, 78-82, 1938.

Moffett, Donovan C., "A Survey of Teachers' Needs in Health Education and Physical Education," *Research Quarterly of the American Association for Health, Physical Education and Recreation*, 20:417, December 1949.

Moulton, Gertrude E., "The Relationship of Physical Education to Health Education and Recreation," *Journal of Health and Physical Education*, 18:570-71, 614-18, October 1947.

Nash, Jay B., *Opportunities in Physical Education, Health, and Recreation*, rev. ed. New York: Vocational Guidance Manuals, Inc., 1953.

———, *Physical Education: Interpretations and Objectives*. New York: A. S. Barnes and Co., Inc., 1948.

———, Francis J. Moench, and Jeannette B. Saurborn, *Physical Education: Organization and Administration*. New York: A. S. Barnes and Co., 1951.

National Conference on Undergraduate Professional Preparation in Health Education, Physical Education and Recreation. Chicago: The Athletic Institute, 1948.

Nixon, Eugene W. and Frederick W. Cozens, *An Introduction to Physical Education*, 4th ed. Philadelphia: W. B. Saunders Co., 1952.

Oberteuffer, Delbert, *Physical Education*. New York: Harper and Brothers, 1951.

Palmer, Chester A., "Physical Education as Your Career," *Journal of the American Association for Health, Physical Education and Recreation*, 24:17, March 1953.

Physical Education for Children of Elementary School Age. Chicago: The Athletic Institute, 1951.

Professional Preparation of the Woman Teacher of Physical Education, Field Service Bulletin, Vol. 13, No. 1. Normal, Illinois: Illinois State Normal University Press, 1950.

Refuse, Janet, and Dorothy A. Cates, "Rehabilitation of the Handicapped Child," *Journal of the American Association for Health, Physical Education and Recreation*, 22:19, June 1951.

Rogers, J. E., "Physical Education in Education," *Journal of Health and Physical Education*, 19:650, December 1948.

Scheerer, William W., *High School Intramural Program*. Minneapolis: Burgess Publishing Co., 1951.

Sehon, Elizabeth, Marian Anderson, Winifred Hodgkins, and Gladys Van Fossen, *Physical Education Methods for Elementary Schools*, 2d ed. Philadelphia: W. B. Saunders Co., 1953.

Seymour, Emory, "Impressions of a First Convention," *Journal of the American Association for Health, Physical Education and Recreation*, 20:581, November 1949.

Staley, Seward C., "The History of Sport," *Journal of Health and Physical Education*, 8:522, November 1937.

Steinhaus, Arthur H., "What Is This Dance?," *Journal of the American Association for Health, Physical Education and Recreation*, 23:10, February 1952.

Sterner, William S., "Preparing Teachers to Coach Physical Activities," *Research Quarterly of the American Association for Health, Physical Education and Recreation*, 22:158, May 1951.

Swenson, Jean, "A Coeducational Sports Day," *Journal of Health and Physical Education*, 18:266, April 1947.

Taylor, Thomas William, "The Unseen Target," *Journal of the American Association for Health, Physical Education and Recreation*, 24:15, June 1953.

Taylor, Wiley W., "Those Who Can't See Need Physical Education Most," *Journal of the American Association for Health, Physical Education and Recreation*, 23:20, May 1952.

Vannier, Maryhelen, and Mildred Foster, *Teaching Physical Education in Elementary Schools*. Philadelphia: W. B. Saunders Co., 1954.

Voltmer, Edward F., and Arthur A. Esslinger, *The Organization and Administration of Physical Education*. New York: Appleton-Century-Crofts, Inc. 1949.

Watkins, James H., "Intramurals in the High School," *Journal of the American Association for Health, Physical Education and Recreation*, 21:281, May 1950.

Wayman, Agnes R., *A Modern Philosophy of Physical Education*. Philadelphia: W. B. Saunders Co., 1938.

Williams, Jesse Feiring, "Education Through the Physical," *Journal of Health and Physical Education*, 13:523, November 1942.

———, *The Principles of Physical Education*, 6th ed. Philadelphia: W. B. Saunders Co., 1954.

———, and Clifford L. Brownell, *The Administration of Health Education and Physical Education*. Philadelphia: W. B. Saunders Co., 1951.

Wilson, Julie, "Dance Education for the Growing Child," *Journal of Health and Physical Education*, 19:326, May 1948.

Wolffe, Joseph B., "New Horizons in Health, Physical Education, and Recreation," *Journal of Health and Physical Education*, 18:699, November 1947.

Wolfson, Berbuce J., "Dance—A Medium of Education," *Journal of the American Association for Health, Physical Education and Recreation*, 21:50, January 1950.

HEALTH EDUCATION

Abernathy, Ruth, and Elsa Schneider, "Health—An Essential of Freedom," *Journal of the National Education Association*, 37:450, October 1948.

Allen, Ross L., "Health Education as Your Career," *Journal of the American Association for Health, Physical Education and Recreation*, 24:19, October 1953.

Bennett, Bruce L., "Improving College Health Teaching," *Journal of the American Association for Health, Physical Education and Recreation,* 23:24, December 1952.

Brownell, Clifford L., *Principles of Health Education Applied.* New York: McGraw-Hill Book Co., Inc., 1949.

Etheredge, Maude L., *Health Facts for College Students,* 6th ed. Philadelphia: W. B. Saunders Co., 1953.

Grout, Ruth E., *Health Teaching in Schools,* 2d ed. Philadelphia: W. B. Saunders Co., 1953.

Health Education, 4th ed. Report of the Joint Committee on Health Problems In Education of the N.E.A. and A.M.A. Washington, D. C.: National Education Association, 1948.

Health in Schools, Twentieth Yearbook, American Association of School Administrators. Washington, D. C.: National Education Association, 1951.

Hein, Fred V., "More Than the Three R's," *Today's Health,* 28:13, September 1950.

————, "Your Child and His School," *Today's Health,* 29:12, January 1951.

Hill, Patricia J., "Unmet Needs in Teacher Education for Health," *Journal of the American Association for Health, Physical Education and Recreation,* 25:21, January 1954.

Kilander, H. E., *Conference on the Undergraduate Professional Preparation of Students Majoring in Health Education.* Washington, D. C.: Office of Education, Federal Security Agency, 1950.

————, "Today's Needs in Health Education," *Journal of the American Association for Health, Physical Education and Recreation,* 22:24, January 1951.

Melby, Ernest O., "Teaching Health for Freedom," *Journal of the American Association for Health, Physical Education and Recreation,* 23:20, October 1952.

Oberteuffer, Delbert, *School Health Education.* New York: Harper and Brothers, 1949.

Rash, J. K., "Duties of Professional Health Educators," *The Journal of School Health,* 20:10, December 1950.

Rugen, Mabel E., ed., "The Physical Educator Asks About Health," *Journal of the American Association for Health, Physical Education, and Recreation,* 23:21, February 1952.

Ryan, Grace L., and Leon A. McDermott, "Health Education and the Physical Sciences," *Journal of the American Association for Health, Physical Education and Recreation,* 23:10, November 1953.

Scrivener, Katherine A., "Health is Elementary—A Symposium," *Journal of the American Association for Health, Physical Education and Recreation,* 24:8, December 1953.

"Suggested School Health Policies (Part III)," *Journal of Health and Physical Education,* 17:146, March 1946.

Williams, Jesse Feiring, *Personal Hygiene Applied,* 9th ed. Philadelphia: W. B. Saunders Company, 1950.

RECREATION

Allen, Catherine L., "Training Student Leaders in Group Recreation," *Journal of the American Association for Health, Physical Education and Recreation,* 20:315, May 1949.

Anderson, Jackson, "Industrial Recreation," *Journal of the American Association for Health, Physical Education and Recreation,* 21:36, November 1950.

————, "Training Student Leaders in Group Recreation," *Journal of the American Association for Health, Physical Education and Recreation,* 20:315, March 1950.

Barrett, Lewis R., "Education's Role in Community Recreation," *Journal of the National Education Association,* 20:123, February 1951.

Benson, Ruell E., and Jacob A. Goldberg, *The Camp Counselor.* New York: McGraw-Hill Book Co., Inc., 1951.

Burns, Gerald P., "The Role of Sports and Games in Organized Camping," *Journal of the American Association for Health, Physical Education and Recreation,* 20:314, May 1949.

Butler, George D., *Introduction to Community Recreation,* 2d ed. New York: McGraw-Hill Book Co., Inc., 1949.

Clark, Leslie, "The School Camp in Winter," *Journal of the American Association for Health, Physical Education and Recreation,* 23:10, January 1952.

Drought, Rose Alice, *Camping Manual.* New York: A. S. Barnes and Co., 1943.

Educational Policies for Community Recreation. Washington, D. C.: National Education Association, 1940.

Fitzgerald, Gerald B., *Community Organization for Recreation.* New York: A. S. Barnes and Co., Inc., 1948.

————, "Recreation as Your Career," *Journal of the American Association for Health, Physical Education and Recreation,* 23:27, November 1952.

Goodhue, Sarah E., "Camping—Introduction to School," *Journal of the American Association for Health, Physical Education and Recreation,* 25:37, January 1954.

Hartwig, Marie, and Florence Peterson, *Camp Counselor Training Handbook.* Minneapolis: Burgess Publishing Co., 1950.

"Hospital Recreation," *Journal of the American Association for Health, Physical Education and Recreation,* 22:24, May 1951.

Joy, Barbara E., "Getting More Real Camping Into Camps," *Journal of Health and Physical Education,* 19:18, January 1948.

Kauffman, Earl, Jr., "Is Recreation a Profession?," *Journal of the American Association for Health, Physical Education and Recreation,* 20:568, November 1949.

Kauffman, Earl, Jr., "Recreation in Today's Schools," *Journal of the American Association for Health, Physical Education and Recreation,* 23:16, March 1952.

Kessel, J. Bertram, "A.A.H.P.E.R. Recreation Policy Statement," *Journal of the American Association for Health, Physical Education and Recreation,* Part I, 24:19, November 1952; Part II, 24:29, December 1952.

Lave, Rudolf, "The Rubbish Playground," *Journal of the American Association for Health, Physical Education and Recreation,* 24:18, April 1953.

MacMillan, Dorothy Lou, *Outdoor Education.* Laramie, Wyoming: Bureau of Educational Research and Services, 1952.

Makintosh, Helen K., *Camping and Outdoor Experiences in the School Program,* Bulletin 1947, No. 4. Washington, D. C.: United States Government Printing Office, 1947.

Marous, Richard S., "After-School Recreation," *Journal of the American Association for Health, Physical Education and Recreation,* 24:12, February 1953.

Masters, Hugh V., "Values of School Camping," *Journal of the American Association for Health, Physical Education and Recreation,* 22:14, January 1951.

Menninger, William O., *Enjoying Leisure Time.* Chicago: Science Research Associates, 1951.

Meyer, Harold D., and Charles K. Brightbill, *Community Recreation.* Boston: D. C. Heath and Co., 1948.

————, *State Recreation: Its Organization and Administration.* New York: A. S. Barnes and Co., Inc., 1950.

Miller, Ben W., "Hostelling—New Roads to Youth," *Journal of the American Association for Health, Physical Education and Recreation,* 22:20, January 1951.

Mordy, Margaret, "Recreation Tomorrow," *Journal of Health and Physical Education,* 16:71, February 1945.

Mortenson, Martin, "Training Leaders in Camping and Outdoor Education," *Journal of the American Association for Health, Physical Education and Recreation,* 23:14, June 1952.

National Recreation Association, *Personal Standards in Recreation Leadership.* New York: The Association, 1949.

————, "Recreation Salaries," *Recreation,* 46:4, September 1952.

Phillips, B. E., "Hospital Recreation is Unique," *Journal of the American Association for Health, Physical Education and Recreation,* 23:29, May 1952.

Pike, Kenneth V., "School Camping Has Come to Stay," *Journal of the American Association for Health, Physical Education and Recreation,* 22:23, June 1951.

Raub, George E., and J. Kenneth Shotts, "A Close-Up of School Camping," *Journal of the American Association for Health, Physical Education and Recreation,* 23:22, May 1952.

Romney, G. Ott, *Off-the-Job Living: A Modern Concept of Recreation in the Post-War World.* New York: A. S. Barnes and Co., 1945.

Randall, Ollie A., "Need for Recreation for the Aged," *Journal of the American Association for Health, Physical Education and Recreation,* 22:24, February 1951.

Smith, Julian W., "Community School Camping," *Journal of the American Association for Health, Physical Education and Recreation,* 22:41, June 1951.

Staff of Oliver General Hospital, Augusta, Ga., "We Prescribe Recreation," *Journal of the American Association for Health, Physical Education and Recreation,* 22:12, November 1951.

Thurston, Lee M., *Community School Camping.* Lansing, Michigan: Superintendent of Public Instruction, 1951.

Wilson, Norma B., "A Playground Project for Small Children," *Journal of Health and Physical Education,* 18:578, October 1947.

HISTORY

Dulles, Foster R., *America Learns to Play.* New York: D. Appleton-Century Co., 1940.

Gardiner, E. N., *Greek Athletic Sports and Festivals.* New York: The MacMillan Co., 1910.

Leonard, Fred E., *A Guide to the History of Physical Education,* rev. ed. (Revised by G. B. Affleck). Philadelphia: Lee and Febiger, 1947.

"Pioneer Women in Physical Education," *Supplement, Research Quarterly of the American Association for Health and Physical Education,* 12:615-703, October 1941.

Rice, Emmett A., *A Brief History of Physical Education,* rev. ed. New York: A. S. Barnes and Co., 1950.

Schwendener, Norma, *A History of Physical Education in the United States.* New York: A. S. Barnes and Co., 1942.

Van Dalen, D. B., Elmer D. Mitchell, and Bruce L. Bennett, *A World History of Physical Education.* New York: Prentice-Hall, Inc., 1953.

TEACHING AND LEADERSHIP

American Association for Health, Physical Education and Recreation, *Developing Democratic Human Relations Through Health Education, Physical Education and Recreation,* First Yearbook. Washington, D. C.: The Association, 1951.

————, *Children in Focus,* Second Yearbook. Washington, D. C.: The Association, 1954.

Avery, Elizabeth S., "So You Plan to Have a Meeting," *Journal of the American Association for Health, Physical Education and Recreation,* 24:22, December 1953.

Baruch, Dorothy M., *Understanding Young Children.* New York: Bureau of Publications, Teachers College, Columbia University, 1949.

Baxter, B., *Teacher-Pupil Relationships.* New York: The Macmillan Co., 1941.

Bucher, Charles A., "Physical Education—Medium for Promoting International Good Will," *Journal of the American Association for Health, Physical Education and Recreation,* 23:32, November 1952.

Chambers, Merritt M., and Elaine Exton, *Youth, Key to America's Future.* Washington, D. C.: American Council on Education, 1949.

"Child Growth and Development, Characteristics and Needs," *Journal of the American Association for Health, Physical Education and Recreation,* 20:333, April 1949.

Commission on Teacher Education, American Council on Education, *Helping Teachers Understand Children.* Washington, D. C.: The Council, 1946.

Cunningham, Ruth, and associates, *Understanding Group Behavior of Boys and Girls.* New York: Bureau of Publications, Teachers College, Columbia University, 1951.

Davies, Dorothy, and Londa Jaquith, "Look at Your Bulletin Board!," *Journal of the American Association for Health, Physical Education and Recreation,* 24:11, April 1953.

Drlica, Karl F., "Rowing as an Experience in Democracy," *Journal of the American Association for Health, Physical Education and Recreation,* 24:32, June 1953.

Education of Partially Seeing Children. New York: National Society for the Prevention of Blindness, Inc., 1952.

Frazier, Benjamin W., *Teaching as a Career,* Bulletin 1947, No. 11. Washington, D. C.: Government Printing Office, 1947.

Harmon, Glennice L., "They Ask Me Why I Teach," *Journal of the National Education Association,* 37:375, September 1948.

Hartley, Ruth E., Lawrence K. Frank, and Robert M. Goldenson, *Understanding Children's Play.* New York: Columbia University Press, 1952.

Hodgkins, Jean, "Making Use of Student Leaders," *Journal of the American Association for Health, Physical Education and Recreation,* 21:222, April 1950.

Leavitt, Norma M., "Improving Public Relations Through A Volleyball Demonstration," *Journal of Health and Physical Education,* 19:25, January 1948.

Letton, Mildred C., and Adele M. Ries, *Clubs Are Fun.* Chicago: Science Research Associates, 1952.

Lindsay, Margaret, "Ask Yourself Some Questions," *Journal of the National Education Association,* 40:173, March 1951.

Lyons, William J., "What the Community Expects of Its Teachers," *School Life,* 30:18, November 1947.

Mikula, Thomas, "Winning Isn't All," *Journal of the American Association for Health, Physical Education and Recreation,* 25:17, October 1953.

Moser, Clarence G., *Understanding Boys.* New York: Association Press, 1953.

Nelson, Gordon L., "Professional Ideals," *Journal of the American Association for Health, Physical Education and Recreation,* 24:18, January 1953.

Nordly, Carl, "Training Student Officials," *Journal of Health and Physical Education,* 17:16, January 1946.

Oberteuffer, Delbert, "Sportsmanship—Whose Responsibility?," *Journal of Health and Physical Education,* 19:543, October 1948.

Perry, Dorothy, and Irene Gilbert, "Student Coaches and Officials Clubs," *Journal of Health and Physical Education,* 17:429, October 1946.

"Prescription for Your Bulletin Board," *Journal of the National Education Association,* 39:680, December 1950.

Programs of the Federal Government Affecting Children and Youth. Washington, D. C.: Government Printing Office, 1951.

Rautman, Arthur, "The Physical Education Teacher as a Personal Model," *Journal of the American Association for Health, Physical Education and Recreation,* 21:10, January 1950.

Sanford, Jean R., "Learning to Officiate is Fun," *Journal of the American Association for Health, Physical Education and Recreation,* 24:29, January 1953.

Solomon, Ben, *Leadership of Youth.* Putnam Valley, New York: Youth Service, Inc., 1950.

"Sportsmanship as a Characteristic of Enlightened People," *Journal of Health and Physical Education,* 19:596, November 1948.

Tunis, John, *Democracy in Sports.* New York, A. S. Barnes and Co., 1941.

Weitzman, Ellis, *Guiding Children's Social Growth.* Chicago: Science Research Associates, n.d.

"What You Should Know About Student Major Clubs," *Journal of the American Association for Health, Physical Education and Recreation,* 23:19, September 1952.

Wilson, Roy K., "Teaching Offers Greatest Opportunities," *Journal of the National Education Association,* 37:434, October 1948.

SAFETY

Compilation of Laws Relating to Recreation. Sacramento: State of California Commission, 1950.

Guenther, Donald P., "Problems Involving Legal Liability," *Journal of the American Association for Health, Physical Education and Recreation,* 20:511, October 1949.

Laws and Regulations Relating to Organized Camping. Sacramento: State of California Recreation Commission, 1951.

Leibee, Howard C., *Liability for Accidents in Physical Education, Athletics, and Recreation.* Ann Arbor, Michigan: Ann Arbor Publishers, 1952.

Lloyd, Frank S., George E. Deaver, and Floyd R. Eastwood, *Safety in Athletics.* Philadelphia: W. B. Saunders Co., 1937.

The Physical Education Instructor and Safety. Washington, D. C.: National Education Association, 1948.

Price, Hartley, "The Role of Physical Education in Accident Prevention," *The Athletic Journal,* 28:51-55, February 1948.

Safety is Good Business. New York: National Association of Insurance Agents and Association of Casualty and Surety Companies, 1952.

Seaton, Don Cash, *Safety in Sports.* New York: Prentice-Hall, Inc., 1948.

STANDARDS

Ashcraft, J. Holley, "A Sane Competitive Program for Junior High School Boys," *Journal of the American Association for Health, Physical Education and Recreation,* 24:20, November 1953.

De Groot, Dudley, "Code of Ethics for Football Coaches," *Journal of the American Association for Health, Physical Education and Recreation,* 24:21, February 1953.

Desirable Athletic Competition for Children. Washington, D. C.: American Association for Health, Physical Education and Recreation, 1952.

Educational Policies Commission, *School Athletics: Problems and Policies.* Washington, D. C.: National Education Association and American Association of School Administrators, 1954.

Fait, Hollis, "Needed: A Policy on Junior-High School Interschool Athletics," *Journal of the American Association for Health, Physical Education and Recreation,* 21:20, October 1950.

Health and Physical Education for All American Children and Youth. Washington, D. C.: National Education Association, 1945.

Lowman, C. L., "A Consideration of Teen-Age Athletics," *Journal of Health and Physical Education,* 12:398, September 1941.

McNeeley, Simon A., "Of Mouse and Men," *Journal of the American Association for Health, Physical Education and Recreation,* 23:27, December 1952.

Standards in Athletics for Boys in Secondary Schools. Washington, D. C.: American Association for Health, Physical Education and Recreation, 1949.

Standards in Athletics for Girls and Women, rev. ed. Washington, D. C.: National Section for Girls' and Women's Athletics, American Association for Health, Physical Education and Recreation, 1948.

Steinhaus, Arthur H., "Boxers Brains Swapped for Medals," *Journal of the American Association for Health, Physical Education and Recreation,* 22:21, October 1951.

FACILITIES AND EQUIPMENT

Bourquardez, Virginia, and Charles Heilman, *Sports Equipment: Selection Care, and Repair.* New York: Prentice-Hall, Inc., 1953.

Champlin, Ellis H., and Caswell M. Miles, "Functional Planning and Standards," *Journal of the American Association for Health, Physical Education and Recreation,* 22:18, February 1951.

The College Physical Education Association, *College Facilities for Physical Education, Health Education and Recreation.* Washington, D. C.: American Association for Health, Physical Education and Recreation, 1947.

Jack, Harold K., "Facilities for Health and Physical Education," *Journal of the American Association for Health, Physical Education and Recreation,* 22:22, February 1951.

Luehring, Frederick W., *Swimming Pool Standards.* New York: A. S. Barnes and Company, 1939.

Mayer, Kenneth L., *Purchase, Care and Repair of Athletic Equipment.* St. Louis: Educational Publishers, Inc., 1948.

McKee, Stanley, "The All-Weather Playground," *Journal of the American Association for Health, Physical Education and Recreation,* 20:175, March 1949.

National Facilities Conference, *Guide for Planning Facilities for Athletics, Recreation, Physical and Health Education.* Washington, D. C.: American Association for Health, Physical Education and Recreation, 1947.

Index

A

Acquaintances, 140-141
Activities:
  physical education, 53, 255
  in school programs, 183
Adjustment, personal, 310
  to professional work, 306
Administrative positions, 32, 293
Administrators:
  duties, 212
  functions, 212
  qualifications, 80, 96
  recreation, 45
Adults:
  avocational interests, 325
  recreation, 48
Advancement, professional, 65-67
Affiliation with professional organizations, 318-319
Agencies, health:
  private, 78
  public, 79
Agencies, voluntary, 81
Agencies, youth-serving. 98-99
Aim:
  general statement, 237
  health education, 243
  physical education, 238
  recreation, 245
American Association for Health, Physical Education and Recreation:
  code, 280
  membership, 61, 320
    student, 152, 320
  placement services, 296
American Camping Association, 98

American Physical Education Association, 228
  (see also AAHPER)
American Public Health Association, 61, 319
American Recreation Society, 319
  purposes, 280
American Red Cross, positions, 293
Anderson, William G., 233
Applications, letters of, 299
Appraisal charts, 14-19
Appraisal, personal, 8
Assistance, state, 81
Athletics:
  cardinal principles (boys), 357
  creed, 335
  desirable practices (girls), 359
  extramurals, 157
  intramurals, 156
  participation, 144
  sportsmanship code, 336
  varsity assistance, 157-159
Attributes, personal (see Personal attributes)
Avocational interests, 325

B

Boy Scouts:
  camping, 94
  executives, 106
  National Training School, 106
  nature of work, 106
  opportunities, 108
  organization of, 231
  requirements, 106-107
  salaries, 107
  working conditions, 107

Boys' Clubs:
nature of work, 108
opportunities, 110
organization chart, 109
requirements, 108
working conditions, 108
Brightbill, Charles K., 245
Brosius, George, 232
Butler, George D., 245

C

Camp:
counselors, 96, 305
positions, 293
Camp Fire Girls:
nature of work, 112
opportunities, 113
organization, 231
requirements, 112
working conditions, 112, 113
Camping:
organized camping, 94, 98
and outdoor education, 11, 94, 98
administration, 96
nature of work, 95
opportunities, 97
practical experiences in, 193
requirements, 95
working conditions, 97
Camps:
number, 94
organization, 94
private, 94
school, 11, 193
special, 94
Careers:
advantages, 72, 73
agency:
private health, 78, 79
public health, 78, 79
youth, 99-113
camping and outdoor education,
94-98
choice of, 4, 334
corrective physical education, 90-92
dance, 55
dissatisfaction in choice, 7
essentials of, 4
exercise therapy, 82
nature of, 4
physical therapy, 82

Careers (Cont'd):
planning for, 4, 19, 25
recreational therapy, 81
re-evaluation, guide to, 4-5, 331
related field, 77, 78
safety education, 92
sources of information, 22
therapeutics, 86
Catholic Youth Organization, 118
Certification:
decrease in, 29
number qualifying, 29
physical therapist, 83
requirements, 273
responsibility for, 274
Characteristics, personal, 62, 315
Children:
adequate program for, 31, 253
and camping, 94-98
corrective work for, 91
development of, 8
education of, 175
enjoyment of, 28
growth of, 175-176
handicapped, 240
health needs of, 259-266
hospital recreation for, 195
knowledge of, 155, 174-176, 180-188,
196-197
leadership of, 8, 9
noon-hour programs for, 164, 174
observation of, 175-176, 180-181
play of, 244
provisions for, 240
relationships with, 218, 221
and school camping, 193, 194
Civil Service, requirements in therapy,
87
Classroom teachers, 216
Coach, duties of, 37-38
Coaching:
opportunities, 63
positions, 290
Coeducation:
co-physical education, 210
corecreation, 211
College:
buildings and classrooms, 129
cultural opportunities, 130
faculty, ranks and titles, 131-132
library, 129

College *(Cont'd)*:
  placement services, 295
  recreational facilities and programs, 129-130
  rules and regulations, 127
  scholarships and loan funds, 128-129
  student activities, 130
  working opportunities, 128
College life, planning, 125
Combinations:
  major, 56-60
  minor, 56-60
  recommended, 56
  teaching, 58
Commercial recreation:
  nature of work, 115
  opportunities, 116
  requirements, 115
  working conditions, 116
Conduct, professional, 152, 205, 315
Contracts:
  as agreements, 303 *(see* Placement)
  ethics, 304
  release from, 304
Contributions to profession, 320-321
Corrective physical education:
  elementary school, 91
  nature of work, 90
  opportunities, 92
  requirements, 90
  working conditions, 91
Courses:
  curriculum, 50
  general education, 50
  health education, 51-52
  physical education, 51-55
  professional education, 50-53
  public health preparation, 77
  recreation, 52, 55
  science, 50-52
Curriculum, 50-55

D

Dance, values of, 145, 256-258
Debate, values of, 146
Degrees, advanced, 66
Department of Health, Education, and Welfare, 229
Development, personal and social, 137
Dramatics, values of, 146

Driver Education, 92-93
Duties:
  health education, 42-43
  physical education, 32-33
    charts, 34-35
  recreation, 47-49

E

Economic status of teachers and leaders, 276-277
Education:
  change in emphasis, 227
  concern of, 8
  influence of, 225-227
  nature, 173-175
  purpose, 174
  responsibility for, 275
Employment:
  full-time, 155, 287
  health education *(see* Placement)
  information, 155, 163
  opportunities:
    health education, 40-41
    physical education, 29-31
    recreation, 46-47
  part-time, 155, 288
  questions concerning, 287
  summer, 155, 288
English, command of, 13
Enrollment, 30-31
  since World War II, 30
Environment, working:
  health education, 42-43
  physical education, 33
  recreation, 47
Equipment, 262
Ethics:
  code of, 275
    for physical education, 342
    for recreation personnel, 343
    for teachers, 338
Evaluation, 26, 209
Examinations:
  preparing for, 135
  taking, 136
Exercise therapy:
  nature of work, 87
  opportunities, 88
  requirements, 87
  working conditions, 88

Experience:
  practical, 191
    in camping and outdoor educa-
      tion, 193
    in hospital recreation, 195
    in youth agencies, 191-192
  voluntary, 165, 170
Extramural athletics:
  leadership, 157
  managers, 157-158
  organization, 157, 259

F

Facilities, physical education, 33, 262
Faculty, 131-132
Field work, 179, 189
Fraternal groups, 147
Freeark, C. H., 148
Friends, 140-141
Future Teachers of America:
  affiliation, 152
  pledge, 337
  purpose, 346

G

Germany, physical education, 226-227
Girl Scouts:
  camping, 94
  executives, 111
  nature of work, 110-111
  opportunities, 111-112
  organization, 231
  requirements, 110-111
  working conditions, 111
Goal, physical education, 31
Graduate study, 32, 40, 66-67, 321
Growth:
  professional, 207, 315 (see also
    Professional growth)
  in schools, 233
Guidance:
  in laboratory experiences, 172, 189-
    190
  supervisory, 172
Gymnastics, 226-228, 256-258

H

Habits, personal, 138-139
Hart, Frank W., 219

Health:
  aspects of, 10
  courses, 79
  definition, 10, 241
  environment, 260
  instruction, 260
  needs of children, 259
  services, 260
Health agencies:
  job opportunities, 80-81
  nature of work, 78-79
  public and private, 78
  requirements, 78
  working conditions, 79-80
Health education:
  aim, 243
  chart, 242
  contributions, 247
  duties, 43-44
  history, 227-229
  importance, 9
  instruction, 243
  nature of, 9
  objectives, 244
  philosophy, 241
  placement, 41
  platform, 244, 353
  positions, 42, 292
  preparation in, 235
  as a profession, 39, 43
  program, 10, 184, 260
    community, 184
    school, 184
    voluntary, 185
  qualifications, 12-13
  working environment, 43, 79
Home, observation of, 177
Hospital recreation, 187, 195
Hoyman, Howard S., 241

I

Industrial recreation:
  nature of work, 113
  opportunities, 114
  requirements, 113
  working conditions, 114
Intelligence, 12
Internship, 191
Interschool athletics, principles, 357

Interviews:
  conduct of, 302
  personal, 300 (*see also* Placement)
  preparing for, 301
Intramurals:
  administration, 156
  leadership, 156-157
  organization, 157, 259

J

Jobs (*see* Employment)
Journalism, 146

L

Laboratory experiences:
  additional, 188
  most valuable, 188
  professional, 171-197
    field work, 189
    importance, 173-179
    internship, 191
    observation, 180
    participation, 182
    purpose of, 171-173
    student teaching, 189
Leaders:
  effectiveness, 171
  recreation, 48
  youth, 217
Leadership:
  ability, 13, 152, 250
  clubs, 6, 159
  community programs, 161
  cooperation in, 165
  democratic, 165
  development, 151-166
  experience, 154
  good, 153, 251
  high school programs, 160, 164
  municipal programs, 161
  noon-hour programs, 164
  opportunities:
    extramural athletics, 157-158
    intramural athletics, 156-157
  possibilities, 155-165
  professional, 203, 250
  qualities, 153-154
  recreation programs, 160
  and teaching, 182

Leadership (*Cont'd*):
  youth, 99
  youth-serving agencies, 162
Leavitt, Norma M., 144, 156
Lee, Joseph, 244
Lewis, Dio, 232
Library, 129
  personal, 318
  use of, 317
Ling, Per Hendrick, 232
Literature, professional, 316-318
Living accommodations, 128
Locke, John, 228

M

McKinney, Fred, 140
Major and minor combinations, 3,
  56-58
Manners, 138
Membership in professional organizations, 152
Mental Health, 12
Music, 145
Mutual Security Agency, 80

N

Nachtegall, Franz, 232
National Education Association, 61,
  319
  code of ethics, 275, 281, 338
National Foundation for Infantile
  Paralysis, scholarships for physical therapy, 85
National Recreation Association, 231,
  272, 280, 319
  placement services, 296
National Section for Girls' and
  Women's Sports, 259
Nature specialists, 98

O

Observation:
  of children, 175-176
  of the community, 178-179
  of homes, 177
  methods, 180-182
  of schools, 176-177

Occupational therapy:
  nature of work, 85
  opportunities, 86
  professional courses, 86
  requirements, 85
  working conditions, 86
Office of Education, United States,
    276, 281
Olympic Games, 229
Opportunities:
  health agencies, 80-81
  health education, 60-61
  physical education, 60-61
  recreation, 62
Orientation:
  to college, 126
  getting acquainted:
    with college, 127-150
    with faculty, 130-133
Outdoor Education, 94-97 (see also
    Camping)

                        P

Parents:
  contacts with, 218
  interest of, 217
Parent-Teacher Associations, 278
Participation, 182
  in college activities, 141, 147
    athletics, 144
    dance, 145
    debate, 146
    dramatics, 146
    fraternal groups, 147
    journalism, 146
    music, 145
    student government, 147
    student organizations, 146
  democratic, 151-152
  and scholarship, 143
  voluntary, 102, 191
Personal attributes, 17, 39, 44, 77, 83,
    97, 204
Personal grooming, 137
Personal rating, 14-19
Philosophy, 236
  education, 236, 247
  health education, 241
  physical education, 237
  recreation, 244

Physical activities:
  skill in, 13, 83, 247, 252
Physical health, 12
Physical education:
  activities, 9, 53, 183, 255
  adult life, 9
  aim, 238
  ancient Greece, 225-226
  code of ethics, 342
  contributions of, 9, 247
  demand for teachers, 29-30
  duties:
    of coach, 37-38
    of men teachers, 35-37
    of women teachers, 35-36
  educational significance, 9, 247
  employment, 29 (see also Employ-
    ment)
  equipment, 262
  experiences, 239
  facilities, 262
  goal, 31
  history, 225, 227
  literature, 316
  nature of, 9
  philosophy of, 237
  platform for, 237, 239, 347
  positions, types of, 32, 33
    coaching, 290
    college, 291
    elementary school, 289
    secondary school, 290
  preparation, 53, 232-234
  a profession, 26-29
    for men, 28
    for women, 26-28
  program of, 9, 183, 253
  qualifications for, 12-13
  in Rome, 225-226
  in United States, 227
  working environment, 33
Physical therapy, 82
  American Physical Therapy Asso-
    ciation, 83
  American Registry of Physical
    Therapists, 83
  nature of work, 83
  physical therapy technicians, 83
  requirements, 83
  working conditions, 84-85
Physical training, 226

Placement:
  college services, 295
  contracts. 303
  health education, 40
    table showing, 41
  individual efforts, 297
  information, 294
  interviews, 300
  private agency, 296
  professional services, 296
  references and recommendations, 298
  state agencies, 296
Planning:
  careers, 4, 7
  conferences and meetings, 308
  cooperative, 210
  course work and study, 134-136
  future work, 305
  programs, 209
  responsibility, 209
  for teaching, 209
  time, 133
Play, 27, 248
  of parents and children, 27
Playgrounds, development of, 230
Positions:
  coaching, 290
  foreign, 294
  health education, 41, 42
  letters of application, 298
  physical education, 32-33, 289
    college, 32, 42, 291-292
    elementary school, 32-33, 289
    secondary school, 32-33, 290
  recreation, 46-47, 288, 293
  in related fields, 78-119, 293
  starting work, 309
Practice teaching (*see* Student teaching)
Preparation:
  educational, 49-58
  health education, 55, 234
  physical education, 53, 234
  for professional duties, 308
  recreation, 55, 234, 275
  related fields, 78-116
Price, Hartley D., 144, 156
Profession:
  characteristics of, 269
  influence of members, 281

Profession (*Cont'd*):
  nature of, 269-283
  strength of, 281
Professional:
  adjustment to work, 207, 306
  assets, 315
  attitude, 204
  conduct, 315
  growth, 207, 315-325
  laboratory experiences, 171-197
  leadership, 203, 250
  literature, 316-318
  organizations, 61, 93-98, 280
    affiliation with, 318
    contributions to, 320-321
  preparation, 49-58, 78-116, 232
  starting work, 308
Professional athletics, 116
  nature of work, 116-117
  opportunities, 118
  requirements, 116-117
  working conditions, 117-118
Professional attitude, 204
Professional growth, 315-325
Professional organizations, 61, 93-98, 228, 283
  American Association for Health, Physical Education, and Recreation, 61
  American Camping Association, 98
  American Public Health Association, 61
  American Recreation Society, 280
  American Red Cross, 93
  National Education Association, 61, 281
  National Recreation Association, 61, 280
  National Safety Council, 94
Professional relationships:
  with administrators, 211
  with classroom teachers, 216
  with other groups, 277
  with parents, 217
  with supervising teachers and leaders, 214
  with supervisors, 213
  with young people, 218, 252
  with youth leaders, 217
Professional students, 154

Professional work:
adjustment to, 207
Programs, 53
  activities, 255-258
  adequate, 31
  community recreation, 183, 186
  effective, 251
  extramural, 33
    leadership, 158
  hospital recreation, 187
  industrial recreation, 113
  intramural, 33, 156
  occupational therapy, 85
  physical education, 183, 227, 255-258
    elementary and secondary school,
      255-258
  public health, 184
  school health, 184
  school recreation, 186
  voluntary agencies, 186
  voluntary health agencies, 185
  youth agencies, 184
Prospects:
  health education, 65
  physical education, 65
  recreation, 65

                        R

Rating, personal, 20
Recommendations, 298 (see also
  Placement)
Recreation:
  activities, 10-11
  agencies, 11
  aim, 245
  code of ethics, 343
  contributions of, 249
  definition, 245
  director, 70-71
  as government function, 276
  growth of, 299
  history, 229-232
  hospital, 187, 195
  industrial, 187
  nature of, 10, 245
  philosophy, 244
  platform, 246, 355
  positions, 46, 293
  preparation, 55, 235, 275
  as a profession, 44, 271

Recreation (Cont'd):
  program, 183-186, 261
    community, 183
    hospital, 187
    industrial, 187
    school, 186
    in voluntary agencies, 186
  provisions for, 11
  qualifications, 12, 13
  standards, 274
Recreational therapy, 88-89
  nature of work, 89
  opportunities, 89
  requirements, 89
  working conditions, 89
Recruitment, responsibility for, 274
References, 298 (see also Placement)
Relationships, professional, 211 (see
  also Professional relationships)
Relaxation, 9
Requirements, 52-55 (see also Curriculum)
Resourcefulness, social, 139
Responsibilities:
  acceptance of, 208
  for evaluation, 209
  leadership, 172, 216
  personal, 204
  planning, 209
  professional, 204-222
  teacher, 171, 215
Rhythmical activities, 256, 258
Romney, G. Ott, 245

                        S

Safety education:
  American Automobile Association,
    93
  American Red Cross, 93
  National Safety Council, 93
  nature of work, 92
  opportunities, 93
  requirements, 92-93
  working conditions, 93
Salaries:
  health agencies, 80
  recreation, 276
  teachers', 276
Sargent, Dudley, 233
Scholarship, 12

Scholarships, 128-129
  and loan funds, 128-129
  physical therapy, 85
School enrollment, 30-31 (see Enrollment)
Science, effect on programs, 227
Self-appraisal:
  chart, 14-18
  summary, 19
Skills:
  fundamental, 256
  in physical activities, 13, 252
Snow, W. B., 82
Specialization, 321-322
Sports, 156, 256, 258
  desirable practices for girls and women, 359-363
  English, 227
  principles for boys, 357
Sportsmanship, code of, 336
Standards:
  athletics, 357-359
  conduct, 205
  health, 66
  National Section for Girls' and Women's Sports, 259, 359
  professional, 205
  program, 259
  undergraduate preparation, 280
Status, teaching and leadership, 273-281
Student:
  government, 147
  membership in AAHPER, 152
  organizations, 146
  participants, 187-189
Student teaching, 189
Students, and college life, 125-148, 320
Success, characteristics for, 38
Supervising leaders and teachers, 214
Supervision, 213
Supervisors, qualifications of, 45, 80

T

Teachers:
  Bill of Rights for, 338
  classroom, 216
  community adjustments, 62
  community relationships, 61
  demand for, 29

Teachers (Cont'd):
  economic status, 62
  experienced, 67-68
  incomes, 276 (see Salary)
  living accommodations, 306
  married women, 71
  new, 67-68
  three-year, 68-69
  salaries, 62-64
  shortage of, 29-30, 58-59
Teaching:
  ability, 13
  advantages, 62
  and leadership, 182
  load, 31
  as a profession, 271
  retirement, 62, 64-65
  salaries, 62, 276
  security, 64-65
  status, 273, 276-278
  undergraduate experiences, 171-197
Tead, Ordway, 221
Tensions, 9
Therapeutics, 81
  exercise, 86-87
  occupational, 85-86
  physical, 82-85
  recreational, 88-89
  values of, 195
Transfer students, 7-8
Travel and professional growth, 323
Turnvereins, 230

U

United Nations Educational, Scientific, and Cultural Organization, 281
United States Office of Education, 276

V

Varsity athletics, 157-159
Varsity letter, 15
Veterans Administration, therapeutic work, 87-88, 195
Vocation:
  change, 6, 66
  choice, 7
  selection, 3, 269
Voice, 13
Volunteer work, 135, 191

W

Writing, for publication, 320
Work opportunities, 128
World Health Organization, 80, 228

Y

Young Men's Christian Association, 94, 100-103
  camp programs, 94
  founding of, 231
  nature of work, 100-101
  opportunities, 100-101
  requirements, 103
  secretary, 101
  working conditions, 101-102
Young Women's Christian Association, 94, 103-105
  camp programs, 94
  director, 105
  founding, 231
  nature of work, 103

Y.W.C.A. *(Con't)*:
  opportunities, 104
  requirements, 103
  working conditions, 103
Youth:
  activities, 178-179
  characteristics, 219-220
  counseling and guiding, 33
  leaders, 62, 192, 217
  leadership of, 28, 172, 250
  programs for, 173
  qualifications for work with, 99
  relationships with, 218-221
Youth agencies:
  Boy Scouts, 94, 106-108
  Boys' Clubs, 108-110
  Camp Fire Girls, 94, 112-113
  Girl Scouts, 94, 110-111
  YMCA, 94, 100-103
  YWCA, 94, 103-105
Youth organizations, 98 *(see also* Youth agencies)
Youth-serving agencies, experience in, 192 *(see also* Youth agencies)